Advances in

OPTICAL *and* ELECTRON
MICROSCOPY

Volume 5

Advances in

OPTICAL *and* ELECTRON MICROSCOPY

Volume 5

Edited by

R. BARER

Department of Human Biology and Anatomy,
University of Sheffield, England

AND

V. E. COSSLETT

Department of Physics,
Cavendish Laboratory, University of Cambridge,
England

ACADEMIC PRESS · 1973
LONDON AND NEW YORK
a subsidiary of Harcourt Brace Jovanovich, publishers

ACADEMIC PRESS INC. (LONDON) LTD.
24/28 Oval Road,
London NW1

United States Edition published by
ACADEMIC PRESS INC.
111 Fifth Avenue
New York, New York 10003

Library of Congress Catalog Card Number: 65–25134
ISBN: 0-12-029905-4

PRINTED IN GREAT BRITAIN BY
THE ABERDEEN UNIVERSITY PRESS LIMITED
ABERDEEN, SCOTLAND

Contributors

HAROLD P. ERICKSON,* *Medical Research Council, Laboratory of Molecular Biology, Cambridge, England* (p. 163).

JOHN H. EVANS, *AERE, Harwell, Berkshire, England* (p. 1).

J. GAHM, *Carl Zeiss, Oberkochen, West Germany* (p. 115).

D. F. HARDY,† *Department of Applied Physics, Cornell University, Ithaca, New York, U.S.A.* (p. 201).

R. T. JOY, *Zoology Department, The University, Nottingham, England* (p. 297).

H. PILLER, *Carl Zeiss, Oberkochen, West Germany* (p. 95).

K. PRESTON, JR., *The Perkin-Elmer Corporation, Connecticut, U.S.A.* (p. 43).

R. H. WADE, *Département de Recherche Fondamentale, Laboratoire de Physique du Solide, Centre d'Etudes Nucléaires de Grenoble, Grenoble, France* (p. 239).

* Present address: Department of Anatomy, Duke University, Medical Center, Durham, N.C. 27710, U.S.A.

† Present address, Department of Applied Physics, University of Hull, Hull, HU6 7RX, England.

v

Preface

Developments in microscopy, in its optical form as well as its electron counterpart, continue unabated. New instruments and improvements in existing ones, new techniques of observation, greater convenience of operation, automatic processing of data, all flood in on us. The growth in the number and size of journals on the subject mirror this activity, to the point where it becomes difficult for even the specialist microscopist to keep abreast of it, let alone the occasional user. It is part of the function of this Series to provide surveys of such developing areas of research, as the contents of the present volume bear witness.

In optical microscopy the emphasis is once again on quantitation. The complexity of modern systems is so great that it is increasingly difficult to compete with current research in the laboratories of some of the larger manufacturers. Accordingly we have asked contributors from Perkin-Elmer (Preston) and Zeiss (Piller and Gahm) to give accounts of the philosophy underlying some of their work. Such accounts are not readily available elsewhere and it is hoped that they will provide useful surveys of current thinking in this important field. On a different topic Evans reviews methods of remote control microscopy based on his long experience at AERE Harwell.

In electron microscopy advances continue to be made in instrument design, including specimen stages for dynamic experiments, in new methods of observation, and in image interpretation. Three articles on various aspects of this latter topic appeared in the previous volume, and now we have an account of the Fourier theory of image formation by Erickson. In observational techniques, the present state of the art of imaging magnetic domain structures is described by Wade and that for biological specimens in the wet state by Joy. With the trend to even higher operating voltages, Hardy sets out the advantages and disadvantages of superconducting electron lenses.

As previously, we believe it will be of interest to list the topics on which articles for future volumes are being commissioned. Suggestions for and offers of articles on other subjects of current interest in microscopy will be gratefully received.

Use of lasers in microscopy
New techniques in optical lens design
Fluorescence microspectrometry
Non-standard phase contrast systems

Scanning microabsorptiometry
"Vital" microscopy
Extraterrestrial microscopy
High resolution electron microscopy
Display of results in microprobe analysis
Localisation of enzymes by electron microscopy
Negative staining for electron microscopy
Phase contrast electron microscopy
Cryomicrotomy

January, 1973   V. E. COSSLETT
                                                   R. BARER

Contents

Remote Control Microscopy

JOHN H. EVANS

Automated Microscopy for Cytological Analysis

K. PRESTON, Jr.

A Universal System for Measuring and Processing the Characteristic Geometrical and Optical Magnitudes of Microscopic Objects

H. PILLER

Instruments for Stereometric Analysis with the Microscope —Their Application and Accuracy of Measurement

J. GAHM

The Fourier Transform of an Electron Micrograph—First Order and Second Order Theory of Image Formation

HAROLD P. ERICKSON

Superconducting Electron Lenses

D. F. HARDY

Lorentz Microscopy or Electron Phase Microscopy of Magnetic Objects

R. H. WADE

The Electron Microscopical Observation of Aqueous Biological Specimens

R. T. JOY

Remote Control Microscopy*

JOHN H. EVANS

Metallurgy Division, AERE, Harwell, Berkshire, England

I. Introduction

THE discovery of radio-activity by Becquerel in 1896 was the first of a series of events which led to the operation of the first nuclear reactor in Chicago, USA, in 1942, and the exploding of the atomic bomb in 1945. Since then nuclear power has been successfully developed for peaceful purposes and today nuclear power stations, radio-isotopes, etc. are accepted as commonplace. In fact, nuclear power stations now produce approximately 15% of electric power generated in the United Kingdom and it is estimated that this figure will rise to 60% by the year 2000. The development of a nuclear power programme depends in no small way on the techniques and equipment devised for examination of samples of candidate fuels after irradiation in special testing reactors and full scale fuel elements from power producing reactors. Materials become intensely radio-active after irradiation in a nuclear

* This article is partly based on a lecture given by the author to the Royal Microscopical Society, 1968.

reactor and, in order to protect workers, have to be handled in special shielded cells. Many techniques are used to study the performance of fuels and other reactor components; one of the most powerful tools available to the scientist engaged on post-irradiation examination is the optical microscope.

II. RADIO-ACTIVITY

Radio-activity is the term given to the phenomenon which occurs when an unstable atomic species, or radio-nuclide, spontaneously changes by a process known as radio-active decay with the emission of ionizing radiations. Radio-nuclides usually emit either alpha or beta particles and/or gamma rays.

Radio-activity may occur naturally or may be induced by bombardment with neutrons in a nuclear reactor.

In a nuclear reactor, fissile atoms in the fuel, e.g. uranium 235, split into two nuclei releasing a vast amount of energy and also two or three neutrons which can penetrate other fissile nuclei causing further fission and releasing more energy and more neutrons. This sequence is known as a chain reaction and the new nuclei produced are called fission products.

Most of the energy released during fission is in the form of heat which is used to produce steam for the generation of electricity.

Any material exposed to a neutron flux in a reactor will become radio-active to a greater or lesser degree. In the case of the nuclear fuel high levels of β and γ radiations are present whereas in the case of graphite (used in some types of reactor) the radiation may be very low and arise from impurities in the graphite.

III. RADIOLOGICAL PROTECTION

When working with radio-active materials the radiations against which protection must be provided consist of alpha and beta particles, X- and gamma rays and neutrons. Apart from the external hazard of direct radiation there is the internal hazard due to the inhalation or ingestion of these materials and protection against both these hazards is necessary. Each type of radiation presents a different problem and the method of protection is varied to suit each particular case.

1. Alpha particles (α) are high energy ionized helium nuclei. They have a low penetrating power and can be stopped by a few centimetres of air, or a sheet of paper. They will not penetrate the surfaces layers of the skin, therefore they do not constitute an external hazard.

However, alpha emitting material is extremely dangerous when inside the body as most finds its way to the skeleton from which it irradiates the bone marrow, damaging the blood forming organs. It is essential to contain alpha active material to prevent ingestion but heavy shielding is not normally required.

2. Beta particles (β) are high energy electrons having greater penetrating power than alpha particles but can be stopped by thick cardboard, Perspex, or a thin sheet of metal such as aluminium. Beta particles will penetrate the skin and irradiate the underlying tissue.

3. X- and gamma (γ) rays are electromagnetic radiations of high penetrating power and can irradiate all the body organs from outside the body. To shield workers from these radiations thick, high density materials are necessary, e.g. lead, cast iron, or concrete. The thickness required depends on the density of the shield material, the energy of the radiation, and the strength of the emitting source.

4. Neutrons. These are penetrating particles and can only be stopped by composite shielding made up of moderating material (such as plastics), dense material (such as lead), and neutron absorbers (such as cadmium).

The type of shielding necessary, therefore, to protect workers will depend on the types of radiation present. In the case of unirradiated plutonium bearing materials, for instance, only the alpha hazard has to be considered and so these are handled in "glove boxes" constructed of a metal frame with Perspex panels fitted with Neoprene gloves (see Section VI B.1 and Fig. 9). The atmosphere inside the box is usually maintained at a pressure of $\frac{1}{2}$ to 1 in. of water negative to that in the laboratory to ensure that any leaks will be into the glove box.

When dealing with irradiated reactor fuels in which all types of radio-activity may be present, it is necessary to protect workers from both internal and external hazards by enclosing the work in sealed boxes (to contain the material) that are surrounded by dense shielding (to attenuate the more penetrating radiations). These measures must be sufficient to reduce exposure of personnel to dose limits not exceeding those recommended by the International Commission on Radiological Protection (ICRP).

The development of atomic energy has been responsible for the emergence of a new profession known as "health physics". The health physicist gives advice on all aspects of work on radio-active materials including the setting of standards of safe working levels of exposure to different types of radiations and the development of methods of radiological protection. A comprehensive range of instruments is available for monitoring all types of radiation, air sampling, etc. Regular checking

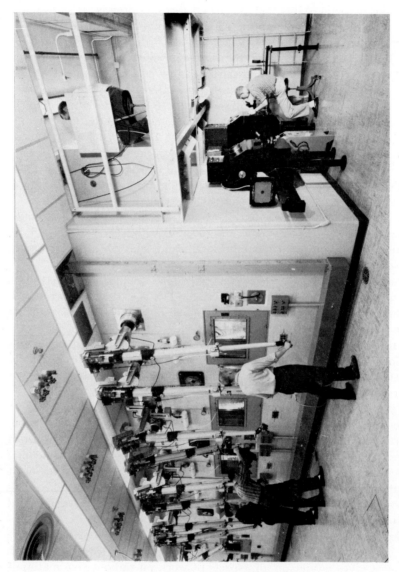

Fig. 1. Concrete shielded cells fitted with master/slave manipulators. (Courtesy of Oak Ridge Laboratory; operated by Union Carbide Corporation for the US Atomic Energy Commission.)

of personnel is carried out by means of small ionization chambers and special film "badges" worn by workers handling irradiated materials. Film badges are changed at frequent intervals—usually every two weeks —and the accumulated dose is recorded for each worker.

Although the hazards involved in handling intensely radio-active materials are formidable, as a result of the development of safe remote handling techniques, the only protective clothing necessary under normal conditions is a laboratory coat. In some "hot" laboratories even this is dispensed with and workers wear normal clothing—see Fig. 1 which shows concrete shielded cells on the left and two lead shielded optical microscopes on the right of the photograph.

IV. SHIELDED CELLS

Materials which emit γ and X rays have to be handled behind thick walls of dense materials. Generally, two types of cell are used for post-irradiation examination; these are briefly described below. For a more detailed account of shielded cells see Venables (1969) and Campbell (1970).

A. *Types of Cell*

1. *Lead Shielded Cell.* An example of this type of cell is shown diagrammatically in Fig. 2. The walls and floor are constructed of lead bricks (up to 10 in. thick) shaped so that joints between rows are stepped, thus eliminating a "shine path" for gamma radiation. Handling within the inner containment alpha box is carried out with fingers attached to the end of tong shafts which are supported in spheres of tungsten or uranium. The spheres are usually floated on a cushion of air introduced between the sphere and its housing. A PVC gaiter fitted around the tong shaft prevents the seepage of contaminated dust along tong shafts. The roof of the cell is constructed of steel plates.

2. *Concrete Shielded Cell.* Generally concrete cells (Fig. 3) are used to shield very large, highly radio-active components such as fuel elements (which may be up to 7 ft long), test rigs from Materials Testing Reactors, etc. They are also used to shield large pieces of test equipment such as tensile test machines, autoclaves, etc. The walls, from 4 ft to 5 ft 6 in. thick, are made of concrete in a range of densities from 150–350 lb ft^{-3}. Handling is carried out by master/slave manipulators; the in-cell component, known as the "slave arm", is mechanically and electrically linked to and follows movements of the master arm operated by the cell technician.

Microscopes for examining active materials are usually housed in

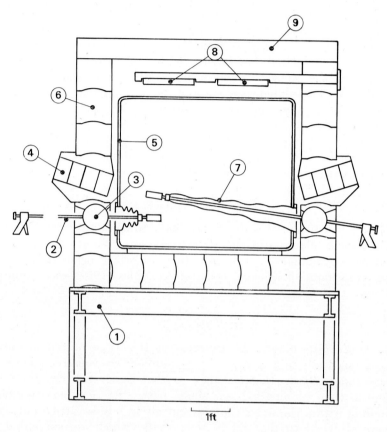

FIG. 2. Lead shielded cell; 1. Plinth; 2. Tong shaft; 3. Sphere unit; 4. Window; 5. "Alpha" box (fitted with Perspex panels); 6. Lead wall; 7. PVC gaiter; 8. Sodium lamps; 9. Roof shielding.

lead shielded cells as these are smaller and more compact than concrete cells and this results in a shorter optical ray path with less loss of illumination. Another advantage of housing a microscope in a lead shielded cell is that one wall of the cell can be made as a sliding door which, after removal of the radio-active sample, can be opened allowing the microscope to be adjusted or cleaned by inserting a hand into a glove fitted to the alpha box panel (Fig. 18).

B. *Windows*

Operations carried out in shielded cells are viewed through windows in the shielding wall. They are made of (*a*) rectangular glass blocks, or

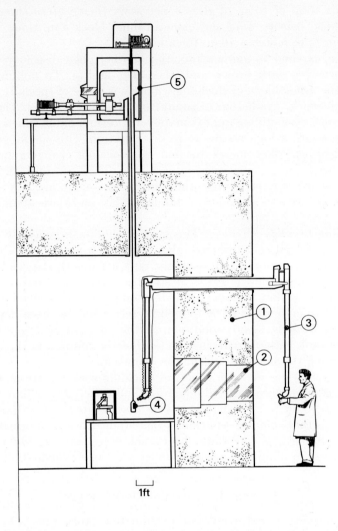

FIG. 3. Concrete shielded cell with lead shielded microscope cell above. 1. Concrete wall; 2. Window; 3. Master/slave manipulator; 4. Transfer bucket; 5. Lead shielded microscope cell.

(*b*) a tank filled with a colourless dense liquid such as zinc bromide. In either case the shielding value of the window must match that of the walls.

1. *Glass Windows*. Glass used for shielding windows is available in a range of densities from 2·67 to 6·1 g cm^{-3}. As an example of shielding

values a total of 16 in. of glass is necessary (made up of three blocks 4 in. thick, density $4 \cdot 3$ g cm^{-3} and an inner block 4 in. thick, density $6 \cdot 1$ g cm^{-3}) to match a 10 in. thick lead wall.

When exposed to gamma radiation normal glass discolours and in time becomes dark brown and, therefore, useless. To minimize this effect the inside block of shielding windows is made of specially treated glass known as "radiation resistant" or "stabilized" glass. The treatment consists of adding approximately 1% cerium oxide which endows the glass with a high resistance to discoloration. This special glass has a slight brown coloration as cast but this does not change appreciably during use.

Microscope objectives and other glass components inside a shielded microscope are also available in stabilized glass and these are discussed later.

2. *Zinc Bromide Windows.* This type of window is generally used in concrete shielded cells although glass windows are also available. The zinc bromide solution is contained in a tank fitted with glass end plates; the in-cell glass plate is made of stabilized glass. A disadvantage of this window is that the zinc bromide solution becomes cloudy after a period of time and has to be filtered. A technique has been developed which removes the cloudy solution from the tank, filters it, and returns it to the tank without reducing the level of the solution in the tank so maintaining the shielding during the operation.

Note. Chromatic aberration effects in shielding windows are minimized by use of monochromatic illumination and generally sodium vapour lamps are used for cell lighting. One disadvantage of sodium light however is that colour detail cannot be obtained; when information on colour is important, e.g. study of corrosion films, supplementary lamps can be used to illuminate samples under periscope examination.

V. Post-Irradiation Examination

The purpose of post-irradiation examination procedures is to determine any changes which may have occurred during irradiation of candidate fuel materials, fuel cladding, etc. in Materials Testing Reactors and also to monitor the behaviour of full scale fuel elements from power producing reactors.

During reactor irradiation changes may occur in the material, e.g. decrease in density in fuel materials due to formation of small bubbles of fission product gases xenon and krypton, corrosion of cladding, etc. and many techniques are used to detect changes in the material and also to measure these changes.

A typical scheme for examination of material irradiated in a Materials Testing Reactor is shown schematically below:

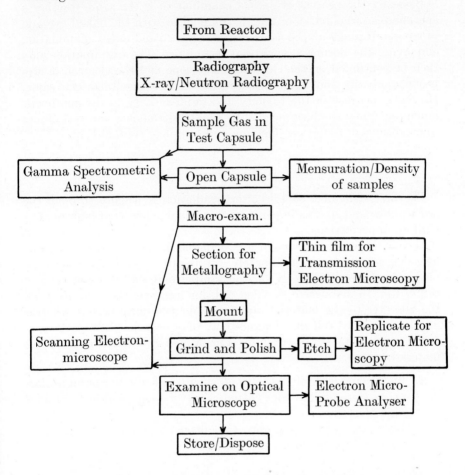

A more detailed account of these techniques and examples of the information which they yield is given by Lambert (1968).

Optical instruments are used in many of these stages of examination, such as reading micrometers when carrying out mensuration, setting up cut-off machines when sectioning material for metallographic examination, etc. The remainder of this paper deals with the optical examination of irradiated samples in both the "as irradiated" form, and after grinding and polishing.

Mention is also made of techniques for making replicas and thin films for electron microscopy.

VI. Optical Examination

Basically the process of optical examination is the same whether a specimen is radio-active or not. It commences with the naked eye and progresses through all the usual stages of macro and micro examination employing the normal preparation techniques. The examination may then be continued on the electron microscope and the electron micro-probe analyser, and again the process is fundamentally the same. However, because of the toxicity and radio-activity of the specimens much ingenuity has been needed to adapt instruments and techniques to conditions of radiation shielding and complete containment.

A. *Low Power Examination*

The first sight of a sample after irradiation is usually through the cell window and so it is imperative that the window is of high quality with no imperfections.

Several types of instrument are available for visual examination at low magnification (approximately up to 10 ×) and the choice of instrument depends largely on the sample material and the type of cell in use. In a concrete shielded cell, for instance, the distance from the observer to the material under examination may be 8 ft whereas in a lead shielded cell this distance may only be 2 ft.

There are two ways of obtaining a magnified view of the radio-active material:

(a) by viewing it through the window with either a pair of binoculars or a stereo-microscope fitted with a long working distance objective, or

(b) by means of a cranked optic tube fitted either inside the shielding wall or "up and over" the wall.

1. *Through-window Examination*

a. *Binoculars*. These may be either standard (8 ×30 or 10 ×50) binoculars supported on a tripod, or a specially made close-range binocular viewer that can be used from infinity down to 2 ft. They provide a bright, erect, stereo image and allow the cell operator to use both manipulators whilst viewing the work. A disadvantage is that it is not convenient to use camera equipment for recording.

b. *Stereo-microscope*. The most popular instrument of this type is that made by Zeiss (W. Germany) and known as the Epi-Technoscope. It was originally developed for surgical operating work and can be fitted with both camera equipment and an observation tube for a second observer. A range of interchangeable objective lenses is available for distances 250–2000 mm; for lead cells the 800 or 1250 mm lens is used and for concrete cells the 2000 mm is necessary. The microscope is supported on a rollable stand and allows the cell operator to view the work and use both manipulators simultaneously. The magnification changer gives a range of approximately $5 \times$ to $30 \times$.

All optics are outside the cell and so unstabilized glass is used.

2. *Periscopes*

There are several ways of utilizing the periscope principle depending on the cell construction.

a. *Lead cells*. One type of periscope used in lead shielded cells at AERE is shown in Fig. 4. The optic tube is cranked within the lead wall so that there is no direct shine path for gamma radiation. Extra lead shielding is used to maintain the shielding thickness. In the illustration, a binocular eyepiece is used for viewing. For a stereo

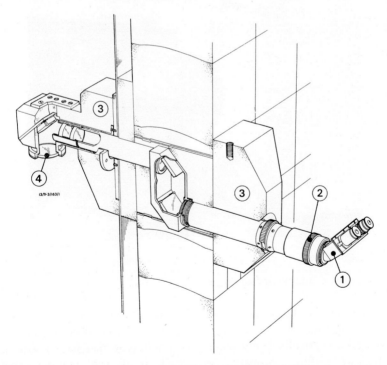

Fig. 4. Harwell design cranked optic tube for lead cells. 1. Binocular eyepiece; 2. Focussing collar; 3. Additional lead shielding; 4. Alpha seal.

image the arrangement shown in Fig. 5 is used and in this case a Zeiss Epi-Technoscope and camera system is attached to the end of the periscope thus enabling the full range of magnifications to be used.

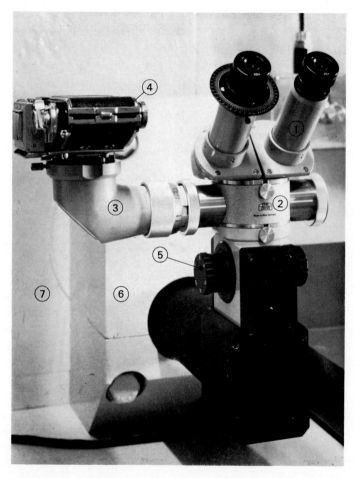

Fig. 5. Epi-Technoscope and camera fitted to cranked optic tube shown in Fig. 4. 1. Binocular eyepiece; 2. Beam splitter; 3. Camera tube; 4. Reflex camera; 5. Magnification changer; 6. Additional lead shielding; 7. Lead cell.

b. *Concrete cells*. For viewing in concrete cells the type of instrument shown in Fig. 6 is used and may be mono- or stereoscopic. It may view a fixed area vertically below the in-cell portion or may have a scanning mechanism enabling the whole cell area to be viewed. The periscope is mounted in a tube inserted in a hole in the concrete shield wall and this method of mounting enables the periscope to be withdrawn from the tube for cleaning or adjustment to be carried out. In the instrument illustrated a "zoom" control at the viewing position gives a continuously variable magnification of ×1 to ×60 with image quality comparable with that of a standard stereo microscope.

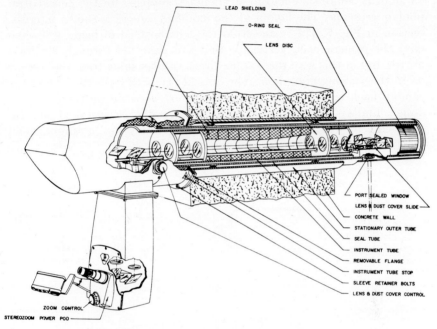

LEAD SHIELDING

O-RING SEAL

LENS DISC

PORT SEALED WINDOW
LENS & DUST COVER SLIDE
CONCRETE WALL
STATIONARY OUTER TUBE
SEAL TUBE
INSTRUMENT TUBE
REMOVABLE FLANGE
INSTRUMENT TUBE STOP
SLEEVE RETAINER BOLTS
LENS & DUST COVER CONTROL

ZOOM CONTROL
STEREOZOOM POWER POD

FIG. 6. Cutaway diagram showing major components of remote stereomicroscope. (Courtesy Bausch & Lomb Inc., Rochester, New York.)

Most periscopes for concrete cells are custom ordered to suit a particular cell. One manufacturer, however, offers a range of standard optic tubes in straight and cranked forms that can be screwed together to suit any particular cell layout with a saving in cost.

Another type of viewing device for concrete cells consists of a straight tube filled with high quality stabilized glass, and is mounted horizontally in the concrete shield wall. A lens on the "hot" side of the shielding wall projects an image through one or more lenses to the eyepiece on the "cold" side of the wall.

3. *Macro Camera*

Frequently the results obtained with the instruments used for low power examination leave much to be desired in both resolution and flatness/depth of field. It is also difficult to photograph samples in vertical illumination—necessary for polished metallographic sections. To overcome these difficulties an instrument has been developed at the AERE which is based on a standard macro-camera and utilizes standard macro-lenses (although made of unstabilized glass, these were used for 18 months before they had to be changed) supplied for the Zeiss Ultraphot microscope. The layout of the modified camera is shown in cross-section in Fig. 7. The image from the lens, instead of being projected onto the camera back vertically above, is deflected through 90° by a mirror and in this way there is no direct gamma shine from the sample on to the viewing/film plane. The optical ray path from the lens to the camera back is 80 cm so that the lenses are used within their original design limits; the camera, therefore, can only be installed in lead shielded cells with walls up to 10 in. thick. An internal uranium shield

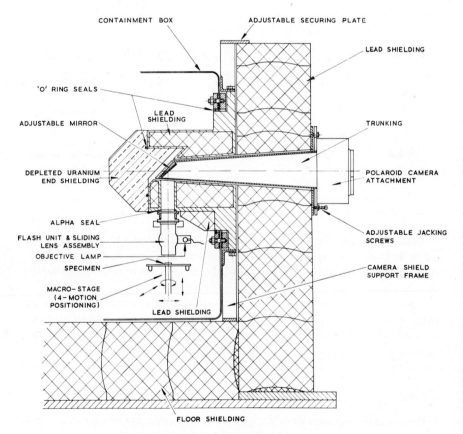

Fig. 7. Sectional view of shielded Macro camera.

is used to compensate for loss of shielding where the image is projected, through the wall, onto the camera back.

The lenses are mounted on a sliding bar and can be positioned below the mirror by means of a tong. The sliding bar only accommodates two lenses but others in the Luminar range can be interchanged. The lenses most frequently used are illustrated in Fig. 8.

Fig. 8. Shielded Macro camera-lens Arrangement. 1. $2 \cdot 5 \times -5 \times$ Luminar; 2. Diaphragm operating lever; 3. Tungsten lamp/flash unit; 4. Epi-Luminar $f = 100$ mm; 5. 15 W Lamp; 6. Stage; 7. Uranium shielding.

a. *Luminar* $2 \cdot 5 \times -5 \times$: used for examination and photography of unmounted samples. Illumination is provided by a "Texturelite Ringflash" unit, incorporating four tungsten lamps and four adjacent flash tubes, mounted around the lens. This allows a choice of lighting directions and has proved to be a versatile unit in use. The practical magnification range available varies between $2 \times$ and $4 \times$ and is changed by a capstan fitted around the objective and operated by a tong.

b. *Epi-luminar* (*f* = *100 mm*): used principally for polished sections of samples that require vertical incident illumination. The lighting is provided by a 15 W lamp attached to lens. Oblique illumination is also possible by using two supplementary low voltage lamps supported in tongs.

Only one magnification, 8 ×, is possible with this lens. If desired, a further magnification step, for viewing only, can be obtained by means of a 6 × focusing magnifier used to view the image on a clear glass screen in the camera back.

The shutter is a focal plane type. Focusing is achieved by raising or lowering the sample on the stage unit.

In addition to the instruments mentioned in this section other standard inspection devices, such as "Boroscopes"; "Intrascopes", are also used for viewing in some cells.

B. *Microscope Examination*

After the initial examination with a low power instrument, sections cut from the sample are mounted in a pre-formed Bakelite holder and prepared using standard metallographic grinding and polishing techniques (Gray, 1968, Krautwedel, 1969). Polished (and etched) sections are then examined using a shielded optical microscope.

1. *Alpha active materials*

As mentioned under "Radiological Protection" when no beta or gamma radiation is present (as in the case of plutonium bearing fuels being developed for the Fast Breeder Reactor) only the alpha activity has to be considered and microscopes are available that can be housed in a Perspex alpha box as shown in Fig. 9. Here an optical flat, fitted in the tube below the binocular eyepieces, prevents leakage of alpha active dust from the box. Microscope controls are operated through Neoprene gloves fitted to ports on the front panel. "Posting" of samples, etc. is carried out through a special opening in one of the panels using a sealed PVC bag technique which, at all times, ensures no leakage of atmosphere from the box.

2. *Irradiated materials*

A major part of the examination of reactor irradiated materials is carried out with an optical microscope, usually of the inverted stage (Le Chatelier) type, and several microscope manufacturers now produce a remote control model for installation in a shielded cell. This section describes how two makes of metallurgical microscope were converted for remote control at AERE, Harwell, and also gives details of some commercially available instruments.

FIG. 9. Microscope in Perspex glove box for examination of unirradiated alpha active materials. 1. Glove box; 2. Glove port; 3. Microscope; 4. Alpha seal housing. (Courtesy E. Leitz, Wetzlar.)

a. *Microscope optics.* Due to the radiation browning effect in normal glass, optical components in that part of a remote control microscope situated inside a shielded cell should be made from radiation resistant glass. This ensures that these components, which cannot be easily replaced, are not affected by gamma radiation during the lifetime of the microscope. Objectives are particularly vulnerable to radiation browning due to their close proximity to the radio-active samples and specially computed radiation resistant objectives, made from glass containing approximately 1% cerium oxide are available from most of the manufacturers of remote microscopes. Figure 10 compares the

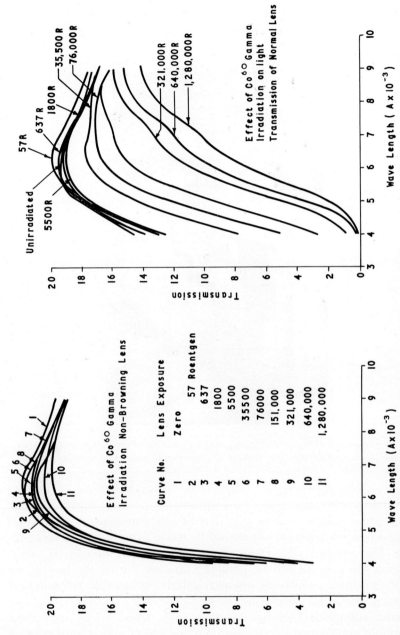

FIG. 10. Comparison of spectral transmission of protected and non-protected objectives. (Courtesy Bausch & Lomb Inc., Rochester, N.Y.)

change in transmission characteristics of "protected" and "non-protected" objectives after irradiation with Co^{60}.

The cost of protected objectives can be as much as 2 or 3 times that of normal objectives of the same quality; at present only achromatic types are available in protected glass. One manufacturer claims it is more economical to use standard objectives until brown and replace them with a new set. Using a sample of uranium oxide of 50 curie activity, four objectives were irradiated with gamma rays; a fifth objective was not treated and used as a control. The transmission of each objective was measured before and after irradiation using light of 2850°K colour temperature or 540 nm wavelength. The results are given in Table I. (Reproduced with permission from M. Ohuchi, Japan Atomic Energy Institute and T. Katoh, Union Optical Co. Ltd. Tokyo, Japan.) It can be seen that the transmission value of the irradiated objectives is only slightly decreased and no difference could, in fact, be detected in photomicrographs taken with each objective after the test.

TABLE I

Objective	Irradiation time hours	Dose Roentgen	Transmission % 2850°K	540 nm
1	0	0	100	100
2	5	7×10^4	98	98
3	10	$1 \cdot 4 \times 10^5$	97	97
4	45	$6 \cdot 5 \times 10^5$	95·6	95
5	70	1×10^6	92	93

Note. The difference in behaviour of standard non-protected objectives in this and the previous test using Co^{60} is due to the relative energies of the gamma ray from each source of 2·5 MeV for Co^{60} and approximately 1 MeV for fission products. The test using uranium oxide is, however, more relevant in this context as Co^{60} is seldom examined on a remote microscope, whereas uranium oxide, as a fuel for some types of reactor, is of great interest and is more typical of the material usually examined on remote optical microscopes.

There is no general agreement amongst workers in this field and it remains a matter of personal choice whether or not to use protected objectives. The author has used standard objectives in a remote microscope in daily use at AERE for 18 months before they had to be discarded.

b. *Remote control microscopes.* The first section traces the evolution of one make of metallurgical microscope, from a relatively simple version modified at the AERE, to a sophisticated instrument operated entirely by remote control. The microscope is capable of the highest standard of microscopy using all the available techniques, except macro and, by positioning all the remote controls at the viewing position, operator fatigue is minimized.

In the second section details are given of how another standard metallurgical microscope was modified for remote control and how in this instrument certain improvements were incorporated which extended the magnification range of the microscope and made it more comfortable to operate.

To conclude, some commercially available remote microscopes are described briefly and salient features of each noted.

A remote control microscope should meet the following requirements. (It is assumed that adequate radiological protection is provided.)

(i) first class optical performance and all usual techniques, bright field, polarized light, Köhler illumination etc.

(ii) complete remote operation, i.e. from outside the shielded cell.

(iii) designed and installed so that there is easy access for maintenance, cleaning, etc.

(iv) reliable

(v) comfortable to use (often a remote microscope is more comfortable to use than a normal inverted stage instrument).

(vi) all fixed optical components inside the cell should be made of stabilized glass.

It is usual to place a remote microscope in a cell separated from the main metallographic preparation cell to minimize contamination problems and to allow access to the microscope via gloves in the alpha box panel (after removal of sample and opening shielding door).

(i) *Reichert MeF microscopes.* Several factors led to the choice of the Reichert MeF model (Reichert, Vienna) as the first remote microscope to be used at the AERE. It was compact, had good polarizing equipment, and could be equipped for micro-hardness testing; in addition such a model, in use in one of the metallography laboratories, was available for installation in a shielded cell.

The first samples irradiated in the Harwell and Windscale reactors were relatively low in activity and two cells, shielded with 4 in. thick lead walls, were built to house the metallographic preparation equipment and the microscope. These early cells were open topped and did not have an inner containment box (Fig. 11). Contamination problems were experienced with the open topped preparation cell.

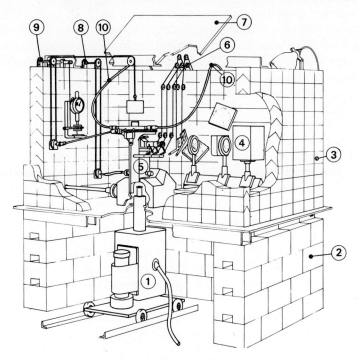

FIG. 11. Reichert MeF microscope in lead shielded cell at A.E.R.E. 1. TV camera; 2. Concrete block plinth; 3. Lead bricks; 4. microscope lamp; 5. Microscope; 6. Diaphragm controls; 7. Mirror; 8. Fine focus control; 9. Stage rotation control; 10. Stage traverse controls.

The microscope diaphragm controls were operated by "cord and pulley" from outside the cell. The stage traverse was operated by Bowden cables and rotating shafts were used for stage rotation and coarse focus. Objectives were changed by a tong fitted in one of the lead walls. The microscope lamp was situated inside the cell and adjustments, when necessary, were carried out before placing the radio-active sample on the stage. At that time, no cranked optic tubes were available and so a television channel (Sykes, 1959) was used to transmit the image out of the cell to a 14 in. television monitor; the image from the projection ocular was projected on to the television camera fitted with a CPS Emitron (EMI) camera tube. The television channel introduced a $10 \times$ enlargement to the normal microscope magnification. Photomicrographs were made by photographing the television monitor screen with a modified studio camera fitted with a wide angle lens.

This rather primitive equipment was used until an increase in the activity of samples (due to higher neutron fluxes becoming available in the Test Reactors) made the shielding inadequate, and so a new metallographic facility was designed and constructed. Whereas the first preparation cells housed the grinding, polishing and etching equipment, the new installation was constructed of five interconnected cells each used for a separate stage in the preparation of samples. The cells were shielded by 4 in. of lead and in this case gas tight alpha boxes were used at a negative pressure of 1 in. water to improve contamination control. The Reichert microscope used in the previous cell was re-covered and modified for use in one of the lead cells in the new line.

Since the new cells were fitted with roofs made of steel plates, "through the wall" rather than "over the wall" controls were used. Stage traverse drives were operated by Bowden cables from a gear box on the inside wall of the cell. The stage traverse controls were also used to operate a plotting table which allowed features of interest on the specimen to be drawn automatically. The microscope lamp was positioned outside the cell and the light projected through an optical system in the wall. Objective changing was carried out by means of a push-pull rod which was also used to load the micro-hardness tester. Cranked optic tubes were still not available and so the original television channel was used for viewing and photomicrography.

Due to an increase in the demand for metallographic examination two further Reichert microscopes were installed at the AERE between 1958 and 1960. Based on the MeF model and using the experience of the previous shielded instruments, the new microscopes were modified for remote control by the manufacturers before delivery to the site. The new microscope (Fig. 12) shown prior to installation in the lead shielded cell, was equipped for examination in bright/dark field, phase contrast, micro hardness testing and was fitted with cranked optic tubes, developed by Reicherts for this work. The microscope was installed in an alpha box shielded with 10 in. thick lead bricks. One wall of the cell was a removable door which, after removal of the sample, could be opened enabling adjustments and cleaning of the microscope to be performed using Neoprene gloves fitted in the alpha box panel. The metallographic preparation equipment was housed in an adjacent interconnected lead shielded cell.

Many of the methods previously used for operating the microscope were again used, but in some cases new controls were fitted. Figure 13 shows diagrammatically how the controls were connected to the microscope. A detailed description of the microscope is given by Greer-Spencer (1961).

FIG. 12. Reichert remote microscope before installation in lead cell.

The use of optic tubes for transmitting the illumination into and the image out of the cell represented a major improvement in the design of remote microscopes since the two disadvantages of television viewing, i.e. lack of colour and loss of resolution due to the line scan, were overcome. A camera 6·5 ×9 cm (later 4 in. ×5 in.) was used for photomicrography.

All microscope controls could be operated comfortably from the working face of the cell and lamp adjustments could be made while looking down the eyepieces. This was a great improvement over the original arrangement where the lamp was inside the cell. Television was also available for group viewing.

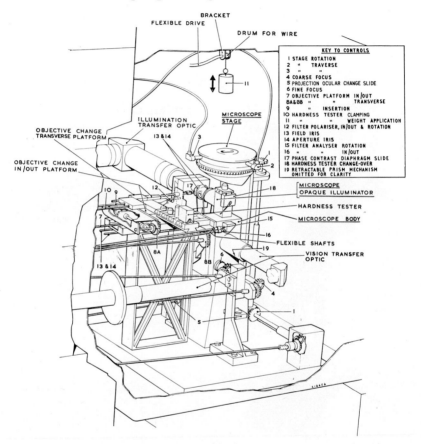

FIG. 13. Remote controls for Reichert remote microscope shown in Fig. 12.

At about the same time as these cells were commissioned, another remote version of the Reichert MeF microscope was introduced jointly by the Shandon Scientific Company and Reichert Company. This model incorporated many of the design features of the Harwell model but introduced the use of small electric motors to drive the stage traverses and rotation. Centre zero ammeters on the control console indicated the stage displacement, thus facilitating repositioning of samples after repolishing, etc. Microswitches were fitted to prevent overtravel of the stage.

These microscopes were the forerunners of the current Reichert remote microscopes known as the "Telatom" (Fig. 14). All controls are rotary which eliminates the possibility of contamination from the cell inherent in the push-pull design. Small electric motors are used for the stage traverses and rotation; all other microscope adjustments are made via mechanical through-the-wall controls. Objective changing is

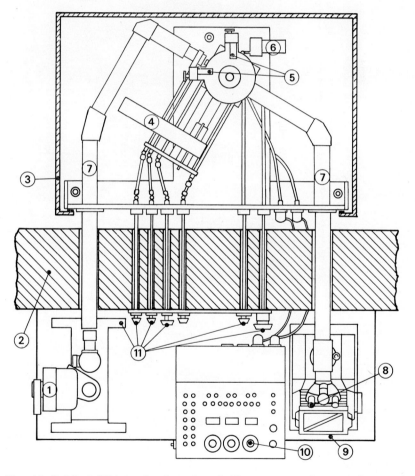

Fig. 14. Reichert "Telatom"—plan view. 1. Mercury vapour/tungsten lamp unit; 2. Lead shielding wall; 3. Alpha box; 4. Objective magazine; 5. Stage traverse motors; 6. Stage rotation motor; 7. Optic tubes; 8. Binocular; 9. Bellows camera; 10. Control unit; 11. Rotary controls.

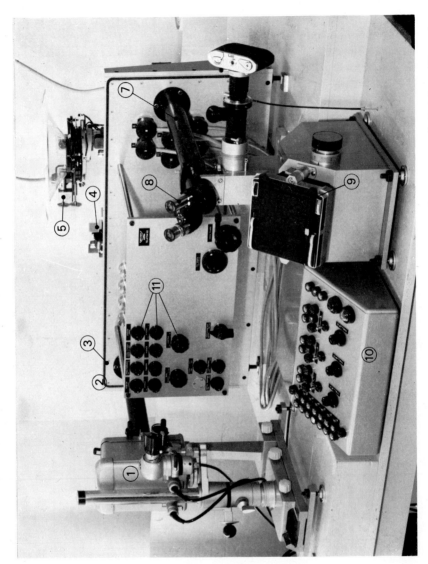

Fig. 15. Reichert "Telatom". (See Fig. 14 for Key.) (Figs. 14 and 15 courtesy C. Reichert, Vienna.)

carried out by a mechanism in place of a tong. The microscope operating face together with binocular viewer and camera is shown in Fig. 15. All mechanical controls are conveniently grouped on the lead wall and the electrical controls, warning lamps (showing stage displacement, elevation, etc.) are housed in a console.

The microscope is fitted with accessories for all the normal illumination methods including polarized light, phase contrast, etc. A range of non-browning achromatic objectives is available.

(ii) *Zeiss Neophot.* When further remote microscopes were required at the AERE, commercially made remote controlled instruments were on an approximately two year delivery and so a survey was made of other standard instruments which could be adapted, and it was decided to purchase two Zeiss Jena Neophot Mk. I (East Germany) microscopes for conversion at AERE.

The adaption connected the remote controls to the vertical illuminator (i.e. aperture and field iris diaphragms, polarizer and analyser and objective changing gear) so that they can be disconnected easily. The micro-illuminator is removable and can be replaced with the macro-equipment supplied with the microscope (this is a major limitation with most remote microscopes, due to the fact that controls in the illuminator unit are arranged so that the macro unit cannot be utilized, and means that the minimum magnification is approximately 20 × whereas with the macro unit it is approximately 5 ×). Another useful feature of the converted Neophot is the objectives, mounted on a turret, which can be rotated with the stage in the lowered position.

Figure 16 shows how the microscope is aligned in a cell shielded by 7 in. lead bricks (the cell is shown on top of the concrete shielded cell, Fig. 3). Note that the need for long cranked optic tubes is avoided; the viewing optic tube is straight. With a radio-active sample on the stage the microscopist is adequately protected from gamma radiation by the extra lead shielding used as shown (5). If for some reason the sample is dropped, and gamma radiation can then "shine" through the unshielded optic tube, the microscopist is not seated at the viewing position but is using the tong unit fitted in the lead door to recover the sample and replace it on the stage. The lamp is situated on the door face of the cell and the light is reflected into the microscope by a large mirror (16). The original optical bench is sealed into the alpha box.

Figure 17 is a photograph of the microscope in the cell before fitting the alpha box panel. In Fig. 18 can be seen the panel with a glove through which the micro-macro changeover is made; also fitted in the panel are the gaiter for the tong shaft and the optical flat through which the illumination passes from the lamp into the microscope.

Speed controlled electric motors are used for the stage traverse, rotation, and for a "super stage" (used on top of the normal stage) that serves to increase stage movement from 17×17 mm to 40×25 mm. Each

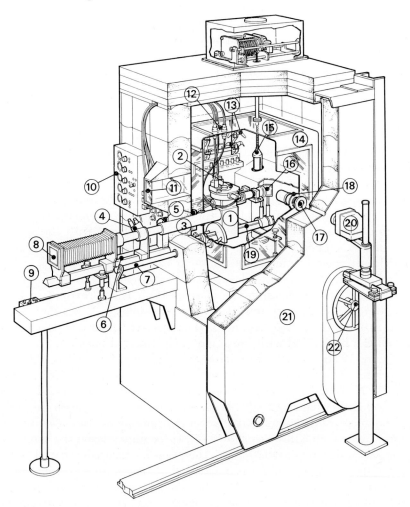

Fig. 16. Diagram of Zeiss Neophot microscope in lead shielded cell.

Key to Figs. 16, 17 and 18

1. Microscope stand; 2. Motorized stage; 3. Image optic tube; 4. Binocular; 5. Extra lead shielding; 6. Coarse focus rod; 7. Fine focus rod; 8. Bellows camera; 9. Control box; 10. Control panel; 11. Shielding window; 12. Electrical connectors; 13. Tong "fingers"; 14. Alpha box; 15. Transfer bucket; 16. Mirror; 17. Alpha seal; 18. Illumination optic tube; 19. Optical bench; 20. Microscope lamp; 21. Sliding door; 22. Door operating wheel; 23. Motor drive objective nosepiece; 24. Macro illuminator on stand; 25. Glove; 26. Tong gaiter; 27. Perspex panel.

stage motor is geared to a synchro-torque transmitter that is connected to torque receivers on the control panel fixed to the cell wall at the viewing position. These receivers give indication of stage displacement.

FIG. 17. Zeiss Neophot microscope installed in lead cell; Alpha box panel not fitted.

Focusing is achieved by means of rods mounted alongside the optical bench (which are provided on the standard instrument) connected by universal joints, through rotary seals in the alpha box panel to the focusing knobs on the body of the instrument.

Objectives are mounted on a motor driven nosepiece and can be interchanged with the stage in the lowered position. The microhardness tester (Hannemann type) is loaded by hand inserted in the glove; no change-over lens/indenter mechanism is required in this type since the diamond is mounted in the front lens of the objective. The mechanical controls are grouped on the lead wall and the electrical controls (for stage movements, objective changing) are housed in a box which can be used either at the eyepiece position or at the end of the bellows camera.

FIG. 18. As Fig. 17 with Alpha box panel in position.

The special optics necessary to compensate for the increased optical path length were supplied by Carl Zeiss (Jena, East Germany) and the stage motors, positional indicators, etc. were fitted by A. Rundle Limited.

(iii) *Commercially available remote microscopes.* Several microscope manufacturers now offer a "remote control" model for use in a shielded cell; this section gives brief details of their main features.

1. *Leitz MM5 RT*. One of the latest additions to the range of special remote control microscopes is manufactured by Ernst Leitz, GmBh, Wetzlar, West Germany, and is shown in Fig. 19 (the front wall of the cell has been removed). It has many features of the Leitz metallurgical microscope MM5, such as large viewing screen, bellows camera for film sizes up to 13 ×18 cm, 450 W xenon lamp, and is equipped for examinations in bright and dark field, polarized light, etc. A micro-hardness tester can be fitted.

FIG. 19. Leitz MM5 RT remote microscope installed in lead shielded cell (front wall removed).

The microscope is supplied as an integrated unit, ready for installation in a shielded cell (Fig. 20). The stand, mounted on a baseplate, is drilled to accept an alpha box (supplied by customer). All remote controls, electrical and mechanical, together with the optic tubes for illumination and image transmission, are passed through a metal tunnel connecting the stand to the viewing position outside the cell. The microscope is mounted on a trolley and, after removal of the front shield wall, can be withdrawn from the cell for maintenance. The motorized stage is controlled by a "Joystick" and the XY displacement is indicated on a cathode ray tube located at the viewing position. A switch returns the stage to the centre position when required. All controls are grouped on a panel mounted on the front cell wall and can be operated while seated at the viewing position. A revolving nosepiece accepts six objectives, or five objectives and a micro-hardness tester; objectives are changed by rotating a knob on the control panel.

FIG. 20. Side view of Leitz MM5 RT showing tunnel connecting microscope stand and viewing unit outside cell. (Fig. 19 and 20 courtesy E. Leitz, Wetzlar).

All optical components and objectives are made from radiation resistant glass.

The tunnel enclosing the remote controls and optic tubes simplifies installation in the shielded cell and, as the microscope is supplied as an integrated unit, alignment problems are avoided.

2. *Union Optical Company, "Farom"*. In 1968 the Union Optical Co. Ltd., in collaboration with the Japan Atomic Energy Research

Institute, introduced a new instrument for the examination of radio-active materials. Known as "Farom" it is similar in design to the Reichert "Telatom" and employs cranked optic tubes which can be supplied to suit the customer's cell.

A general view of the microscope before installation in a cell is shown in Fig. 21, and a typical cell layout is shown schematically in Fig. 22.

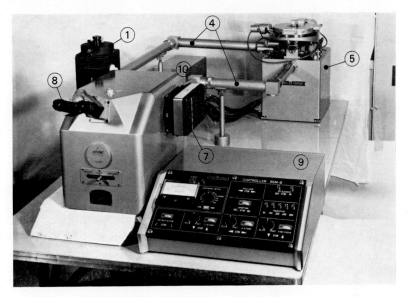

Fig. 21. Union optical "Farom" remote control microscope, Figs. 21 and 22. (See Fig. 22 for key.) (Courtesy Union Optical Company, Tokyo.)

The microscope controls are operated exclusively by small electric motors and, as no mechanical controls are used, installation in a shielded cell is simplified.

The stage X and Y movements (25 ×25 mm) are greater than normal on this type of microscope, which is an advantage when examining samples which can be up to approximately 40 mm diameter. Positional indication is given on meters displayed on the control unit.

All "in cell" optical components are manufactured from radiation resistant glass; objectives, however, are only available in unstabilized glass and have to be changed when brown (see p. 19). The motorized revolving nosepiece has provision for five objectives. When changing objectives, the stage is automatically raised and, when the selected objective is in position, lowered again. The fine focus, used to bring the image into focus, has a travel of 2 mm.

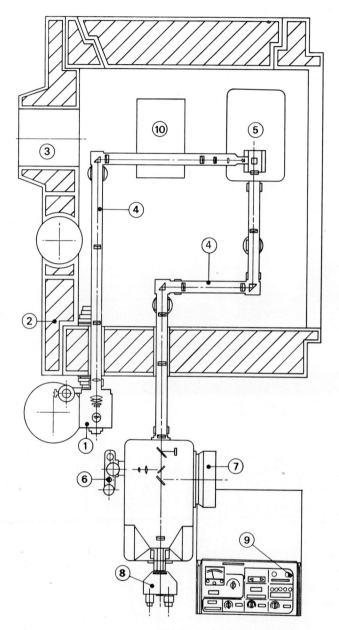

Fig. 22. Plan view of Union Optical "Farom". 1. Lamp; 2. Shielding wall; 3. Cell window; 4. Optic tubes; 5. Microscope; 6. 35 mm camera; 7. Polaroid camera; 8. Binocular; 9. Control unit; 10. Relay box.

Bright field and polarized light equipment are fitted. Illumination is provided by a 300 W xenon lamp. A choice of several camera systems is available and a built-in exposure meter on the control unit determines exposure values. A lever on the control unit directs the image to the binocular eyepieces, or 35 mm camera, or Polaroid camera.

3. *Bausch and Lomb.* Bausch and Lomb manufacture two remote control microscopes, (i) a "Blister" model for installation in a shielded "blister" built onto the outside face of a main cell wall; the microscope stand is sited inside the blister and the lamp and camera/viewer are outside, (ii) an in-cell model in which the microscope stand and lamp are housed in the main concrete shielded cell and the image is directed through the cell wall to the viewing/camera position.

Fig. 23. Bausch and Lomb blister type remote control microscope. (Courtesy Bausch and Lomb Inc., Rochester, New York.)

The blister model is most frequently used and is shown in Fig. 23. The microscope stand is housed in a separate cell attached to the main cell and is usually shielded with 8 in. thick walls of steel or cast iron. The layout is such that cranked optic tubes are not necessary and results in a very compact arrangement.

Samples are transferred from the preparation cell to the microscope through a channel in the cell wall.

The microscope is equipped for examination in bright field, polarized light and sensitive tint. All glass components, including the four objectives on a revolving turret, inside the blister, are made from radiation resistant glass. All remote controls are grouped at the viewing position, the fine focus control is also operable from the camera back by means of a rod mounted below the optical bench.

It is not possible to use a hardness tester with this microscope and a separate instrument is available for this technique.

4. *Brachet "Telemicroscope".* The latest version of this microscope, first introduced in 1958, appeared in 1965 and is shown in Fig. 24. The remote controls, together with the illumination and image are brought out of the cell through a metal tunnel connecting the microscope stand and the viewing/control position (similar to Leitz MM5 RT).

The microscope is equipped for examination in bright and dark field, oblique and incident illumination, and polarized light. The lamp, 100 W mercury vapour or 250 W xenon, is situated outside the cell; if housed inside the cell, remote controls are provided. (Brachet advise against housing the lamp inside the cell however.)

Several interesting features are provided:

(1) Automatic centering of the stage.
(2) Stage movement of 80×80 mm allowing examination of large samples (upper limit probably governed by shielding).
(3) Automatic scanning of samples at $100 \times$ magnification coupled to automatic camera system for 400 exposures with built in negative numbering enabling mosaics to be prepared.
(4) Micro-hardness tester which completes its sequence of operation automatically.
(5) Motorized objective turret for 8 parfocalized objectives.

The microscope can also be used for macro examination at $10 \times$ magnification on viewing screen.

For use in cell up to 300 mm wall thickness.

5. *Other makes.* Although no British made remote microscope has been developed, several Vickers projection microscopes have been adapted for use in shielded cells at the Windscale Works of the UKAEA. The manufacturer modified the body of the microscope to enable the image beam to emerge horizontally from the cell, allowing suitable shielding to be used. Other remote controls, such as focusing, diaphragm controls, analyser and polarizer control, were carried out by the AEA staff and the motorized stage and super stage drives were carried out by A. Rundle (Upper Norwood) Ltd., Ashford, Kent.

Two Vickers M55 microscopes have been converted for remote operation at the Whiteshell Nuclear Research Establishment, Manitoba, Canada—described by Wilkins (1967). Focusing, objective selection, and stage traverse are motorized. Three objectives give macro $4 \cdot 75 \times$– $13 \cdot 3 \times$. It is not possible to change from micro to macro so one instrument is used for each technique.

Accessories. Remote microscopes can usually be fitted with the

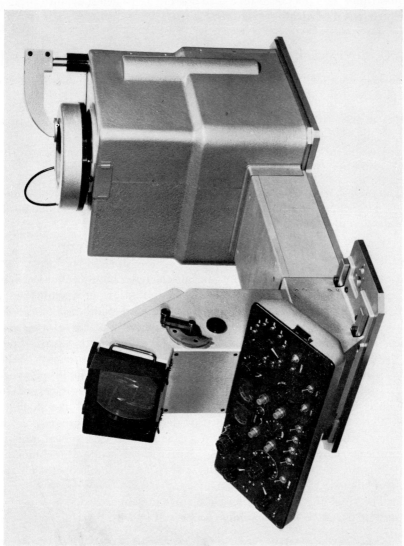

FIG. 24. Brachet "Telemicroscope". (Courtesy Etablissements Cerf, CAEM, Paris.)

normal accessories such as viewing screens, measuring and comparison eyepieces, and quantitative analysis equipment. At the AERE a "Quantimet 720" has been linked to one of the Reichert remote control microscopes described on page 22.

VII. Comparison of Microscope Features and Installations

In this chapter, two methods of providing a remote control microscope have been described:

(a) a standard microscope can be modified, for installation in a shielded cell, by the user

or (b) a special remote control model can be purchased from one of the manufacturers who now offer this type of microscope.

The choice will probably be made after consideration of local conditions, i.e. degree of sophistication required, availability of skilled staff, timescale and cost.

A. Standard microscope modified by user

1. In this case, an instrument can be selected which meets as nearly as possible the requirements of the examination programme, e.g. capability of changing from micro- to macro-examination. Those microscope accessories not required, e.g. phase contrast, dark field, micro-hardness tester, need not be provided with remote controls and, as the cost of modifying a microscope may be five times the cost of the basic instrument, a saving in the overall cost of the cell can be achieved.

2. Inevitably, special optical components and/or modifications to the basic instrument are necessary to enable it to be used in a shielded cell. These modifications may be provided by the microscope manufacturer, which is preferred, or by a specialist firm or by local labour. In any case, close liaison is necessary between the user and technicians carrying out the work if high quality results and reliable operation are to be achieved.

3. The shielding can be tailored to the exact microscope layout and it may be easier to fit a new microscope cell in with existing cells.

B. Commercial remote control microscopes

1. It can be seen from the descriptions given in this article that the range of special microscopes for use in shielded cells varies considerably in design, degree of sophistication and price (from £10 000 to £25 000). Usually, such a microscope is provided with remote controls for all

functions and if any are not required this will result in unnecessary expenditure.

2. Some designs, in which all controls, together with optic tubes etc. pass through a single duct are simpler to install and are less likely to become misaligned during use.

3. If skilled labour is not available this type of microscope with remote controls, special optics, etc. fitted by the manufacturer, should be chosen.

In either of the cases given, the installation of a remote control microscope should be carried out so that easy access is provided for maintenance and cleaning either by:

(a) building one wall of the cell as a sliding door which, after removal of the sample, can be opened and operations carried out through gloves fitted in the alpha (containment) box panel or:

(b) mounting the microscope on a trolley which can be wheeled out of the shielding.

C. *Ease of operation*

In addition to providing easy access to the microscope for maintenance, close attention should be paid to the layout of the cell operating face. The following points help to minimize operator fatigue:

1. All remote controls should be within easy reach of the operator when seated at the eyepiece or camera positions.

2. Use of parfocal objectives mounted on a motor driven turret; it is particularly advantageous if the turret can be rotated whilst the stage is in the lowered position, thus obviating the need to raise and lower the stage each time an objective is changed.

3. Ability to switch parfocal image between eyepiece and camera systems.

D. *Other desirable features*

1. The use of small d.c. motors to operate microscope controls. Stepping motors have recently been used at the AERE for extremely accurate microscope stage movements. (For a description of this type of motor see Causer, 1970). Although most microscope controls can be successfully motorized, mechanical operation is preferable for control of diaphragms and fine focus.

2. A large stage movement, up to 40×40 mm, to allow examination of, for example, complete fuel element sections.

3. Optic tubes should be as short as possible with the minimum number of cranks (consistent with shielding requirements), to ensure

minimum loss of illumination and misalignment during use. If a door is provided, the microscope lamp could be located inside the cell, thus eliminating the need for one optic tube. (The lamp would be adjusted before introduction of sample.)

VIII. OTHER TECHNIQUES

In addition to the optical techniques described, other instruments, e.g. electron microscope, scanning electron microscope and electron microprobe analyser are used for examination of irradiation materials.

A. *Electron Microscopy*

Two of the fission products formed in nuclear fuels are the gases xenon and krypton; they are produced on an atomic scale and under certain circumstances can build up to form sub-microscopic bubbles 20 Å to 1000 Å in diameter. In order to resolve such small detail it is necessary to utilize the electron microscope which can either examine two-stage plastic/carbon replicas or thin films of the actual material.

1. *Replicas*

Standard replication techniques have been adapted for use in shielded cells, (Bainbridge and Hudson, 1965). The first replicas taken are usually grossly contaminated and so are discarded; subsequent replicas are generally low enough in $\beta\gamma$ activity to be brought out of the cell and processed in a standard carbon evaporator/shadowing unit. The final carbon replica can then be examined in the electron microscope as normal, although care must be taken to prevent break up or loss of the replica which could be an ingestion hazard.

2. *Thin Films*

The production of thin films from bulk irradiated samples is now a routine operation in many atomic energy laboratories and the AERE work has been described by Bainbridge (1968). Thin films are produced by electropolishing 2·3 mm discs (to fit a standard electron microscope sample holder) of the sample material until approximately 1000 Å thick. They can then be examined in the electron microscope and are sufficiently low in $\beta\gamma$ activity to be adequately shielded by the microscope column. Care must be taken to prevent break up or loss of the thin film as this could become an ingestion hazard.

A recent addition to the equipment installed at AERE for the study of irradiated materials is the 1 MeV electron microscope and this is used to examine films of uranium metal up to $\frac{1}{2}$ μm thick (Foreman and Hudson, 1970).

B. *Scanning Electron Microscopy*

The Scanning Electron Microscope is now extensively used for examination of irradiated samples. It has the advantage that it can examine the surface of samples in the "as-irradiated" condition, i.e. no preparation is necessary. Because of its range of magnification and large depth of focus it has been used to supplement the information obtained with the optical microscope. Samples are usually larger, and therefore more active, than thin films and for this reason additional precautions are necessary when loading and unloading the scanning electron microscope. Once the specimen is in the instrument the column shielding is adequate to protect the operator.

C. *Electron Microprobe Analysis*

This technique is now standard practice to study irradiation induced changes in reactor materials, including analysis of fission product inclusions, corrosion effects in fuel cans, etc. (Lambert, 1968). Several makes of standard instrument have been modified for examination of radio-active samples and at least one manufacturer now offers a specially built analyser for this work. An important design requirement in a modified instrument is the shielding of the X-ray spectrometers from $\beta\gamma$ radiations from the sample which give rise to excessive noise and consequent loss of sensitivity.

IX. SUMMARY

Remote control microscopy, now carried out in nuclear laboratories in many countries, is an important part of the post-irradiation examination of reactor materials. This chapter describes how radioactive samples, although hazardous, can be safely examined in shielded cells. Optical equipment has been adapted for use in cells and details are given of how two models of metallurgical microscope were adapted for remote operation together with descriptions of commercially available microscopes for this work. In conclusion the salient features of each type of microscope are given along with comments on developments which have led to ease and efficiency of operation. Techniques employing the electron microscope and electron micro-probe analyser are briefly described.

ACKNOWLEDGEMENTS

The author would like to thank colleagues at the AERE Harwell and other establishments for help in preparing this article, and also Dr. K. S. B. Rose and Mr. J. B. Sayers for helpful comments on the manuscript. Thanks are also due to manufacturers for supplying details and photographs of equipment for examination of irradiated material.

REFERENCES

Bainbridge, J. E. and Hudson, B. (1965). AERE Unclassified Report 4965.
Bainbridge, J. E. (1968). AERE Unclassified Report 5677.
Campbell, D. (1970). *Nuclear Energy*, **11** (Sept./Oct.) (5).
Causer, R. (1970). "Engineering Review" July, Standards Group, AERE, Harwell.
Foreman, A. J. E. and Hudson, B. (1970). 7th International Conference on Electron Microsocopy (Grenoble) Vol. 1, p. 77.
Gray, R. J. (1968). American Society for Testing Materials STP-430, pp. 17–62.
Greer-Spencer, J. G. (1961). AERE Unclassified Report 2549.
Krautwedel, H. L. (1969). *Metallography*, **2**, 2/3, p. 191.
Lambert, J. D. B. (1968). *Nuclear Energy* January, pp. 2–12, March pp. 34–45, May pp. 66–75.
Recommendations of the International Commission on Radiological Protection, Publication no. 9 (1966), Pergamon Press, Oxford.
Sykes, E. C. (1959). British Institute of Radio Engineers Convention, Session 7.
Venables, J. H. (1969). Conference on Lead Shielding and Nuclear Safety, Lead Development Association, London.
Wilkins, B. J. S. (1967). Proceedings of 15th Conference on Remote Systems Technology, p. 296. American Nuclear Society.

Automated Microscopy for Cytological Analysis

K. PRESTON, Jr.

The Perkin-Elmer Corporation, Norwalk, Connecticut, USA

I. INTRODUCTION

IN three of the earlier volumes of this series the reader has been exposed to discussions of semi-automatic and automatic measurement techniques in visible light microscopy. In Volume 3 Humphries (1969) described a series of both manual and semi-automatic techniques for determining particle size, shape and volume. Various specialized microscopes and microscope attachments were discussed having a variety of grids and reticles which were useful for specific measurement tasks. In Volume 2 Mendelsohn *et al.* (1968) described the CYDAC CYtological DAta Conversion) system which has available both an electronic and a mechanical television microscope capable of logging microscope images on magnetic tape. Methods of automatically processing images of chromosome spreads, human white blood cells, and other tissues using an off-line computer were described giving an indication of the power of digital computer programs for high speed picture processing. In Volume 4 Beadle (1971) described an automatic microscope system, called the Quantimet, which is characterized by being completely automatic and exhibits extraordinary speed of performance. This machine was developed primarily for metallurgical applications in high speed particle analysis and, in a general sense, is not programmable in its picture processing operations.

Fig. 1. The CELLSCAN/GLOPR system for use in automated microscopical picture processing. (1) Xenon lamp power supply; (2) auto-focus mechanism; (3) television microscope; (4) slide traverse mechanism; (5) finding and framing computer; (6) ASR-35 teletype; (7) GLOPR computer; (8) Varian 620i computer system.

This chapter contributes the first complete description of a new generation of microscope image processors wherein the user has at his immediate disposal not only the image logging capability of a television microscope but also the picture processing capability of an on-line system of several digital computers. (See Fig. 1.) Whereas in the CYDAC system the microscope was manipulated manually by the user and images were processed off-line using a large general purpose machine the CELLSCAN™/GLOPR™ system described here has a microscope which is automated in almost all of its functions. Furthermore two special purpose and one general purpose computer are included as an on-line facility. The user communicates with both the computers and the microscope via a teletype keyboard. The language used for communication is a new language called GLOL which is a high level computer language such as FORTRAN, ALGOL, etc. Its structure permits the user to write programs in which single commands are used to select the color of illumination in the microscope, to position the microscope stage, and to transmit selected images from the microscope to the computer for analysis. The GLOL language also permits the user to cause microscope images to be logged in either digitized or quantized form on magnetic tape and to be recalled from magnetic tape as required during picture processing experiments. Finally, the language permits the user to code picture processing procedures, to observe their action on the computer display, to modify them as desired, and to file them for future use and reference.

Two somewhat similar systems are now under construction; one, in the United States the other in Great Britain. In the United States there is the Spectre II system which is being developed by a group led by Lipkin (1969) and in Great Britain Rutovitz and others (1970) are developing another such system as part of a program being carried out by the Medical Research Council. Other systems of interest also have come into being which are similar to CYDAC in that all functions are not automated and/or most computation is done off-line or via time-sharing. These include the TICAS system of Wied *et al.* (1968) and those systems developed by Ledley (1969) at the National Biomedical Research Foundation, by Nathan and Selzer (1968) at the Jet Propulsion Laboratory and by Neurath and others (1970) at the New England Medical Center.

The primary purpose of this chapter is to describe CELLSCAN/ GLOPR rather than to draw parallels with these other systems. The interested reader should therefore review the references cited above in order to make system comparisons. Since CELLSCAN/GLOPR has been used primarily in hematology, this chapter begins by providing the background necessary to understand this particular branch of cytological analysis. After thus setting the stage in a specific task-oriented manner, this chapter continues by describing the characteristics of the CELLSCAN/GLOPR automatic microscope, giving illustrations of the images formed with this system, and then proceeding with a discussion of specific picture processing techniques and recent results which have been obtained in the field of automated cytology.

II. White Blood Cell Differentiation

A. *General*

The major classes of human blood cells are shown in Fig. 2. There are two major classes; the erythrocytes (red cells) and the leukocytes (white cells). The leukocytes are further sub-classified into those cells which show a granular cytoplasm (granulocytes) and those which do not (monocytes and lymphocytes). Finally the granulocytes are sub-divided according to the way in which they react to the common biological stain called "Wright's stain" (methylene blue eosinate). The subclasses of the class granulocyte are the eosinophil (cytoplasmic granules stain red), the neutrophil (cytoplasmic granules stain faintly), and the basophil (cytoplasmic granules stain purple). In addition there are also many types of commonly occurring abnormal leukocytes as well as certain rare types of leukocytes which are not discussed in this chapter.

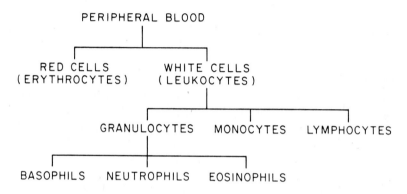

Fɪɢ. 2. Major classes and sub-classes of peripheral blood cells.

Quantitative information on the patient's health is obtained by per-forming what is called the "white blood cell differential count" or "WBCD". To perform this count 100 leukocytes are observed through the microscope and are categorized according to the categories shown in Fig. 2. Because of the low rate of occurrence of the eosinophil (3%) and of the basophil (0·5%) the statistical validity of the 100-cell differential count is subject to question. However, for reasons of economy and due to the scarcity of qualified clinical technologists, most WBCD's are taken at the 100-cell level. The man-hours spent on performing these counts represent an enormous volume of effort. In the United States alone millions of man-hours are allocated to this task annually. Unfortunately, due to the fatiguing nature of the work and the difficulty of obtaining suitably trained technologists, perform-ance is often far from satisfactory. Therefore this area of effort is a prime target for automation if such automation may be achieved within the usual constraints of economy. One reason that automation of this operation has not yet been achieved is due to the extreme difficulty of mechanizing the extraordinary capabilities of the human eye/brain system in performing the complex pattern recognition tasks involved.

B. *Blood Film Preparation*

The first step in performing the WBCD is to extract a small sample of blood (a few drops are sufficient) either by finger-puncture or by veni-puncture. This blood is then carefully spread on a microscope slide, allowed to dry, and stained with Wright's stain. At this point the examination of the blood film under the microscope commences. Ordinarily, due to the difficulty of manually spreading the blood in a thin uniform film, the clinical technologist must search under low power (100 ×) until a "good" region of the blood film is located. Unfortunately, as has been shown by Ingram and Minter (1969), the white blood cell differential count varies from point to point on the manually prepared blood film. Thus the process of selecting the area in which cells are to be observed places an unknown bias in the final results.

TABLE I

Differential leukocyte counts on spinner and conventional smears
(After Ingram and Minter, 1969)

Smear	Granulocytes	Lymphocytes	Monocytes	Degenerate cells (Total %)
Conventional	56·1 + 7·2*	39·3 + 8·2	6 + 3	18·6
Spinner†	63·2 + 5·8	32·2 + 3·4	4·6 + 3·4	2·8

* Percentage of the three cell types ± 2 Std. Dev. shown for whole blood smears on which 500 consecutive cells were classified.
† All spinner smears represented were spun at 7000 rev/min.

In 1967 Preston and Norgren (1971) devised a method of automating the preparation of blood films so as to achieve complete uniformity over the entire area of the microscope slide. To do this a technique was adapted for the preparation of blood films which was then in use for producing uniform layers of photoresist on silicon slices in manufacturing transistors. The transistor industry applies such films by a process called "spinning". Spinning involves mounting the silicon slice on a chuck, flooding it with photoresist, and spinning it about an axis of symmetry perpendicular to the surface upon which the photoresist was applied. With the proper combination of acceleration, deceleration, rev/min and spin time, it is possible to produce extraordinarily uniform films of photoresist. By means of a rigorous investigation, Preston and Ingram were able to achieve equally good results on films of human blood. This development has been a significant step forward in the automation of the WBCD. As can be seen from Table I not only is the uniformity of the distribution of white blood cells improved by spinning

FIG. 3. Typical blood film spinner.

but also the number of white blood cells disrupted is far less than those disrupted when using manual techniques.

A typical blood film spinner is shown in Fig. 3. This figure shows the chuck for holding the microscope slide and the bowl in which it is recessed. The purpose of the bowl is to catch the excess blood which is cast off during spinning. Figure 3 also shows a spun blood film which has been stained with Wright's stain. Figure 4 shows spun blood films made by both flooding the microscope slide with blood and by using a few drops. This figure also affords comparison with a good manually made film. All films shown are stained with Wright's stain. The spun film may be made to cover an area as large as several square centimeters. This area is large enough to permit a WBCD to be performed on several thousand cells if desired. This feat would be difficult if not impossible with a manually prepared blood film. Spun blood films may also be made on microscope cover slips using a spinner with a chuck modified for this purpose.

Fig. 4. Stained films of human blood on microscope slides. Left to right: spun film made by initially flooding microscope slide; spun film made from two drops of blood placed in centre of slide; manually spread film.

III. THE AUTOMATIC MICROSCOPE

A. *General*

With the advent of spinning for blood film preparation, the automatic microscope for use in white blood cell differential counting need not be programmed for the difficult task of searching for a "good" area on the microscope slide. The CELLSCAN/GLOPR system uses a standard Leitz Ortholux microscope. The microscope slide is manually loaded on the microscope stage under oil immersion and the microscope is adjusted by the user for initial focus on the blood cells. After this operation has been carried out, the user returns to the teletype keyboard and simply types the command FIND. This activates a special purpose image processing unit which we call the "finding and framing" computer which automatically locates leukocytes in the blood film. Since there are approximately 1000 erythrocytes per leukocyte, this image processing unit must reject 100 000 erythrocytes in the process of finding sufficient leukocytes for a 100 cell WBCD.

B. *Oscillating Mirror Scanner*

The inter-relationships between the leukocyte finding computer and the automatic microscope within the overall CELLSCAN/GLOPR system are shown in the system block diagram given in Fig. 5. The

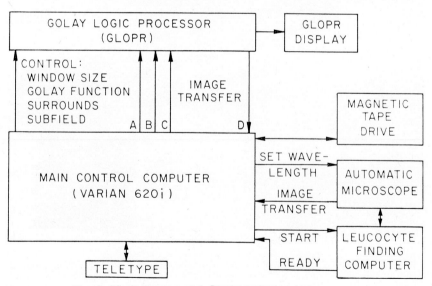

FIG. 5. Block diagram of the CELLSCAN/GLOPR system.

heart of the automatic microscope is an oscillating-mirror television scanner which mounts on the microscope body in the place ordinarily occupied by the trinocular tube used for photography. This scanner is an extremely simple, reliable and accurate mechanism for both photo-microgrammetry and photomicrometry.

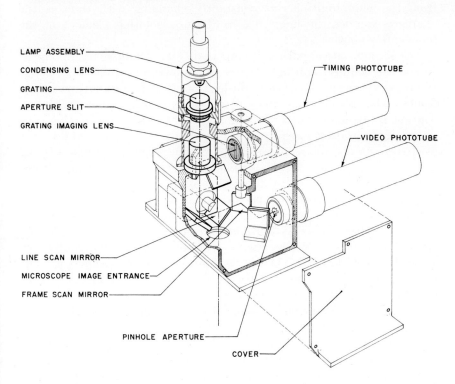

LAMP ASSEMBLY

CONDENSING LENS

GRATING

APERTURE SLIT

GRATING IMAGING LENS

TIMING PHOTOTUBE

VIDEO PHOTOTUBE

LINE SCAN MIRROR

MICROSCOPE IMAGE ENTRANCE

FRAME SCAN MIRROR

PINHOLE APERTURE

COVER

HIGH RESOLUTION IMAGE SCANNER

FIG. 6. Isometric drawing of the galvanometer scanner used in the CELLSCAN/GLOPR television microscope.

Two optical paths are provided within the scanner. (See Fig. 6). In one path the image produced by the microscope objective is formed in reflection from two moving mirrors. The first of these mirrors moves at the television line frequency and is therefore called the "horizontal mirror". The other mirror which oscillates at the television frame rate is the "vertical mirror". After reflecting off the front surfaces of the horizontal and vertical mirrors, the image is formed on an aperture which is one resolution element in diameter in the plane of the image.

Behind this aperture is a photomultiplier called the "video photomultipler". The output current of this photomultiplier is proportional to the light flux passing through the aperture. As the horizontal and vertical mirrors oscillate, the image formed by the microscope optics is swept in a raster-fashion across this aperture. Thus the current from the photomultiplier is constantly changing with time as the aperture samples the light flux from one resolution element of the image after another.

The second optical path is illuminated from a light source mounted within the scanner. This light source illuminates a grating whose image is formed via the back surface of the horizontal mirror on a slit aperture in front of what is called the "timing" or "synchronizing" photomultiplier. The slit is aligned parallel to the image of the bars of the grating. The image of the grating sweeps past this aperture as the horizontal mirror oscillates. As the image of each bar of the grating passes across the aperture, a pulse of current is emitted by the synchronizing photomultiplier which is used to direct the computer to sample the video signal. Despite scan to scan perturbations in the motion of the horizontal mirror each synchronizing pulse produced by the synchronizing photomultiplier occurs at the exact instant when the proper image element is imaged on the aperture in front of the video photomultiplier. Thus the CELLSCAN/GLOPR oscillating mirror scanner is self-compensating for positional perturbations in the horizontal scan direction. This allows the horizontal mirror to be driven in any mode desired. It is our current practice to use a simple sinusoidal scan generator to drive the horizontal mirror rather than the traditional "saw-tooth" scan generator.

The advantages of oscillating mirror microscope scanners have been discussed in detail by Mansberg and Ohringer (1969). The motion of each mirror is produced by applying the driving current to a galvanometer movement on whose shaft is mounted the mirror in question. Galvanometer motors are typically used in chart recorders and may be built to have an accuracy of at least 1 part in 100. Using a cantilever or "taut-band" suspension for the motor and designing for small angular motions which will not fatigue this suspension, it is possible to achieve an essentially infinite life for the device.

It is important to mention that the two prime advantages of the oscillating mirror scanner are that (1) it may be used with illumination of any wavelength and (2) the same video photodetector is employed to measure the light flux at each image point. This avoids the disadvantage of the essentially monochromatic cathode ray tube scanners as well as the problems of photosurface non-uniformity which are present in all television imaging tubes (such as orthicons, vidicons, etc.).

The disadvantages of a mirror scanner are, of course, that (1) motions cannot be produced which are as rapid as those characteristic of electron beam action and (2), as the scan frequency is increased, the dynamics of the situation cause the positional accuracy of the galvanometer movement to depart from that which is characteristic of its quasistatic performance. In the CELLSCAN/GLOPR oscillating mirror scanner the vertical mirror moves at a sufficiently slow rate (1 scan in approximately 3 s) that linearity is satisfactory. The horizontal mirror, which oscillates at 40 scans s^{-1}, is compensated by the synchronization scheme mentioned above.

C. *Microscope Stage Positioning*

Positioning the microscope slide in the automatic microscope is handled by two separate electro-mechanical systems. Motion along the optical axis, i.e. in the focusing direction, is controlled by means of a closed loop servo-mechanism. The purpose of this servo-mechanism is to hold the microscope slide continuously in focus. This action is performed by electronically analyzing the signal produced by the video photomultiplier. The high frequencies in this signal are processed by an electronic circuit which, through a feed-back mechanism allied with the automatic focus control, maximizes the high frequency content of the signal. This insures that objects presently in the field of view are kept in best focus.

Motion of the microscope stage in the plane of the microscope slide is under control of a commercially available slide positioning unit sold by the Leitz Corporation. This unit is manufactured by the Femco Corp. of Irwin, Pennsylvania (USA). It connects to pulleys on the x and y stage controls via a system of belts which move the stage in a pre-programmed fashion. Travel and velocity in the x direction are adjusted by two separate controls. Each time the stage reaches the preset travel limit in the x direction, it is stepped by a preset increment in the y direction. Thus the stage itself performs a raster scan. This is the type of scan initiated by the FIND command and it continues while the automatic microscope searches for objects of interest on the microscope slide.

D. *Finding and Framing*

The action of the finding and framing computer is constantly to monitor the output of the video photomultiplier as the microscope

3

slide is being searched. During the search portion of the operation the
microscope illumination is set to a band between 570 and 670 nm
(yellow-red). With this illumination Wright's stained leukocyte nuclei
absorb strongly while the Wright's-stained red cells are relatively
transparent. As soon as a Wright's-stained leukocyte nucleus appears
within the field of view of the objective, its location is sensed by the
finding and framing computer. The finding and framing computer
causes the motion of the stage to be arrested at the appropriate instant
of time. The same computer also sets up gating pulses on the signal
from the video photomultiplier which frame the image of the leukocyte
which has been located in a $24 \times 24 \ \mu$m window. The main control
computer is then notified that a leukocyte has been found. Because of
the relatively large separation between leukocyte nuclei in typical

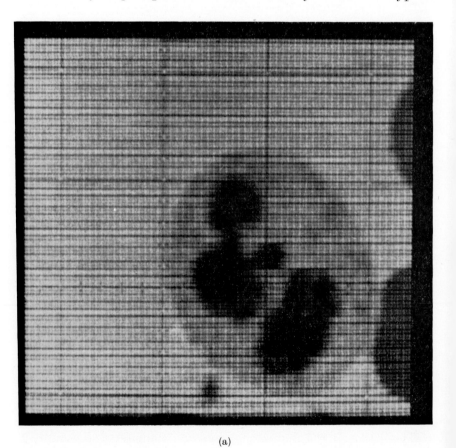

(a)

Fig. 7. For caption see page 58.

blood films the likelihood that a window contains more than one leukocyte is extremely small. When a leukocyte has thus been "captured"
the user is so informed by the main control computer which returns
control to the teletype.

E. *Display and Analysis*

The user now has several options which he may exercise. One option
is simply to display the image of what has been found for visual

(b)

Fɪɢ. 7. For caption see page 58.

analysis. Another option is to record the image in either quantized or digitized form on magnetic tape. The third and final option is to execute an image processing program either on an experimental or "production line" basis.

Two types of scanner display are available in the CELLSCAN/ GLOPR system. One is the standard television display which is illustrated in Fig. 7. This figure shows the five commonly occurring types of white blood cells which were discussed earlier. In forming the display the user may operate the teletype to cause the automatic microscope to change its wavelength of illumination. At the present time blue, green and yellow-red illumination is available, under teletype control.

(c)

Fig. 7. For caption see page 58.

The standard television display, although informative to the human eye, is too qualitiative for accurate photometry. Non-linearities in the light emitted by the phosphor of the display tube as well as non-linearities in the response of the recording medium (photographic film) make precise photometric measurements impossible. An alternative display which shows the television signal in isometric form makes quantitation possible. Figure 8 shows three such displays formed of the neutrophil shown in Fig. 7 using three separate bands of illumination. This form of display is called the contourograph and has been discussed extensively by Preston and Carvalco (1969). It is produced by

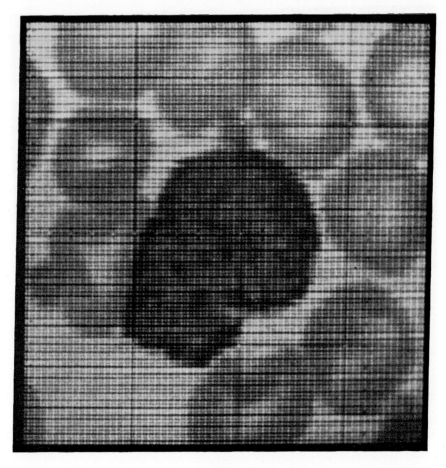

(d)

Fig. 7. For caption see page 58.

combining the output of the video photomultiplier with information derived on the position of the horizontal and vertical mirrors as given by the following equations:

$$v(t) = \alpha_{ov}s_o(t) + \alpha_{vv}s_v(t) \tag{1}$$
$$h(t) = \alpha_{vh}s_v(t) + \alpha_{hh}s_h(t) \tag{2}$$

where $v(t)$ and $h(t)$ are the contourographic vertical and horizontal signals, respectively, $s_o(t)$, $s_v(t)$ and $s_h(t)$ are the scanner video, vertical and horizontal signals, respectively, and the α's are the combining coefficients. Since $v(t)$ incorporates the actual video signal $s_o(t)$, it is

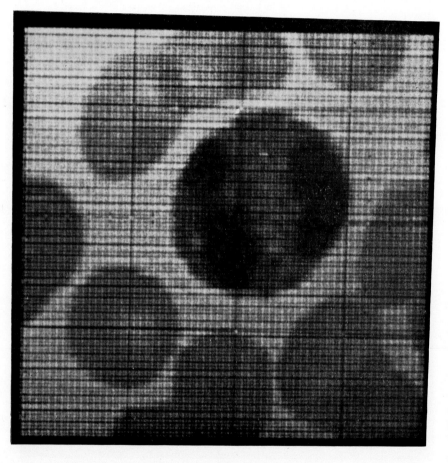

(e)

FIG. 7. Five television images formed by the CELLSCAN/GLOPR system. Left to right: (a) neutrophil; (b) lymphocyte; (c) monocyte; (d) basophil; (e) eosinophil.

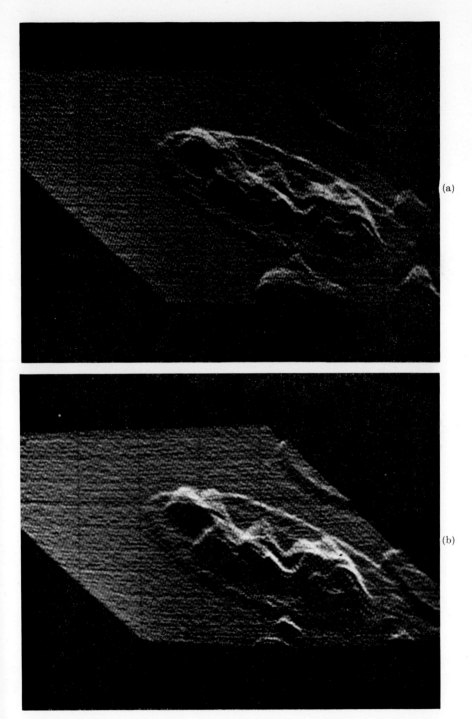

(a)

(b)

FIG. 8. For caption see page 60.

possible (within the deflection linearity of the display oscilloscope) to observe and measure intensity variations throughout the image in a quantitative manner. Since the cytoplasm of the erythrocytes is red and the neutrophil nucleus is blue, blue illumination causes the contourograph to show a relatively light neutrophil nucleus and dark erythrocytes; green, dark neutrophil nucleus, erythrocytes and cytoplasm; yellow-red, dark neutrophil nucleus and light erythrocytes and cytoplasm.

IV. Picture Processing

A. *General*

Once a leukocyte has been located by means of the automatic microscope and displayed, if desired, by the user for visual analysis, the user of CELLSCAN/GLOPR may experiment in analyzing its structure by coding various picture processing programs. Alternatively, he may

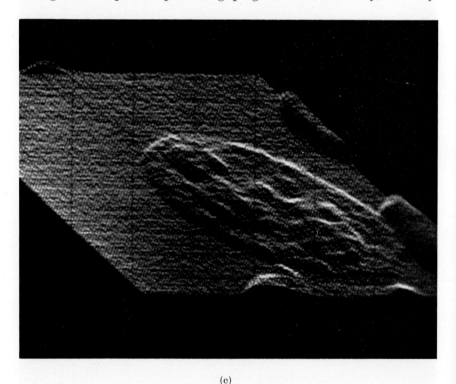

(c)

Fig. 8. Contourographs of the neutrophil image shown in Fig. 7 using illumination in (a) the yellow-red; (b) green; (c) blue.

decide to use previously coded programs to carry out his investigation. It is even possible for him to perform a hands-off operation where he simply instructs the automatic microscope to find a multiplicity of leukocytes and to identify each one according to previously determined tests. Upon his return to the CELLSCAN/GLOPR system the user may then request a printout of the numbers and types of leukocytes located.

B. *Golay Pattern Transformations*

In all cases the picture processing algorithms utilized in the CELLSCAN/GLOPR system are based upon the hexagonal pattern

(a)

FIG. 9. For caption see page 63.

transformations of Golay (1969). A complete description of Golay
transformations and their application to picture processing is beyond
the scope of this chapter. The interested reader is referred to Appendix
I and to a discussion by Preston (1971) at the Symposium on Feature
Extraction and Selection held by the Institute of Electrical and
Electronic Engineers at the Argonne National Laboratory in October
1970.

Golay transformations are implemented in the CELLSCAN/GLOPR
system by means of a computer language called GLOL (Golay LOgic
Language). The complete command structure of GLOL is presented in
Appendix II. This chapter illustrates the use of this image processing

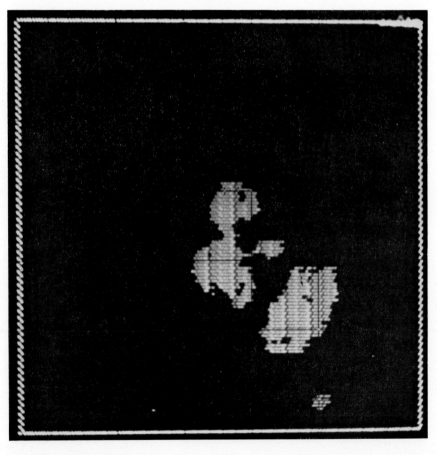

(b)

Fig. 9. For caption see page 63.

language in certain specific applications. To begin with, note that the purpose of any program in GLOL is to manipulate the leukocyte image in such a way that measurements may be made which may be used (1) to identify the class of leukocyte presented and/or (2) to provide diagnostically useful information.

Before manipulating the leukocyte image, it must first be converted into a form suitable for the application of the Golay transformations. Golay transformations require that all images be represented by stacks of black and white (binary) images. Each binary image in the stack is generated by thresholding the initial television image at a

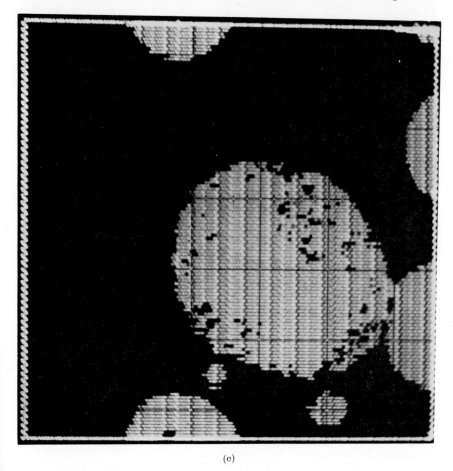

(c)

FIG. 9. Binary images formed by thresholding the neutrophil images shown in Fig. 7 at (a) the peak nuclear density; (b) the minimum nuclear density; (c) the minimum erythrocyte density.

specific photometric level. Image elements darker than this level take
on the binary value 1; all others 0. Three binary images derived from
the neutrophil shown in Fig. 7 are shown in Fig. 9 with a composite
image (made by triple exposure) shown in Fig. 10.

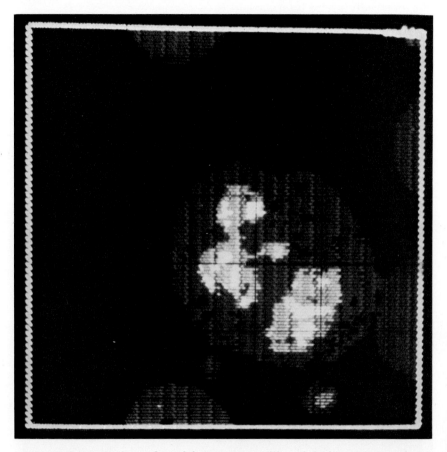

FIG. 10. Composite image formed from a superposition of the binary images shown
in Fig. 9.

The Golay transformations require that image elements be arranged
in an hexagonal lattice where each image element is surrounded by six
nearest neighbours. As has been pointed out by Rosenfeld (1970) the
hexagonal lattice avoids the fundamental connectivity ambiguity of
the square lattice. The action of Golay's hexagonal transformations is
independent of the orientation of the image (as it should be, since the
class to which a white blood cell belongs is the same whether it is

"up-side-down" or "right-side-up"). It turns out that there are only fourteen orientation-independent nearest neighbour configurations which may occur in binary images stored in the hexagonal lattice. For reference these configurations are shown in Fig. 11. They are called the "Golay surrounds".

```
  0 0       1 0       1 1       1 1       1 1       1 1        1 1
0 X 0     0 X 0     0 X 0     0 X 1     1 X 1     1 X 1      1 X 1
  0 0       0 0       0 0       0 0       0 0       1 0        1 1

 ZERO      ONE       TWO      THREE     FOUR      FIVE        SIX


  1 0       1 1       1 1       1 1       1 0       0 0        1 1
0 X 1     0 X 0     0 X 0     0 X 1     0 X 1     1 X 1      0 X 0
  1 0       0 1       1 0       1 0       0 0       0 0        1 1

SEVEN    EIGHT      NINE       TEN     ELEVEN   TWELVE   THIRTEEN
```

FIG. 11. The 14 Golay hexagonal patterns, i.e. the Golay "surrounds".

In coding a procedure in GLOL the user must indicate to the computer:

(1) What surrounds are to be checked in the particular image plane being examined.
(2) What action is to be taken when a particular image element occurs in the presence of these surrounds.
(3) Whether the values of image elements from other image planes are to take part in the decision.

All of these instructions are entered on the teletype in a single line of code called the "Golay statement" (see Appendix I). A statement either causes the contents of a given image plane to be altered or creates a new image plane while retaining the contents of the original image in memory.

Sequences of statements are called "procedures" and may be given a procedure name and filed by the user for future recall. Recalling a procedure causes the specified sequence of Golay transformations to be executed.

Measurements are made by inter-leaving COUNT commands within sequences of Golay statements. Each COUNT command causes all elements in a specified binary image which have the binary value 1 to be counted. This count is tabulated and stored as an element of the measurement vector.

C. *GLOL Procedures*

Simple as the Golay transformations may seem they provide a powerful tool for picture processing. Two specific examples have been given. Figure 9b shows the binary image which results when the neutrophil shown in Fig. 7a is thresholded at a photometric level corresponding to the maximum transmission of its nucleus. Note that only the nucleus appears in the resultant binary image.

One measure which is useful in leukocyte recognition is simply the ratio of nuclear perimeter to nuclear area. Such a computation may be

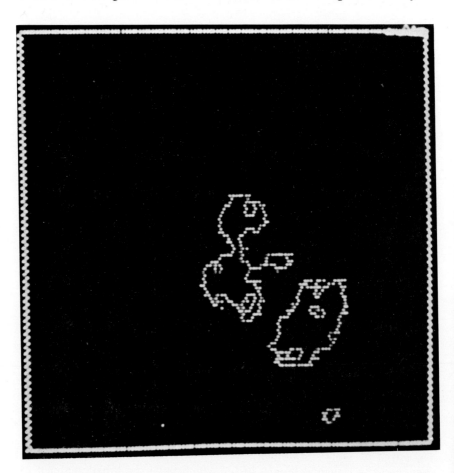

FIG. 12. Binary image resulting when all interior points (binary 1's with the Golay surround No. 6) are removed from the binary image shown in Fig. 12. A count of this image yields a measure of nuclear perimeter.

carried out using a procedure consisting of the following four lines of GLOL code.

```
COUNT A,M(1)
B=M[G'(A)A]6,,
COUNT B,M(2)
ARITHMETIC M(3)=M(2)/M(1)
```

The first line is simply the already discussed COUNT statement which scores as the first element of the measurement vector M(I) the total of all binary 1's in image plane A, i.e. the nuclear area. The second line of code contracts the binary 1's in image plane A to those which are not

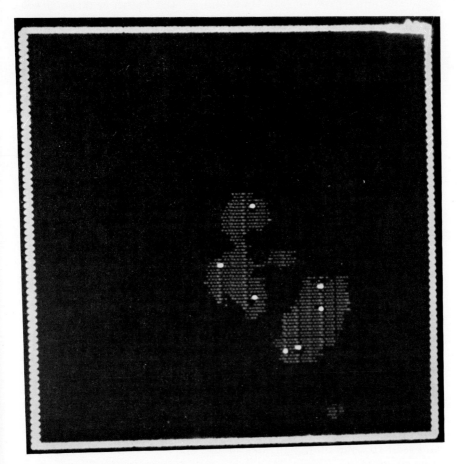

FIG. 13. Composite image showing the contents of the binary image plane (bright points) holding the results of a GLOL void-marking procedure superimposed on the original binary image of the neutrophil nucleus.

interior points, i.e. to those which do not exhibit the sixth Golay surround. The result is placed in image plane B whose contents are shown in Fig. 12. The third line of code counts the total number of binary 1's in image plane B, i.e. totalizes the peripheral points of the nuclear image, and scores these as the second element of measurement vector M(I). Finally, the last line of code is an arithmetic statement which takes the ratio of the first two elements of the measurement vector M(I) and scores these as the third element of the same measurement vector.

In a second example the following GLOL procedure may be used to score the number of nuclear voids and set the fourth element in the measurement vector equal to this number.

$$B=A$$
$$B=M[G(B)+G'(B)B]1{-}13,4,$$
$$C=B-A$$
$$C=M[G'(C)C]1{-}4,4,3$$
$$C=M[G(A)A]1,,$$
$$\text{COUNT C,M(4)}$$

Two image planes (B and C) are used in a manipulation which, after the execution of the third statement, places a cluster of binary 1's in image plane C corresponding to each nuclear void. These clusters are contracted to isolated binary 1's by the fourth statement. The fifth statement erases all other material from image plane C while retaining the isolated binary 1's which are then counted by the sixth statement. The resultant contents of image plane C are shown brightened and superimposed on the contents of image plane A in Fig. 13.

D. *The GLOPR Computer*

Many other relatively complex picture processing operations may be carried out using reasonably simple GLOL procedures. For example, nuclear lobes may be sized and counted, nuclear and cytoplasmic texture measured, cytoplasmic voids located, etc. The great advantage of the simplicity of the associated Golay hexagonal transformations is that they may be performed at high speeds even when using computer logic which operates on only one image point at a time (rather than upon all image points simultaneously). These transformations may be executed using a low cost, special purpose, picture processing computer and lead to computational rates many times faster than comparable general purpose machines. For this purpose we have constructed GLOPR (Golay LOgic PRocessor). This unit is accessed as if it were a fast subroutine by the main control computer.

The present GLOPR deals with 1, 2, or 3 binary image planes in a stack simultaneously. Simple Golay statements may be executed in approximately 50 ms for a 128×128 image. Optionally the user may specify a 64×64 or 32×32 image with corresponding faster execution times. Golay procedures such as those shown above may be executed in less than a second while more complex procedures may take several seconds to execute. These image processing rates are comparable with the speed of the associated automatic microscope in both locating leukocytes on microscope slides and scanning their images into the computer system.

E. *Measurement Analysis*

Using GLOL procedures of only moderate complexity it is possible to measure many leukocyte properties as mentioned above. Once a set of measurements have been made on a leukocyte of an unknown type, the computer must calculate the cell type to which these measurements are most likely to correspond. There are many methods of performing this association ranging from the classical approach taken in multivariate statistical analysis to some of the newer algorithmic approaches taken in such fields as parametric linear programming (See Willner, 1967). We have explored many of these analytical techniques and are evaluating their efficiency. As one might expect, each has its special field of utility.

Although this chapter is primarily concerned with automatic microscopy and associated problems in picture processing, it also briefly reviews here some of the problems inherent in measurement analysis. As is well known, the multivariate statistical approach to object recognition from a given set of measurements is optimum when the distribution of measurements for all classes of images corresponds to the normal or Gaussian distribution (See Anderson, 1958). Where Gaussian statistics do not apply or where multimodality within a class occurs, other approaches are advantageous. The basic problem in classifying a leukocyte from measurements performed on its image is illustrated by the model shown in Fig. 14. This 3-dimensional model shows three clusters lying in a 3-dimensional measurements space. Let us assume that these three clusters represent regions in 3-space where measurements on three classes of leukocytes tend to congregate. For reasons of illustration these clusters are elongated and are aligned with each of the three measurement axes. Classical multivariate analysis seeks to find the plane which may be used to separate the measurements corresponding to one particular class from those measurements representing all other classes. The difficulty encountered by taking such an approach is well illustrated in Fig. 14 since there is in fact no plane which can successfully separate measurements corresponding to any one cluster from the other two clusters. This fact has led us to abandon the classical approach and devise an improved technique called "pair-wise"

FIG. 14. Three-dimensional model showing three separate regions in a 3-dimensional measurement space delineating clusters corresponding to three classes of leukocytes.

data separation. This approach is illustrated in Fig. 15. Measurement space is compartmented by "many" planes in such a manner that each compartment contains only members of one class. As might be expected by an examination of Fig. 15 this approach has been far more successful

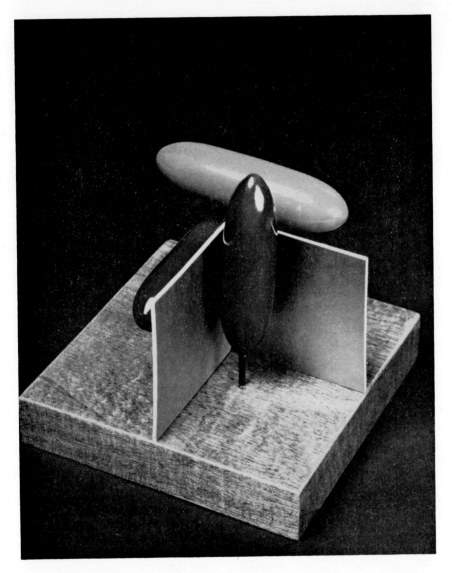

FIG. 15. Illustration showing the use of two planes in 3-dimensional space whose purpose is to separate one cluster from all other clusters.

than the classical single-plane approach. Two planes are shown in Fig. 15 which define a compartment which contains a single cluster. Presently the CELLSCAN/GLOPR system is programmed to perform pair-wise separation for as many as eight white blood cell classes. The pair-wise separation of eight classes requires 28 planes.

V. Recent Results

So far our research has concentrated primarily on analysis of blood films made from normal subjects. Using CELLSCAN/GLOPR in fully automatic, hands-off operations, the system has been made to operate without monitoring for long periods. Our present mode of operation for this type of production line work is to mount a microscope slide on

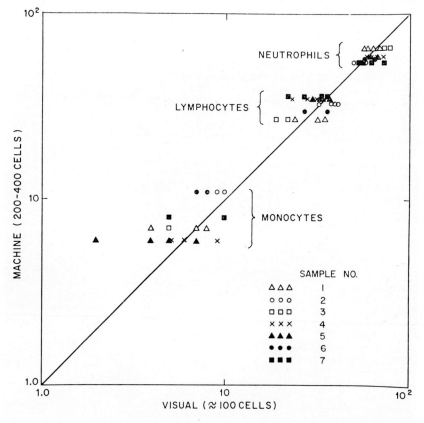

FIG. 16. Graph showing the correlation of white blood cell differential counts made by the CELLSCAN/GLOPR system with visual counts for the same subjects made by clinical technologists.

the automatic microscope at the end of the day, activate the system for a 500–1000 cell WBCD, and retrieve the microscope slide the following morning. In 1970 many overnight runs of this type were performed. During these runs the finding and framing computer detected many thousands of objects which were judged by the main control computer to be leukocytes. Each of the objects was measured, analyzed as to its morphology, and then identified by the machine as being a lymphocyte, granulocyte, or monocyte. When a decison could not be reached, the object was placed in a "don't know" category. All the blood films examined by the machine were then examined visually by at least two clinical technologists at the Norwalk Hospital (Norwalk, Connecticut, USA). The machine WBCD was then plotted against the results of visual WBCD. Results are shown for seven subjects in Fig. 16.

CYTOLOGICAL DATA SHEET EXPERIMENT 067

	NEUTROPHIL			LYMPHOCYTE			MONOCYTE		
TRIMMED NUCLEAR AREA	17	22	27	29	38	47	52	80	107
TOTAL CELL AREA	62	93	124	61	89	117	121	177	234
FINE STRUCTURE INDEX	.36	.47	.58	.23	.28	.33	.18	.26	.34
INCLUSION INDEX	.015	.025	.035	–	.008	.018	–	.023	.051
IRREGULARITY INDEX, FINE	–	2.8	13	.11	.25	.60	.66	3.3	5.8
IRREGULARITY INDEX, COARSE	.40	.82	1.2	–	.06	.19	.28	1.4	2.6
ELONGATION INDEX	–	.093	.315	.008	.013	.018	.004	.026	.048
NUCLEAR TRANSMISSION, Y	.29	.38	.47	.29	.35	.41	.44	.45	.46
CYTOPLASMIC TRANSMISSION, Y	.23	.61	1.0	.44	.65	.86	.47	.66	.85
NUCLEAR TRANSMISSION, G	.20	.21	.22	.18	.19	.20	.20	.28	.36
CYTOPLASMIC TRANSMISSION, G	.25	.40	.55	–	.50	–	–	.50	–

FIG. 17. Cytological data sheet graphing measurements made by the CELLSCAN/GLOPR system on both the morphology and colour of the five classes of human white blood cells. Results taken from a particular patient are shown graphed with respect to the means and 3-sigma limits for the means of the population or patients.

Besides classifying the leukocytes found, the machine measured and tabulated many details on the structure of each cell. These measurements are currently being graphed for each experiment on a data sheet, an example of which is shown in Fig. 17. This data sheet lists a series of indices which are currently under investigation for their possible diagnostic utility. These indices include information on both the nuclear area and overall cell area. Indices derived on fine structure, inclusions, irregularity in the nuclear outline, and nuclear elongation are also included. Finally, four indices are included which are measures of colour, i.e. transmission values of both nucleus and cytoplasm in the 570–670 nm band (yellow-red) and in the 500–550 nm (green). (At the present time sufficient statistical information is not yet available for tabulation of results taken in the blue.) Although some of these measurements are not used in identifying the cell *per se* they appear to provide a "finger-print" of the individual subject. Whether this finger-print is diagnostically useful will not be discovered until many more experiments are performed. However, the ideas presented here may be of interest to those who wish to evaluate the power and utility of automatic microscopy as applied to hematology.

Recently the CELLSCAN/GLOPR system has been applied to two other investigations in automatic microscopy relating to cytological

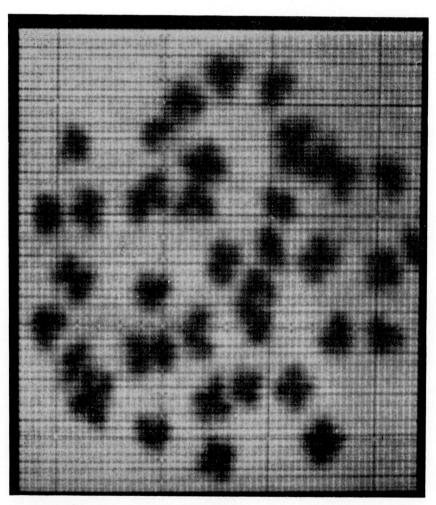

Fig. 18. Television image of a cluster of chromosomes (24×24 μm window).

analysis. One involved a test of the system's ability to do chromosome counting. Figure 18 shows the television image of a cluster of chromosomes (*Pycnoscelus Indicus*) contained in a 24×24 μm window using 128×128 image elements. A GLOL procedure was written for the purpose of counting the chromosomes in the spread. The result is shown in the composite image given in Fig. 19. This shows the contents of the image plane from which the count is taken brightened and superimposed on the contents of the plane containing the original thresholded image. The operation time for this counting procedure was 0·3 s.

Fig. 19. Composite image showing the binary image (bright points) resulting from a GLOL procedure designed to perform a chromosome count superimposed on the original binary image of the chromosome cluster.

Figures 20 and 21 provide the second example which relates to the analysis of epithelial cells in *Papanicolaou* stained cervical smears. Figure 20 shows the television image corresponding to a 48×48 μm window again using 128×128 image elements. Both the nucleus of an epithelial cell and clumps of neutrophils appear in the image. A GLOL procedure was written for the purpose of eliminating the neutrophils from the image and retaining only the epithelial cell nucleus for further analysis. The execution time of this procedure was less than 1 s. The results are shown in Fig. 21 where the contents of the final binary image plane are shown brightened and superimposed upon the contents of the original thresholded image. These results were obtained with the expenditure of only a few man-hours in coding and testing the required procedures. The speed of the CELLSCAN/GLOPR system in executing

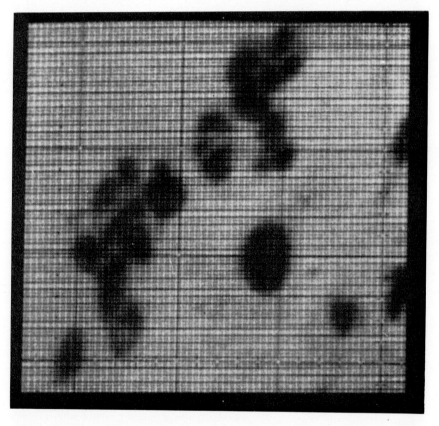

Fig. 20. Television image of a Papanicolaou stained cervical smear (48×48 μm window).

Fig. 21. Composite image showing the contents of the binary image which results from using a GLOL procedure to select the epitherial cell nucleus (bright points) superimposed on the original binary image which contains an epithelial cell and neutrophils.

GLOL commands on a line by line basis and the provision of an instantaneous display of the resultant image make it possible to make rapid advances in new applications of microscopical picture processing. Furthermore, once preliminary results have been obtained on a small set of images, the procedure developed may be tested on large volumes of imagery by operating the system on a hands-off basis for whatever length of time is required.

VI. CONCLUSION

In conclusion it is evident that the past five years have seen great advances in the automation of microscopical measurements in cytology.

We have now reached the point where the microscope combined with the computer acts as a reasonably skilled cyto-technician as regards the examination of the blood cells of normal subjects. We may expect in the future to see further advances which will permit still more sophistication to be built into the machine. When these advances will become available to the everyday clinic is unknown. This will depend entirely on economic factors.

The advantages of the application of the automatic microscope to cytology are clear. They are similar to those of automated data taking in any field. Automation removes the tedium from human endeavour and makes operations more quantitative and precise. It makes possible the transfer of information from one laboratory to another by standardizing the data format. It makes it possible to build data banks of information which are the recorded history of individual subjects as well as of large populations of subjects. Extensive use can be made of this volume of data by determining both population norms and even of individual norms with a breadth and scope never approached by manual methods. This is the strength of automation in cytology. It is our sincere hope and expectation that in the next decade economics will permit the daily use of this technology in the clinical environment.

Acknowledgements

The work leading to the accomplishments reported in this chapter was undertaken through the coordinated efforts of a large number of people. In particular Dr. Marylou Ingram of the University of Rochester has inspired the work of the Perkin-Elmer Corporation in the application of automatic microscopy to problems in hematology and has served as a consultant to the project. Within Perkin-Elmer, A. H. Smith and his associates are to be complimented for the excellent design and fabrication of the oscillating mirror scanner; C. Stahl and his group for the design and construction of GLOPR; A. Reis and his staff for the programming services which lead to the GLOL software system; and P. E. Norgren, J. R. Carvalko and D. DeCava of the author's group for coding of procedures, performance of experiments, and data analysis. Miss Olive Clearwater and her staff and Dr. I. Weisbrot of the Norwalk Hospital provided the visual white blood cell differential counts which permitted the evaluation of machine performance. And, finally, Gennifer Austin provided immeasurable assistance in typing this manuscript while J. Bannister and J. Pascucci and their staffs are responsible for the final illustrations. Funding for the project was provided by the U.S. Department of Defense approved Independent Research and Development in Optical Signal Processing at Perkin-Elmer.

REFERENCES

Anderson, T. W. (1958). "An Introduction to Multivariate Statistical Analysis," J. Wiley & Sons, New York.

Beadle, C. (1971). The quantimet image analysing computer and its applications. *In* "Advances in Optical and Electron Microscopy" (R. Barer and V. E. Cosselett, eds.), Vol. 4, p. 361. Academic Press, London and New York.

Golay, M. J. E. (1969). Hexagonal Parallel pattern transformations, *IEEE Trans. on Comp.* **C-18**, 733.

Humphries, D. W. (1969). Mensuration methods in optical microscopy. *In* "Advances in Optical and Electron Microscopy" (R. Barer and V. E. Cosselett, eds.), Vol. 2, p. 33, Academic Press, London and New York.

Ingram, M. and Minter, F. M. (1969). Semiautomatic preparation of coverglass blood smears using a centrifugal device, *Am. J. Clin. Path.* **51**, 214.

Ledley, R. S. (1969). Automatic pattern recognitions for clinical medicine, *Proc. IEEE*, **57**, 2017.

Lipkin, L. E. (1969). Spectre II: General-purpose microscope input for a computer, *Science, N.Y.* **166**, 328.

Mansberg, H. P. and Ohringer, P. (1969). Design considerations for electronic and electromechanical flying spot scanners, *An. N.Y. Acad. Sci.* **157**, (1), 5.

Mendelsohn, M. L., Mayall, B. H. and Prewit, J. M. S. (1968). Digital transformations and computer analysis of microscopic images. *In* "Advances in Optical and Electron Microscopy" (R. Barer and V. E. Cosselett, eds.), Vol. 2, p. 77. Academic Press, London and New York.

Nathan, R. and Selzer, R. H. (1968). Digital video data handling: Mars, the moon, and men. *In* "Image Processing in Biological Science" (D. Ramsey, ed.), University of California Press.

Neurath, P. W. *et al.* (1970). Combined interactive computer measurement and automatic classification of human chromosomes, *Cytogenetics*, **9**, 434.

Preston, K., Jr. (1971). Feature extraction by Golay hexagonal pattern transforms, *IEEE Trans. on Comp.* **C-20**, 1007.

Preston, K., Jr. and Carvalko, J. R. (1969). Use of the contourograph to evaluate a high-resolution television microscope, *Proc. IEEE*, **57**, (Corres.), 104.

Preston, K., Jr. and Norgren, P. E. (1971). Method of Preparing Blood Smears, U.S. Pat. No. 3,557,267.

Rosenfeld, A. (1970). Connectivity in digital pictures, *J. Assoc. of Comp. Mach.* **17**, 146.

Rutovitz, D. *et al.* (1970). Instrumentation and organization for chromosome measurement and Karyotype analysis. *In* "Pfizer Medical Monographs 5-Human Population Cytogenetics", Edinburgh University Press.

Wied, G. L., Bahr, G. F. and Bartels, P. H. (1968). Taxonomic intra-cellular analytic system (TICAS) for cell identification, *Acta Cytol.* **12**, 180.

Willner, L. B. (1967). On parametric linear programming, *SIAM J. Appl. Math.* **15**, 1253.

Appendix I

Simple GLOL Statements

In analyzing the simple GLOL statement there are four basic sets which must be considered. These sets are

(1) The set of all points in the designated plane which have the value ONE.
(2) The set of all points in the plane which have the value ZERO.
(3) The set of all points in the plane which exhibit the specified surround(s).
(4) The set of all points in the plane which do not exhibit the specified surround(s).

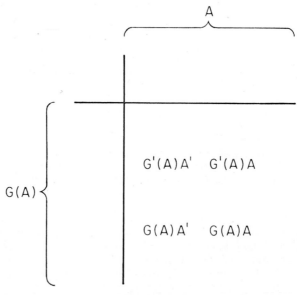

Fig. I-1

If the plane, A, is the designated plane, then these sets are given by A, A′, G(A), G′(A), respectively. The intersection of these sets, as represented by the Boolean algebraic portion of the simple GLOL statement, are best illustrated by a 2-variable Karnaugh map as shown in Fig. I-1. There are, of course, 16 possible configurations of this Karnaugh map. These configurations are shown in Fig. I-2 in what we call a "Karnaugh matrix" whose element is designated by K_{ij}. The diagonal elements of the Karnaugh matrix represent reasonably trivial

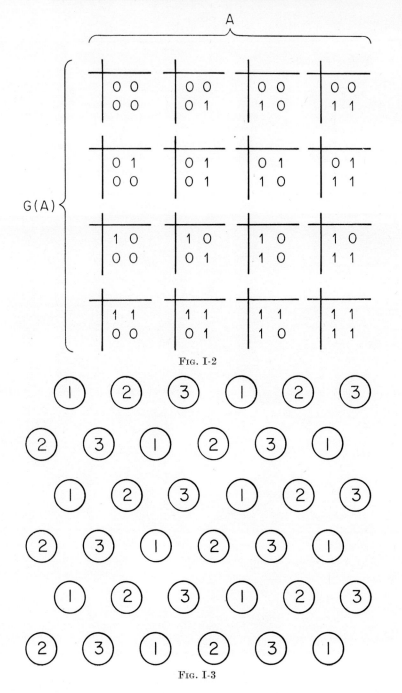

Fig. I-2

Fig. I-3

TABLE I

Matrix Element	Code	Function
K_{14}	G(A)	Marks surrounds
K_{12}	G(A)A	Contracts or "shrinks"
K_{13}	G(A)A′	Contracts and inverts
K_{24}	G(A)+G′(A)A	Expands or "swells"
K_{34}	G(A)+G′(A)A′	Expands and inverts
K_{23}	G(A)A′+G′(A)A	Custers

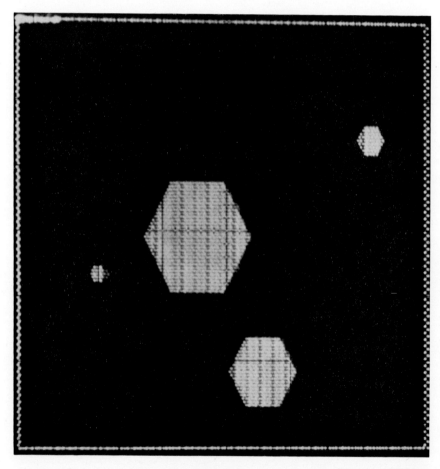

Fig. I-4a

operations, namely, erasure of the contents of the plane (K_{11} and K_{44}), duplication (K_{22}), and inversion (K_{33}). The symmetric elements of the Karnaugh matrix, i.e. K_{1j} and K_{j1} are identical operations if used with what are called "complementary surrounds", i.e. the two subsets of surrounds whose intersection is zero and whose union is all possible surrounds. For example, for K_{12} and K_{21}, we can write two equivalent GLOL statements such as

$$A=M[G(A)A]0\text{--}10,,$$
$$A=M[G'(A)A]11\text{--}13,, \tag{I-1}$$

since surrounds 0–10 are the complement of surrounds 11–13.

FIG. I-4b

Since the four diagonal elements in the Karnaugh matrix represent trivial operations and the symmetrical elements are identical if used with the complementary surrounds, one may describe the properties of "all" simple GLOL statements in a list having only six entries as given in Table I. Further, taking into account the relatedness of K_{12} and K_{13} (both "contracting" operations) and K_{24} and K_{34} (both "expanding" operations), the entries in the table may be seen to describe only four basic operations:

  (1) Marking of points in the plane which have specific surrounds.
  (2) Contracting the number of points which have the value ONE.

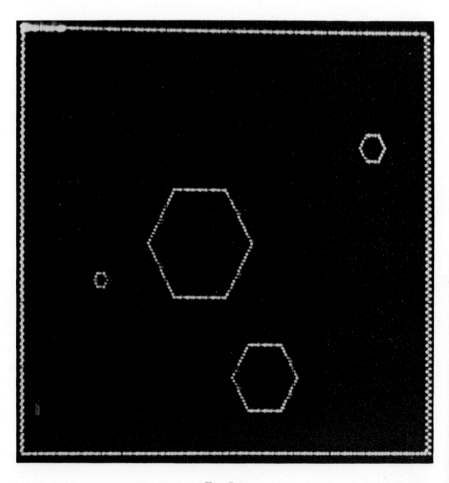

Fig. I-4c

(3) Expanding the number of points which have the value ONE.

(4) Custering the contents of the plane.*

Consider the following simple GLOL statement which generates the plane B based upon the contents of A.

$$B = M[G(A)]N1,, \tag{I-2}$$

This is a marking operation where each picture element in B is ONE

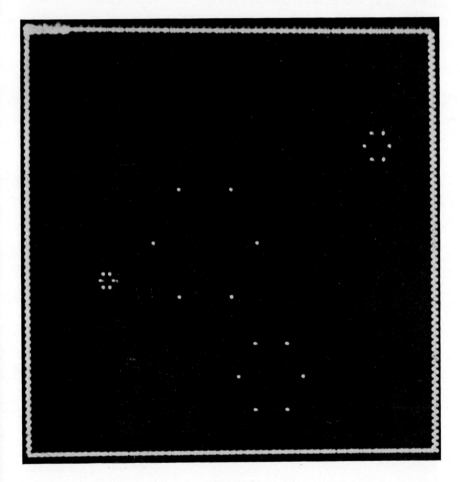

FIG. I-4d

* Custering is an operation which causes "waves" to propagate out from any picture element in the plane which has the value ONE. The pattern generated finally stabilizes in a closed cycle. Custering has been discussed by Kirsch *et al.* (1957) and an example is given in (I-4).

wherever the corresponding element in A has the surround N1. (The comma's after N1 are required in GLOL to call the default option where one iteration is performed and subfields are disregarded.)

The simple GLOL statement give by

$$B = M[G(A)]N1\text{--}N/3\text{--}N4,,\qquad(\text{I-3})$$

creates in B a set of ONE's corresponding to all elements in A which have "any" one of the surrounds N1 through N2 or N3 through N4.

When a simple GLOL statement is written as a replacement statement, the contents of the specified plane are changed; no new plane is

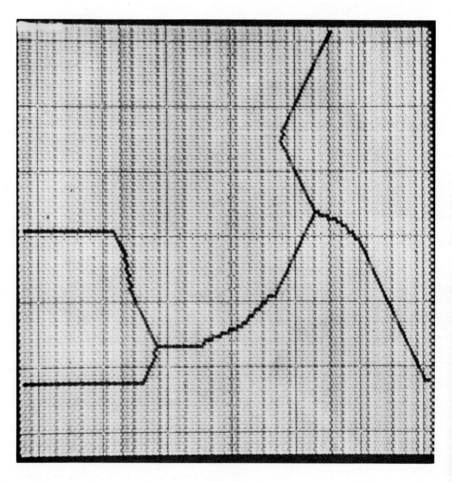

Fig. I-4e

created. The statement which follows is the classical "shrinking" operation (Izzo and Coles, 1962), namely,

$$A = M[G'(A)A]1-4,N1,3 \qquad (I-4)$$

Here picture elements in A are retained during each iteration if they have the binary value ONE and do not have surrounds 1, 2, 3, or 4. The quantity N1 indicates that the statement is to be performed for N1 iterations, i.e. N1 times. Furthermore, in order that a residual isolated ONE always be retained for each contiguous group of ONE's is the initial n×n array, the statement indicates an operation in sub-fields. For example a subfields-of-three map is shown in Fig. I-3.

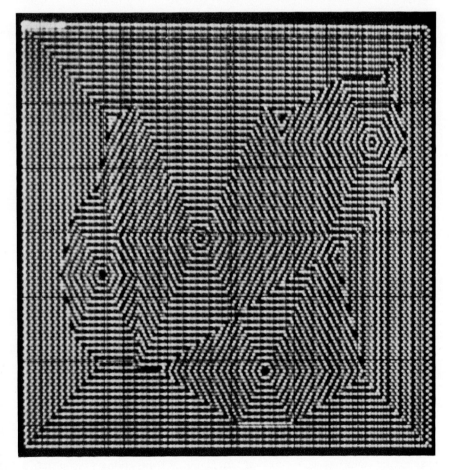

Fig. I-4f

When operating in subfield of three (as above), the GLOL statement is performed three times for each iteration; first, for picture elements in the first subfield; next, in the second subfield; finally, in the third subfield. As discussed by Golay (1969) subfields of four and seven are also possible. Since the order in which subfields are taken may significantly affect the results obtained in executing the GLOL statement, the user may specify the subfield order as indicated by the final numerics in the general GLOL statement.

If A is the binary picture shown in Fig. I-4(a), the contracting or shrinking operation given by statement (I-4) will reduce it, after the appropriate number of iterations, to that shown in Fig. I-4(b). If, instead, a GLOL statement is written which contracts the original image using surrounds 1–5/7–13, the result is an edge map as shown in Fig. I-4(c). If the user desires to contract to corners, then only surround 3 is utilized with the result shown in Fig. I-4(d). The effect of an expanding operation is shown in Fig. I-4(e) and of custering in Fig. I-4(f).

References—Appendix I

Golay, M. J. E. (1969). Hexagonal parallel pattern transformations, *IEEE Trans. on Computers*, **C-18**, 733.

Izzo, N. F. and Coles, W. (1962). Blood cell scanner identified rare cells, *Electronics*, **35**, 52.

Kirsch, R. A., Kahn, L., Ray, C. and Urban, G. H. (1957). Experiments in processing pictorial information with a digital computer, *Proceedings EJCC*, 221.

Appendix II

The GLOL Command Structure

In addition to the Golay statement for performing Golay hexagonal transformations as described in the main body of the text, the GLOL software system incorporates a series of commands which are described in a tabular fashion below. These commands include simple binary logic operations which are carried out between pairs of image planes; definitive commands which set up appropriately sized image storage areas, measurement arrays, and permit the naming of subroutines or "procedures"; tabulator commands which permit measurements to be made and procedure and arrays lists to be generated; identify commands for use in recognizing particular objects of interest; deletives for the purpose of releasing pre-defined storage areas for other purposes; input/output commands for use in controlling the system peripherals; commands relating to the use of the cathode ray tube display systems; executive commands for use in carrying out procedures; commands to the automatic microscope; histogramming commands for use in

forming, manipulating, and displaying photometric histograms; a
selection command for use in image partitioning; arithmetic commands;
as well as commands for looping and branching within a program.

Golay Statement

$$D=[G(A)B+G'(A)C]N1 \ldots N2,N3,N4/N5 \ldots N6$$

Logical operations

A=B+C	Generates image plane A with contents equal to the union of planes B and C.
A=B*C	Generates image plane A with contents equal to the inter- section of planes B and C.
A=B—C	Generates image plane A with contents equal to Exclusive OR of planes B and C.
A=B	Generates image plane A with contents identical to B.
A=0	Sets the contents of image plane A to ZERO.

Definitives

DEFINE SYSTEM N1	Sets window size to 32×32, 64×64, or 128×128.
DEFINE ARRAY V/N1	Allocates N1 memory loca- tions for a measurement array labeled "V".
DEFINE BUFFER A	Allocates memory locations for an image plane labeled "A".
DEFINE PROCEDURE XYZ . . . END PROCEDURE XYZ	Permits the user to enter a series of GLOL commands which are then filed under the procedure name XYZ.

Tabulators

COUNT A,V(N1)	Causes the sum of all binary ONE's to image plane A to be stored as the value of array element V(N1).

CATALOGUE

Causes names of all previously defined procedures and arrays to be listed at the teletype.

Identifiers

IDENTIFY NOW

Multiplies the measurement array with sets of pre-assigned weights, calculates the sums, compares with the appropriate constant, and outputs the resultant object identification. (This command may be used pair-wise for as many as 8 simultaneous object types.)

IDENTIFY TABULATE

Generates a table of the number of objects identified as a function of object type.

Deletives

DELETE BUFFER A

Causes memory locations previously allocated for buffer A to be released.

DELETE PROCEDURE   XYZ

Causes memory locations previously allocated to procedure XYZ to be released.

DELETE ARRAY V(N1)

Causes memory locations previously allocated to array V(N1) to be released.

Input/Output

OUTPUT N1,V(N2–N3)

Causes values N2 through N3 stored in measurement array V to be printed on the teletype (N1 = 1), on paper tape (N1 = 2), on both the teletype and paper tape (N1 = 3), or on magnetic tape (N1 = 4).

PAPER TAPE

Used after DEFINE PROCEDURE XYZ to cause procedure to be loaded from paper tape reader.

END OUPUT	Writes end of file mark on magnetic tape.
WRITE A	Stores the contents of one-bit image plane A on magnetic tape.
READ A,N1	Spools out magnetic tape to the N1th one-bit image and stores it in image plane A.
SEARCH A,N1 . . . N2	Searches magnetic tape for the one-bit image specified and stores it in image plane A.
BACK N1	Back spaces N1 one-bit images.
BEGIN	Rewinds the tape.
END TAPE	Goes to last one-bit image on the tape.
FETCH	Searches magnetic tape for the multi-bit image specified.

Cathode ray tube

| DISPLAY A | Causes the contents of image plane A to be exhibited on the GLOPR display screen. |
| CLEAR | Stops the operation of the display. |

Executives

| EXECUTIVE PROCEDURE XYZ | Causes the procedure XYZ to be carried out. |
| RUN N1 | Causes a list of commands and/or procedures to be executed N1 times. |

Automatic microscope

| FIND | Causes the automatic microscope to locate an object of interest. |
| ACQUIRE A,N1 | Causes a multi-level image to be thresholded at level N1 and stored in image plane A. |

WAVELENGTH N1

Causes the wavelength of illumination used by the scanner to be shifted to a colour having the pre-assigned number N1.

Histogramming

HISTOGRAM A

Causes the photometric histogram of a multibit image to be computed and stored in image array A.

SMOOTH A, N1

Causes the histogram stored in array A to be smoothed by pair-wise averaging for N1 cycles.

GRAPH A

Causes the histogram stored in array A to be placed in an image buffer and displayed.

Selection

PICK A,N1

Causes the N1th isolated ONE in image plane A to be retained and sets all other image elements to ZERO.

Arithmetic

AR $V(N1) = V(N2) + V(N3)$

Causes the sum of $V(N2)$ and $V(N3)$ to be stored in location $V(N1)$.

AR $V(N1) = V(N2) - V(N3)$

Causes the difference of $V(N2)$ and $V(N3)$ to be stored in location $V(N1)$.

AR $V(N1) = V(N2)*V(N3)$

Causes the product of $V(N2)$ and $V(N3)$ to be stored in location $V(N1)$.

AR $V(N1) = V(N2)/V(N3)$

Causes the ratio of $V(N2)$ and $V(N3)$ to be stored in location $V(N1)$.

Loop

DO $V(N1),V(N2),V(N3)$ . . . STOP

Causes the commands listed

to be executed with the loop index going from V(N1) to V(N2) in increments of V(N3).

Branch

IF . . . ELSE . . . STOP

Using an ALGOL-like IF, executes either the first or second list of GLOL commands depending upon the outcome.

Transfer

AID

Causes transfer of control to the Varian 620i AID II system for housekeeping and test purposes.

A Universal System for Measuring and Processing the Characteristic Geometrical and Optical Magnitudes of Microscopic Objects

H. PILLER

Carl Zeiss, Oberkochen, West Germany

I. Introduction

THE microscope can be used to measure two essentially different kinds of magnitude: geometric ones, which include the lengths, areas, and numbers of the various features in the image field; optical ones such as the transmittance or the reflectance of the various features. For many years the geometric magnitudes of a number of grains have been measured by visual setting, devices of a mechanical or electronic nature (point counters) being used to record the observations. Over nearly half a century photoelectric sensors, now chiefly the photo-multiplier tube, have been used to measure optical magnitudes, which is something that the eye cannot do with any accuracy.

In recent years, however, the development of electronic devices not only for recording observations but also for making computations with these, has brought about a great advance.

Work has been extended into both the ultra-violet and the infra-red regions of the spectrum. It can, in fact, be said that quantitative microscopy in all its aspects is now firmly based on the use of photo-electric equipment.

A survey of the literature makes it clear that we are still, in this field, at the stage of fundamental research and that further investigations are required in order to consolidate the progress already made;

this state of affairs will be achieved when the use of photo-electric equipment has become a routine procedure.

On the other hand, the actual results so far obtained are not numerous. It follows that what is really needed now is a universal system for measuring and that basic research should be done to achieve this. There is still a great need to study and compare the various photometric procedures and to compare these also with "classical" quantitative methods in order to be able to decide on the best type of apparatus and how to use it for the purpose in view. This is really more important than the development of special types of apparatus for quickly and conveniently measuring particular selected magnitudes.

In the present paper the general lines of such a universal system are considered. A microscope of the highest quality forms the central section, and this must possess interchangeable mechanical and optical modules. These enable the operator to illuminate the specimen in various ways, to form the image under different optical conditions, and to insert optical devices such as micrometers, compensators, etc., in the path of the rays. Different kinds of calibrated positioning devices for the specimen are required. To such a microscope are added various interchangeable electrical modules, and these can now be obtained commercially at a reasonable cost.

II. Characteristic Magnitudes to be Measured

Tables I and II of magnitudes directly measured and the information derived display the properties that we are discussing. In Table I we compare first each of the three geometric magnitudes with itself and with the two others. When one of these magnitudes is taken with itself, what we have is a comparison of it for different features. Thus, length to length consists of a comparison of the length for different features in the image field, and similarly with areas. Number to number gives a comparison of the numbers of different features. When we take area with length we get the relation between these two magnitudes in a single given feature. When we take number to length we get the distribution of lengths in a given feature and correspondingly for number to area. For these last two we can, of course, make histograms to show the distributions.

Next we take the optical magnitudes one at a time and compare each with the three geometrical magnitudes one at a time. Table I shows that the length column defines one linear co-ordinate in the field, and so the optical magnitude refers to this locus. The area column defines a point in the field and so the optical magnitude refers to this

Table I

Geometrical compared with Geometrical and Optical compared with Geometrical Magnitudes

	Magnitudes directly measured	Length	Area	Number
Geometrical	Length	Comparison of lengths for different features		
	Area	Relation of area to length in a given feature	Comparison of areas for different features	
	Number	Distribution of lengths in a given feature	Distribution of areas in a given feature	Comparison of different numbers of features
Optical	Direct Transmission Factor	Each Magnitude for a line in the field defined by one linear co-ordinate	Each Magnitude for a point in the field defined by two perpendicular linear co-ordinates	Each Magnitude related to numbers of features, whence histograms and mean values are obtained
	Direct-Reflection Factor			
	Path- (or Phase-) Difference			
	Diffuse-Reflection Factor			
	Fluorescence Intensity			

TABLE II

Each Optical Magnitude compared with itself for Various Features

Each shaded rectangle indicates the comparison of one optical magnitude for the various features.

point. The number column defines the numbers of features, so that the optical magnitude refers to the number of features having particular values; histograms and mean values can be obtained from these data. In Table II the same optical magnitudes are compared each with itself and this gives the comparison of this optical magnitude for the various features. In general taking one optical magnitude with another optical magnitude produces nothing for our present discussion. As a special case we may note that any measurement from which the value of the refractive index can be obtained will, when combined with the direct reflection factor, enable the values of the absorption coefficient and of the refractive index to be evaluated by use of Fresnel's equations.

The properties with which we are dealing in measuring these optical magnitudes are respectively, Transmission, Direct-Reflection, Interference, Diffuse Reflection, and Fluorescence. Fluorescence and diffuse reflection are not intrinsic properties of the material, as are the first three, and so they can only be measured under specified conditions.

When any particular magnitude is being measured we can obtain its variation with time, along a given direction in the specimen plane, across the area of the specimen plane, and also with the wave length of the light used. From such "variation" data information can be obtained on temporal processes, and on distribution with area and in space. From the frequency distribution of the various features we can construct histograms and size distribution diagrams; statistical deviations from the mean values (error analysis) and spectral properties can be obtained, either in transmitted or in reflected light. From the spectral curves we can derive a quantitative expression of the colour in white light of the feature.

In general, of course, it will not be possible to measure all the magnitudes given in the tables on any single specimen, even under the best conditions. The operator has to work out in each case the scheme of image-analysis best adapted to his particular problem. For example, in cancer research pattern recognition of differential absorption is applied; in ore mineralogy and in coal studies direct spectral reflectance is used systematically. The measurements made automatically can always be supplemented, according to the needs of the particular case, by measurements made by classical methods and by visual observation (Gahm, 1971).

III. Optical Conditions for Measurement

We now discuss the optical conditions that will enable us to make reliable measurements on the image, for it is on the image formed in the microscope that measurements are made and not directly on the stage object. A microscope of the highest quality should be used, and this should be very carefully adjusted according to the manufacturer's instructions in order to obtain maximum contrast and sharpness of definition of the features in the stage object. It should be kept in mind that while the eye may detect a feature in an imperfect image, this may be beyond the discriminating power of the photo-electric sensor to be employed. No amount of photo-electric hardware and of hard and software for data processing can make up for a failure to obtain the best possible image for them to work on.   We have to remember that whereas the eye is able to compare many features in a field, the photo-electric sensor merely records the intensity of that small field exposed to it at any given moment. When the brightness of the image is inadequate, the sensor may not be able to distinguish between the grey level of one feature and that of another. There is, of course, always a limit to the distinguishing power of the sensor, and this is, in fact, the present limiting factor in all such measurements. Again, where features of the same or similar kind overlap in the field of the sensor, the system cannot work.

We can set out in a general way the main problems of photo-electric measurements.

A. Irradiation of the light sensor with a sufficient amount of energy.

B. Enhancement of contrast and sharpness of delineation of the features in the image field.

C. Isolation of the features (Mertz, 1971).

A. *Irradiation of the Light Sensor with a Sufficient Amount of Energy*

(1) A decision has to be made about the spectral band-width to be used. All that can be stated in a general way is that this should be as large as is possible for obtaining the kind of measurements that are desired; the reason is the need to make the radiance of the lamp as large as possible. It is a mistake to think that accuracy is always increased by greatly reducing the spectral band-width, and there are two arguments against this practice. First, it reduces very greatly the radiance of the lamp; second, the increasing coherence that results from a very small band-width increases the possibility of multiple beam interference at optical surfaces within the microscope. (In this respect the use of laser beams for work of this kind may be dis-advantageous.) Experience has shown the most effective band-width to be 10 to 20 nm.

(2) Within the spectral range being used the spectral density of

radiation should be as large as possible; information about various lamps is supplied by the manufacturers in the form of spectral curves.

(3) The numerical aperture of the system to be used must be decided. This should not be too small because the amount of energy transmitted is proportional to the square of the numerical aperture. On the other hand it should not be too large because this would produce a systematic measuring error (due to conical illumination) greater than the tolerable limit. For reflectance measurements the best value of the numerical aperture lies between 0·1 and 0·2. For the measurement of geometrical magnitudes larger apertures are sometimes advantageous because of the improvement of image resolution but in general the larger the aperture the poorer the contrast. For transmission measurements the illuminating aperture should not exceed about 0·4.

(4) The illumination system of the microscope must be adjusted so as to produce uniform illumination of the aperture of the system to be used. By looking at the back focal plane of the objective, either through the Bertrand lens or with the ocular removed, the image of the illumination aperture diaphragm will be seen limiting the aperture of the system. This area must be totally and uniformly illuminated and as bright as possible under the working conditions; this is obtained by using Köhler illumination and properly adjusting all parts of the illumination system.

Both in transmitted and in reflected light all optical parts that are not essential for the measurements should be removed from the light path, lenses, beam splitters, mirrors and glass plates; this all raises the total transmission factor of the microscope and reduces glare. Likewise a monochromator with a large transmission factor should be used.

With transmitted light the sub-stage condenser, and also the lamp-collector lens, should have a high degree of correction. The use of an "objective" in place of the ordinary sub-stage condenser is even recommended for the best work; in this case one of rather lower power than the actual objective in the observation system is recommended in order to ensure the correct aperture relationship and, for example, we might have the pair: illumination "objective" (N.A. 0.40) and observation objective (N.A. 0·65). All parts should be kept perfectly clean to avoid scattering by dust and dirt; all lenses should be properly focused and all diaphragms properly adjusted.

With birefringent objects contrast can be obtained by the use of polarized light and by suitable adjustment of the analyser.

With reflected light the illumination system should also be one with a high degree of correction and, of course, the actual objective is itself the last element in the illumination system. The choice of reflector comes in here; the prism type transfers distinctly more energy but, of course, the cone axis is necessarily somewhat oblique; in some cases also the background shading produced in the image is undesirable. The glass-plate type gives a cone axis that is normal and there is no shading of the image, but the loss of incident intensity is considerable.

B. *Enhancement of Contrast and Sharpness of Definition of the Features in the Image Field*

(1) The specimen must be prepared in the appropriate way. For transmitted light, the section has to be as thin as is practicable. Attention must be paid to specific, uniform and sufficiently deep staining; it is important to match the refractive index of the embedding medium to that of the specimen to suppress scattering at the boundary; contamination of the embedding medium should be avoided. For reflected light the important points are: optical flatness of the surface and, in particular, no hollowing out at grain boundaries; avoidance of chemical reactions during the grinding and polishing process; cleanliness of specimen to avoid atmospheric tarnish; gentle polishing to avoid production of heat and to minimize deformation of the surface layer. In certain cases definition and contrast may be improved by suitable etching (Schrader, 1957) or by the deposition of an interference layer (Pepperhof, 1965).

They can also be improved by immersing the surface in a suitable oil or other liquid of suitable refractive index; this is largely used for photo-micrography in reflected light. The use of polarized light, with a retardation plate inserted at the 45° position before the objective (antiflex method, see Piller, 1960) is useful in suppressing glare in the microscope.

(2) In addition to the ordinary bright-field technique with the microscope, others can be used; dark-field illumination; phase-contrast, double-beam or differential interference procedures; ultra-violet or infra-red light, for which commercial apparatus is now available working from 250 to 1100 nm. Contrast can be improved by means of photo-micrography, utilizing special development techniques, and then making microdensitometric measurements on the photograph.

(3) Fluorescence can be due either to an inherent property of the feature in the specimen or else to staining with fluorochromes which are taken up differentially by various features; this technique is of particular importance in biological work either to enhance contrast or to indicate the amount of certain chemical components such as nucleic acids, proteins etc.

C. *Isolation of the Features*

In material where the isolation of the various components is difficult, special methods of preparation have to be used. The material can be dressed, according to its nature, by cutting, crushing, sieving, flotation, sedimentation, smearing in such a way that features of the same kind, and if possible also of the same size, such as cells, chromosomes, dust particles, minerals, etc. are separated from others. The preparation is then made so that these features are not in contact with each other. Thus it may be necessary to measure the specimen repeatedly in different conditions of preparation so that each type of feature may be properly measured for the magnitudes required.

IV. Layout of a Universal Measuring System

A. *General Features*

The advantages of a measuring system that can be used both for visual microscopy and for photo-electric measurements are obvious. Technical developments in recent years have made it possible to assemble such a system in a convenient way from commercially available parts at a reasonable cost. In what follows an example of such a universal system is described.

Figures 1 and 2(a, b) show the component parts of the system in the form of block diagrams. Its central part is a large modern microscope enabling the use of all kinds of illumination and contrast enhancement.

In the microscope itself the illumination system comprises everything from the lamp up to the specimen; the observation system comprises everything from the specimen up to the eye, in visual work, or the photo-sensor in photo-electric measurement. As we are dealing here with a larger assembly and automatic measurement, not visual, we shall find it more convenient to define the image-forming system as comprising everything from the lamp up to the optical interface. This comprises: stabilized radiation supply, the stabilization being needed for photometry; radiation modulator, which enables the photo-sensor to disregard unwanted light, which is unmodulated; monochromator of suitable type; microscope, the parts of which we shall not detail here, but auxiliary devices may include polarizing optics, interference systems etc. Since the ordinary visual system is not in use, it is replaced by an optical interface between the microscope proper and the photo-sensors. The control signals generator provides a means of automatic positioning of the scanning stage or other module.

In Fig. 2 are shown the measurement and data-processing system in two forms. In Fig. 2(a), from the optical interface we can go to the right for the measurement of geometrical magnitudes by means of a television camera tube; this feeds into the central processor, which has its own supply unit. This then feeds three ways: the monitor is a visual-display television with an arrangement for restricting the field so as to be able to observe and check what features are actually being measured and what kind of measurement is being carried out. The analog signal display may be used by itself as the reading; the analog-to-digital converter feeds the digital signal display. Alternatively we can go to the left for the measurement of optical magnitudes by means of a photomultiplier tube; this feeds into an amplifier which has its own stabilized supply unit. This then feeds two ways; into the analog signal display or into the analog-to-digital converter and thus to the digital signal display.

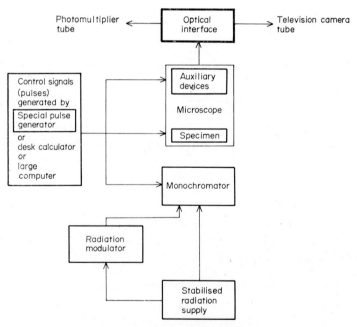

Fig. 1. The image-forming system.

In either case, from the digital signal display unit we can go three ways. First, we can simply have this printed out. Second, we can put it through a code translator to a puncher (cards or tapes). Third, we can put it through an interface to a desk calculator of modern type which can do some processing of the data before feeding to a teletype printer. As the end product of the puncher we have storage of the data, and this can be done also with the processed results from the desk calculator. This system of Fig. 2(a) can be called one for the addition of peripheral units.

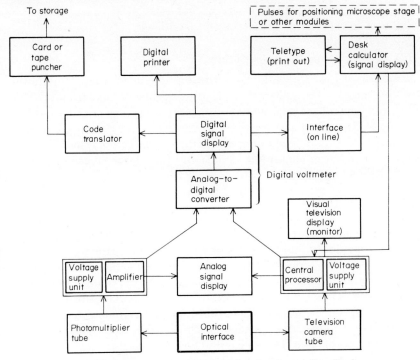

FIG. 2(a). System to which peripheral units can be added.

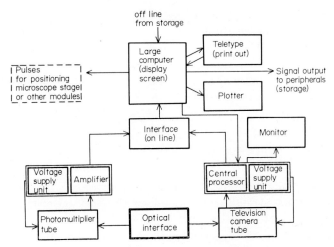

FIG. 2(b). System including a large computer.

In Fig. 2(b), on the other hand, both the central processor on the right and the amplifier on the left feed through an interface to a large computer from which signals can be passed in four ways:

(a) to a digital display or a screen;
(b) to a teletype with print-out and feed-back;
(c) to a plotter;
(d) to peripherals for data storage.

The system of Fig. 2(b) can be described as one using a large computer, and this enables the generation of signals, commanded from storage, which can control the positioning of the scanning stage or other module. It may be remarked that with the ever-increasing efficiency of desk calculators the main remaining advantage of large computers is their ability to process analog input signals and their large storage capacity.

B. *Optical System*

We can now consider some of the parts of the system in more detail. The microscope, as we have mentioned, should be of the largest and most flexible modern design so as to enable the operator to have at his command the whole range of techniques. For the geometrical measurements a scanning microscope stage is used, and interchangeable models are available having different lengths of unit step. The scanning stage moves the specimen in two dimensions, so that signals can be plotted in cartesian co-ordinates (specimen plane scanning). The length of step, or of groups of steps, is usually chosen according to the diameter of the field to be measured; when this is to be viewed by the television tube it is nearly the whole field as seen on the monitor display, but it is only a very small part of this when it is being measured by the photo-multiplier tube. The smallest step is about 0·5 μm while the largest is measured in mm. The highest speed is some 50 steps per second if operated by a control signals generator or 200 steps per second if operated by a computer. The stepping motors can be programmed to control:

(1) The length of a single step or of a group of steps.
(2) The number of steps or of groups of steps.
(3) The speed and direction of movement (line-, s-meander, or comb-pattern scanning).

Stages are being designed which can be rotated in angular steps and also moved along straight lines, allowing the position of the object to be defined by polar co-ordinates.

The specimen is best illuminated by a low voltage lamp with a flat, square-shaped tungsten filament. For special cases, and for ultraviolet light, this can be replaced by a super-pressure xenon lamp. Discharge lamps can be used provided that they are selected to be free from instability due to flicker; stability can be increased by reducing the distance between the electrodes, but this should not be so small as to prevent the proper illumination of the condenser aperture.

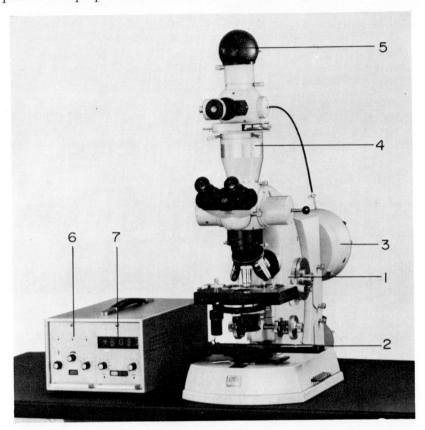

FIG. 3. Equipment for measuring optical characteristic magnitudes: Microscope (1) with continuous interference-filter monochromator (2) and light modulator (3). Opto-mechanical module (photometer attachment) (4) with photomultiplier (5). Amplifier with stabilized high-voltage unit for photomultiplier (6). Digital display unit (decimal display unit (7)).

For a single wave length it is convenient to use a homogeneous monochromatic filter between the lamp and the microscope. The running (continuous spectrum) type of monochromatizing filter is easy to use, but often contains small holes. Where a monochromator is required, this can be of the diffraction grating or prism type; these require specially designed auxiliary lenses. The change of peak wave length can be controlled by hand or else by an electromotor. Means for the automatic positioning of either a monochromatic filter of the running type or for automatic selection of wavelength by means of a mono-chromator are still under development.

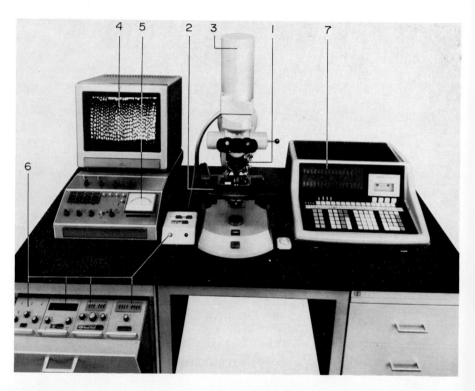

Fig. 4. Equipment for measuring geometrical characteristic magnitudes: Microscope (1) with microscope stage controllable by pulse generator (2). Opto-mechanical module with television camera tube (3) and monitor (4). Signal processing unit built into desk. Analog signal display unit (5). Modular electronic system (6) as shown in Fig. 2(a). Desk computer (7) (Type Wang 700).

For work with a photomultiplier it is advantageous to insert a radiation modulator to produce an alternating signal of a given frequency by means of a rotating or vibrating chopper or a Kerr cell; the reason is that this enables the suppression of disturbing radiation from outside the beam and also of the dark current signal since the indicating device can be made to respond to the modulated signal alone. But there are two disadvantages: first, the maximum speed of sequence of signals is limited by that of the frequency produced by the modulator; second, more complicated apparatus is required to transform the alternating photo-current into the direct current for the output signal.

At the upper end of the body tube of the microscope there is placed the optical interface, which is an opto-mechanical device for doing several things. It enables the different light sensors to be interchanged with the visual ocular; the more quickly this can be done the better the design of the optical interface. This interface also includes a selectable photometer stop which can be chosen and centred to delimit the field to be viewed or measured.

C. *Light Sensors*

The light sensor is either a television camera tube or else a photomultiplier tube, and we can consider the qualities of each type so as to obtain a comparison of these. In general the domain of the television tube is the measurement of geometrical magnitudes, whereas that of the photomultiplier tube is the measurement of optical magnitudes; they are thus complementary. This difference of domain arises from the fact that geometrical magnitudes are characterized by the duration and sequence of signals, whereas optical magnitudes are characterized by amplitudes. Thus quantitative television microscopy is essentially geometric, whereas microscopic photometry is essentially optical. The term "photometry" is used here in its widest sense to include: microphotometry, microspectrophotometry, microdensitometry, microreflectometry, microfluorometry, etc.

The television tube can signal only large differences of brightness between features, up to about 10 divisions between the smallest and the largest, but it does this with extremely high speed. The speed of its signal is determined by that of the electronic image-plane scanner, which has a maximum of about 5×10^6 signals per second. It is obvious that the precision of statistical geometric measurements is improved by enlarging the area of the specimen being measured; this is most conveniently achieved by combining image-plane scanning with specimen-plane scanning.

The television tube has to be placed in the plane of the real image of the stage object (specimen). It should be noted that work with a television tube demands careful adjustment of the illumination so that this is uniform over the whole viewing field, even though a certain degree of shading can be electronically compensated for. The television tube could be used for optical measurements only where this was required to be merely semi-quantitative, as for example, in semi-quantitative pattern recognition.

The photomultiplier tube can signal either fine or else very large differences of light intensity, up to about 200 divisions between the smallest and the largest, but it does this with a relatively low speed.

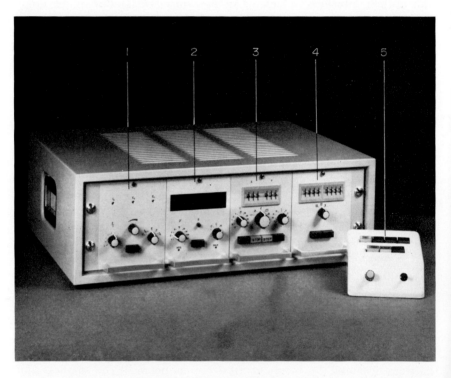

FIG. 5. Modular electronic system for measuring geometrical and optical characteristic magnitudes: Amplifier with stabilized high-voltage unit for photomultiplier (1). Digital signal display unit (decimal display unit) (2). Pulse control generator (3) for modules which can be moved by stepping motors. Code translator (4). Remote control unit for pulse control generator (5).

The speed of its signals is determined by the speed with which the position of the specimen (in specimen-plane scanning) or the peak wave length of the monochromator (in spectral measurements) can be changed. It is also limited by the inertia of the display unit, and the maximum speed is about 200 signals per second.

The photomultiplier tube may be placed either in the plane of the real image of the stage object, or in any other plane where the cross-section of the light bundle does not exceed that of the cathode of the sensor. The photomultiplier tube is used to best advantage where a distinction has to be made between two features differing only slightly in brightness. In such a case specimen-plane scanning has to be done with the smallest possible opening of the photometer stop. The measured results will be uncertain if the area of the photometer stop is big enough to include grain boundaries, edges etc. Work with the photomultiplier demands only uniformity of illumination over the very small area delimited by the photometer stop.

The light sensors are connected to power supply and electrical signalling units—a central processor for the television tube and a pre-amplifier for the photomultiplier tube. The former is controlled either by hand or by a computer and it discriminates the signals or signal groups by means of logic circuits in respect to amplitude, amplitude variation, number of signals, and the relation between these various quantities. Certain auxiliary magnitudes, such as standard grey levels, threshold values, counting marks, etc., are signalled on the monitoring screen, along with the image to be analysed.

D. *Display*

The signals coming from the television tube plus central processor and from the photomultiplier tube plus amplifier can be shown on the same analog display or else they can be converted and shown on the same digital display. We can say at this point that the system shown in Fig. 2(a) is essentially complete in that it has achieved two kinds of display. But peripheral units can be added for convenience:

(1) A digital printer can print out directly.

(2) A code translator can be used to activate a puncher to produce data on punched cards or tapes for storage and further processing by off-line procedures.

(3) A modern desk calculator to analyse the data and then either print it with the aid of a teletype, or else put to storage. It can classify signals with respect to groups having the same threshold values; it can count the number of signals in the groups; it can analyse statistical errors and it can integrate, all very quickly. Such calculations can be very useful in checking the reliability of measurements. Finally it can feed back a number of pulses to the central processor or to the controls of movable modules. This feed-back activates the motor controlling the position of the specimen on the stage and the setting of the mono-chromator and of any auxiliary device such as a compensator.

Figure 2(b), on the other hand, depicts a large computer in place of the system just described; this computer serves both for signal display

and processing. This system only shows to advantage where there is
the need to process a large amount of data, to feed back a large number
of pulses, and to carry out data storage, data processing, feed-back
and reliability checking in the shortest possible time, resulting in a

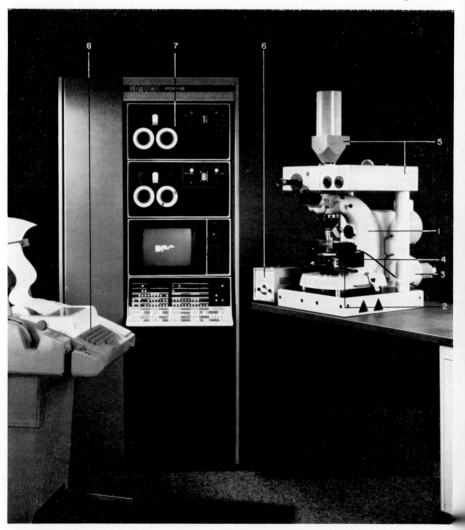

Fig. 6. Equipment for measuring and processing geometrical and optical characteristic
magnitudes: Microscope (1) with continuous interference-filter monochromator (2), light
modulator (3), microscope stage with stepping motors (4) controlled by the computer. Opto-
mechanical module (large photometer attachment) with photomultiplier and television camera
tube (5). Amplifier with stabilized high-voltage unit for photomultiplier (6). "PDP-12" computer (7) with teletype unit (8). See Fig. 2(b).

highly automated system. The development of automation has been rapid in recent years (see, for example, the publications of Wied, 1966, Wied and Bahr, 1970 and Dinner and Kaye, 1971). Some general aspects of this field may be mentioned here (Lang, 1972).

1. Automation is useful only if a large number of measuring signals must be processed in a short time.

2. It does not compensate for errors due to inadequate quality of the microscopic image or to incorrect adjustment of the measuring device.

3. It needs extensive preliminary operations (programming, testing) and work in an air-conditioned environment.

4. It is expensive unless the measuring device or parts of it are permanently in use.

5. It does not replace human activity completely, but only supplements it.

The latter fact is made obvious by the following list of factors which has to be taken into consideration for quantitative image-analysis of a given specimen.

1. Choice of the significant property (size, shape, brightness, colour, adjacent domains of features to be measured etc.).

2. Consideration of sources of errors (systematic errors due to the quality of the specimen, to incorrect adjustment of apparatus, to electric instability, to non-linearity of signal display, etc.); statistical uncertainties due to natural variations of the specimen or to signal noise.

3. Positioning of specimen and adjustment of the measuring field according to factors 1 and 2.

4. Choice of parameter which signifies the property to be measured.

5. Starting measurement.

6. Signal output.

7. Signal processing (calculation and processing of measuring results).

8. Determination and plotting of results and distribution of results (Areal, frequency, spectral, temporal).

Factors 1-6 have to be controlled by the observer, factor 7 may be controlled by the observer or by a desk calculator or by a big computer. Factor 8 is most conveniently controlled by a big computer.

ACKNOWLEDGEMENT

This paper was compiled in close collaboration with Dr. N. F. M. Henry. The author is deeply indebted to him for his generous and valuable advice.

References

The present paper claims no more than to give an outline of a subject that is developing so fast that it is still too early to write a complete account. This being the case, no attempt has been made to provide a full list of references; mention is made only of a few works of general interest that the author has found useful. The reader may well think of many others that could equally well have been on this very short list. In Volume **19**, No. 1 (1971) of *The Microscope* there are papers covering various aspects of image-analysis by means of a television system, along with a good bibliography, and reference may be made to this. It is hoped in the near future that to this can be added a bibliography dealing with the application of the photomultiplier tube to image analysis.

Dinner, P. J. C. and Kaye, B. H. (1971). *Microscope*, **19**, 77–86.

Gahm, J. (1971). *Z. Mitteilungen*, **5**, 249–289.

Lang, W. (1972). *Prakt. Metall.* **9**, 208–226.

Mertz, M. (1971). *Microscope*, **19**, 41–63.

Pepperhof, W. (1965). *Arch. Eisenhütten.* **36**, 941–950.

Piller, H. (1960). *Z. Werkzeitschrift*, No. 34.

Schrader, A. (1957). "Ätzheft." Bornträger, Berlin.

Wied, G. L. (1966). Editor, "Introduction to Quantitative Cytochemistry", Part I. Academic Press, New York and London.

Wied, G. L. and Bahr, G. F. (1970). Editors, "Introduction to Quantitative Cytochemistry", Part II. Academic Press, New York and London.

Wied, G. L. and Bahr, G. F. (1970). Editors, "Automated Cell Identification and Cell Sorting." Academic Press, New York and London.

Instruments for Stereometric Analysis with the Microscope —Their Application and Accuracy of Measurement

J. GAHM

Carl Zeiss, Oberkochen, West Germany

I. GENERAL CONCEPTS

THE determination and description of characteristic values in a microscopic image is summed up by the terms "stereometry", "stereology" and "quantitative image analysis". While the word "stereometry" primarily suggests geometrical characteristics of the object, "stereology" indicates a well-defined area of stereometry on a solid scientific base and "quantitative image analysis" denotes the correlation of geometrical characteristics of the object with local physical properties of the image. The latter are determined with the help of photometric instruments used in microscopy. The technique involves the correlation and recording of the spatial coordinates with such physical characteristics as transmission, absorption, reflection, refractive index, absorption index, tristimulus values, phase differences, concentrations and dry mass. If necessary, this is followed by computer processing and statistical analysis of the data (see general references).

The following two problems are intended to serve as illustrative examples demonstrating the features and methodology of stereometric procedures.

1. *Problem definition:* The circumference L, of a circle, is to be measured with a grid of grid constant a.

$$\text{Circumference } L = \pi D$$

$$D = \text{diameter and } \pi = 3\cdot14$$

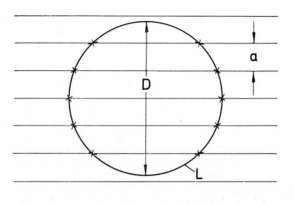

FIG. 1. Circle intersected by group of straight lines.

Assuming that a grid of grid constant $a \ll D$ is superimposed on the circle, the following relations will hold:

$C =$ number of intersections of the grid lines with the circumference L.

$$D \approx a\frac{C}{2}$$

$$L = \frac{\pi}{2}aC$$

This equation is generally applicable for the determination of the length L of any curve in the plane by means of a grid (Fig. 2). Curves of this type do not usually conform to the symmetry of the circle; during the measurement it is therefore necessary to superimpose the grid statistically on a curve trace. This will always require the introduction of the statistical multiplication factor $\pi/2$ in the equation.

2. *Problem definition:* The specific surface of an oriented object is to be determined.

By "specific surface of a phase v" is meant the ratio of the surface S_v of this phase to the volume V of the measured sample or the volume V_v of a given phase v. From the specific surface it is possible to calculate by multiplication with V (or V_v) the absolute surface S_v of the phase in the sample volume.

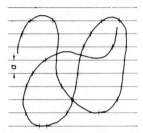

FIG. 2. Curve intersected by group of straight lines.

By "oriented object" is meant a phase that takes up a preferred direction within the sample. In the example given here, the components of the phase are assumed to be arranged in cylindrical form, with the cylinder axes running parallel to each other (Fig. 3) and the sample surfaces perpendicular or parallel to the axes of the cylinders. Let the cylinder shown represent the sum of the partial cylinders. The following relations will apply:

$$\text{Phase surface } S_v = L_v t$$

The circumference L_v in the sample area A can now be determined by means of a grid of grid constant a.

$$S_v = \frac{\pi}{2} a C_v t$$

Using a microscope, the thickness t of a specimen viewed in transmitted light can be determined by focusing on the upper and lower surfaces; thus, the absolute surface S_v of the phase v will have been determined directly. While this type of measurement cannot be performed on a strongly absorbing specimen, there is the following alternative for deriving the characteristics of such samples from the measurable values on their upper surface:

$$t = \frac{V}{A} = \frac{V_v}{A_v}$$

$$S_v = L_v \frac{V}{A} = L_v \frac{V_v}{A_v},$$

i.e.
$$\frac{S_v}{V} = \frac{L_v}{A} \quad \text{or} \quad \frac{S_v}{V_v} = \frac{L_v}{A_v}$$

The right hand terms are values pertaining only to the surface of the sample. These values are directly measurable with the microscope and permit the calculation of the spatial ratio of surface to volume according to the equations given.

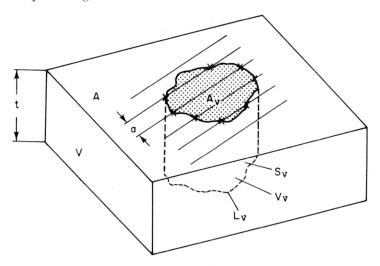

FIG. 3. Oriented object intersected by group of straight lines.

The values A or A_v are determined by calibrating the measuring lines of the grid. It is particularly advantageous to sub-divide in lengths of grid constant a (Fig. 4) because each point of the grid will then correspond to the measuring area a^2 or to the length a. Areas A or A_v are determined by counting the number of points p or p_v found on them. The corresponding equations are

$$A = pa^2$$
$$A_v = p_v a^2,$$

from which the lengths L or L_v of the measuring lines assigned to the sample or the phase can be calculated in the following manner:

$$L = \frac{A}{a} = pa$$

$$L_v = \frac{A_v}{a} = p_v a$$

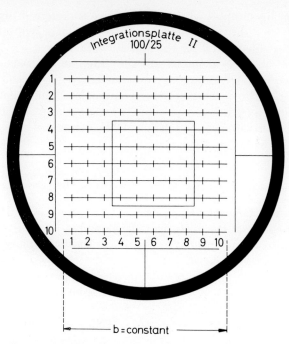

FIG. 4. Point-line pattern II of integrating eyepiece, Carl Zeiss, Oberkochen (Integrationsplatte = point-line pattern).

Depending on the measuring method and knowing a, either the areas A or A_v or the number of image points p or p_v can be determined. An instrument well suited for area measurement is the quantitative microscope coupled with television, while image points are easily measured with a scanning microscope photometer.

Under these conditions the equations given below are applicable for specific surfaces.

$$\frac{S_v}{V} = \frac{L_v}{A} = \frac{\frac{\pi}{2}aC_v}{A} = \frac{\frac{\pi}{2}C_v}{pa} = \frac{\pi}{2}\frac{C_v}{L}$$

$$\frac{S_v}{V_v} = \frac{L_v}{A_v} = \frac{\frac{\pi}{2}aC_v}{A_v} = \frac{\frac{\pi}{2}C_v}{p_v a} = \frac{\pi}{2}\frac{C_v}{L_v}$$

These equations are related in that

$$\frac{S_v}{V} = \frac{S_v}{V_v}\frac{A_v}{A}$$

When observing samples which do not have a preferred direction (i.e. "unaligned" or "isotropic" objects), these formulae will still apply if the factor 2 is substituted for the statistical factor $\pi/2$.

These two examples demonstrate the different approaches that are usually taken in determining stereometric characteristics. The characteristics may be the number of phase components, image points, points of intersection, lengths, and possibly, areas in the plane, from which spatial characteristics are then deduced. Measuring methods and results are essentially based on statistics.

II. MEASURING METHODS AND THEIR OPTIMIZATION

In line with the various requirements of users and governed by technical feasibility, the historical development of stereometry proceeded from *area-measurement techniques* to *linear analyses* and finally to the *point-counting method*.

In the area-measurement technique, the volume components V_v or the weight components G_v are determined from the area components a_v of the phase v.

Linear analysis, a somewhat simpler technique, solves the problem in a similar fashion: a straight line is superimposed on the object and the fractional lengths l_v covering the phase v are measured.

In the point-counting method, a point pattern is superimposed on the object and the number of points p_v falling within phase v is counted.

The heart of these problems is the determination of the volume or weight components of the phase v in the sample, for this information cannot be accurately deduced from the chemical constitution of solid samples because they may include mixed crystals and faults.

The percentile volumetric component V_v° of phase v is under these conditions:

$$V_v^\circ = V_v \times 100 = A_v \times 100 = L_v \times 100 = P_v \times 100$$

$$= \frac{a_v}{\Sigma a_v} \times 100 = \frac{l_v}{\Sigma l_v} \times 100 = \frac{p_v}{\Sigma p_v} \times 100$$

$$= \frac{p_v a^2}{\Sigma p_v \times a^2} \times 100 = \frac{p_v a}{\Sigma p_v a} \times 100 = \frac{p_v}{\Sigma p_v} \times 100$$

The last line of this group of equations is indicative of the identical relationships resulting if the measurement is performed with the point pattern described under Section I 2 (Fig. 4).

From the volumetric percentage V_v° and the specific weights γ_v, the weight percentage G_v° is calculated as follows:

$$G_v^\circ = \frac{\gamma_v V_v^\circ}{\varSigma \gamma_v V_v} \times 100$$

Now the question arises which of these techniques is best suited for determining such general characteristic data as described under Section V. Keeping in mind that accurate measurement calls for a relatively large amount of statistical data (which in turn requires time), it is best to choose a measuring technique that will yield all of the desired stereometric characteristics in one single operational step. Closer examination shows that this can only be done with the linear-analysis technique. Since a linear distance must be quantized by means of a pulse generator in order to achieve satisfactory accuracy, the advantages of the point-analysis technique become available in this process as an extra bonus. This corollary is generally applicable. An optimization of stereometric techniques can be achieved by combining point with line patterns. Such a pattern is used in the example given under Section I 2 and shown in Fig. 4.

III. Optimization of the Measuring Process

The cases to be treated here are representative of those encountered in practice. Visual measurement with the help of grids will be evaluated first. Of primary concern here are the determinations of lengths and surfaces as well as area and volume components of a phase.

Special attention will also be paid to the visual linear analysis; it will be performed in such a manner that all stereometric characteristics are determined in a single work step.

Lastly, a linear analysis will be performed with a grid whose grid constant is small compared with the size of the object.

A. Visual Measurement with Point-line Patterns

Since in many of the stereometric analytical relationships the total length L of the measuring distance or the corresponding measuring area A is obtained, the measurement is simplified if constant and known values are assigned to these magnitudes in advance (Fig. 4). In the case of the quantized lines of a grid, this means that the measuring length $L = pa = K_1$, or the measuring area $A = pa^2 = K_2$, with the magnitudes at first based on the relative and unknown value a.

By means of this measuring field of constant magnitude, other measuring fields of any size $A^* = nA$ or measuring lengths $L^* = nL$

can be constructed through the additive connection of n different measuring positions. The results of the measurements can in this case be based on L^* and A^* or, through averaging, on L and A.

Arrangements of this type are particularly well suited for efficient visual measurement. By a single absolute calibration of these fields with the help of a micrometer, all of the measured relative values can be expressed in absolute terms. In each case the number of points, the fractional lengths and the fractional areas add up to form the value of the full measuring field, and it is therefore necessary to obtain only $(k-1)$ of k phases in the sample.

If, for example, a measuring field of $A = pa^2 = 100a^2$ is given (Fig. 4) and two phases, namely E with 70% of the area and F with 30%, only the phase F with the smaller area needs to be counted. An average of 30 hits must in this case be recorded for F. The area fraction E can then be calculated without counting from $E = 100 - F = 100 - 30 = 70$ hits, which is the equivalent of the area fraction

$$E^\circ = \frac{70}{100} \times 100 = 70\%.$$

If the measurement covered $n = 20$ measuring fields, the measuring area $A^* = 20A = 20a^2 \times 100a^2 = 2000a^2$. E will then have $20 \times 70 = 1400$ measuring points, and F correspondingly $20 \times 30 = 600$ measuring points. The resulting relative area fractions are $E = 1400a^2$ and $F = 600a^2$. By determining the absolute value $a = 10\ \mu m$, it is possible to state the absolute area fractions $E = 1400 \times 10^2 = 1 \cdot 4 \times 10^5\ \mu m^2$ and $F = 600 \times 10^2 = 6 \times 10^4\ \mu m^2$.

Such measuring fields with constant given values greatly simplify the work, particularly during visual measurement with reticles in the eyepiece or in the plane of projection (Fig. 4). The measuring conditions can be further improved by an appropriate choice of the magnification between constant a of the grid and the mean size of the object. This is demonstrated in Fig. 5 by measurements performed on a test object.

The percentile volumes are shown in the diagram as ordinates while the number of measuring positions is plotted as abscissa. The object was a simple, square cell of grid constant $d_4 = 120$ mm in whose corners were arranged squares having a lateral length of $a_4 = 40$ mm. The nominal area fraction taken up by the phase was therefore $(a_4^2/d_4^2)100 = (40^2/120^2)100 = 11\frac{1}{9}\%$. This object was measured with a grid having a constant number of points $p_n = 25$ but a variable grid constant $C_n = 5, 10, 20, 40$ and 60 mm. The measured results represent the average values entered up to the measuring position. The measuring curves are marked by the corresponding parameters a_4/C_n and d_4/C_n. These diagrams show that a pronounced selectivity occurs. Under conditions of $a_4/C_n \approx 1$, a good approximation to the nominal value is achieved at about 30 measuring positions, but large fluctuations from the nominal persist under any other parametric conditions; a uniform smoothing of the curves is attained only if there are more than 100 measuring positions.

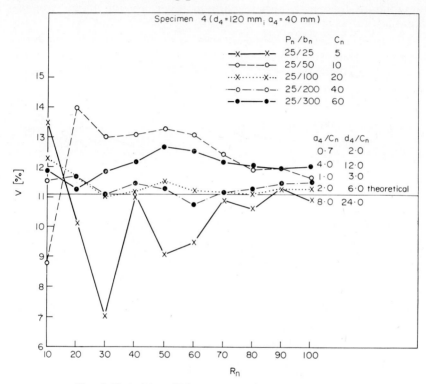

FIG. 5. Test object. Volume measured with point pattern.

A close examination of the measured values furthermore shows that the numbers of the best curves approximate the normal distribution sooner than the data of the other diagrams. These findings confirm the empirical rule according to which in a visual measuring process with grids optimization is usually attained through adjustment of the magnification when the mean particle diameter approximates the point interval of the point-line pattern (Fig. 6).

B. *Visual Linear Analysis*

To ensure that the linear measurement in analyses of the type discussed here is performed with a satisfactory degree of accuracy, the distances must be quantized at fairly close intervals by means of a variable pulse generator. For this purpose, perforated chopper disks with an appropriate light source and photocell may be used whose angular motion is coupled to the motion of the stage via transmission gears. The stage can be moved at will by means of a d.c. motor. Stepping motors with speeds variable over a wide range are also suitable.

The interval between adjacent measuring lines must be chosen to be greater than the largest particle diameter to permit unequivocal counting; this ensures that no particle will be touched by a line more than once.

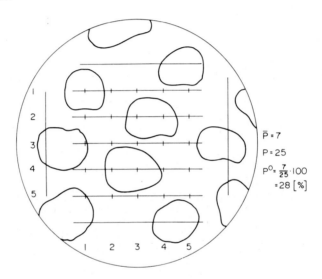

FIG. 6. Optimal fit of point-line pattern.

During visual microscopic measurement, each point of intersection with a phase boundary will then be recorded by pressing a key at the recording unit. This establishes a clear correlation between the points of intersection and the stereometric characteristics. Problems of this type can be handled in an optimum manner by using the logic circuitry of commercially-available desk-top computers in conjunction with flexible programs. Thus it is possible, for instance, to solve many-particle problems and to describe without difficulty the external and internal particle areas simultaneously yet independently (Fig. 6).

During the measuring process, the number of particles and intersections, the fractional lengths of the phases and the entire measuring length are available at any time; this makes it possible to evaluate immediately the number, specific surfaces, area and volume fractions, and contiguity conditions of outer and inner phase areas. At the same time the fractional lengths can be grouped according to any number of schemes, such as, for example, normal, log-normal and RRS distribution (see Section V).

Instruments suitable for recordings of this type are called linear analyzers (Fig. 7). Some of their functions can be performed automatically if the microscopic detector that is used has sufficient resolution with respect to contrast and form, in which case the system is called a phase computer (Fig. 8). A phase computer differs from a scanning microscope photometer in its software.

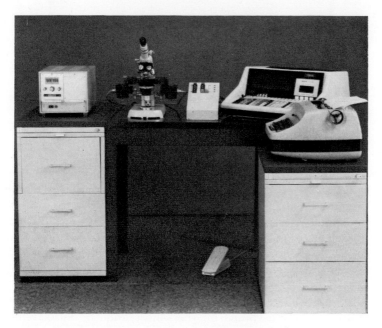

FIG. 7. Linear analyzer (Carl Zeiss, Oberkochen), consisting of microscope with scanning stage, stage control unit, interface, manual input, WANG desk-top computer and typewriter.

Linear analyzers can additionally be programmed to function, with any desired degree of operator comfort, as automatic point counters, particle counters for blood analysis and for other similar tasks. However, for reasons mentioned earlier, it is no longer advisable to practice today the type of point analysis used exclusively only a few years ago.

FIG. 8. Phase calculator (Carl Zeiss, Oberkochen), consisting of microscope with scanning stage, measuring amplifier, digital display unit, digital stage control unit, interface, WANG desk-top computer and typewriter.

C. *Automatic Linear Analysis*

The advantages of the measuring techniques described in Sections III A and III B are derived from visual evaluation and recording of the specimen because full use is made of the human operator's talent to combine and to differentiate shapes. Measuring systems of this kind can be very economical and highly efficient. Among the disadvantages are the great amount of time that is required for the measurement, the subjectivity of the evaluation and the poor statistical averaging during the measurement.

These disadvantages can be largely eliminated if a grid with small grid constants is superposed on the object and the measurement is performed automatically. Initially, a few other problems will be incurred in return, such as reduced contrast resolution due to detector character- istics and poorer form differentiation by the electronic units, because they cannot match the human ability to judge. On the other hand, there will now be quantitative photometric, objective measurement and much less time will be required. Storage of the data and the electronic criteria make it possible to determine the number of particles, projection lengths and absolute surfaces directly and without additional azimuthal averaging. Furthermore, the measured values can be assigned local coordinates and can be recalled at any time for processing. Instrumental requirements for such systems are rather elaborate and make them relatively expensive.

At this point a few words are in order concerning the contrast resolution of automatic image analyzers, for opinions and findings on this subject vary greatly today and comparisons are well-nigh impossible because of a wide divergence in definitions.

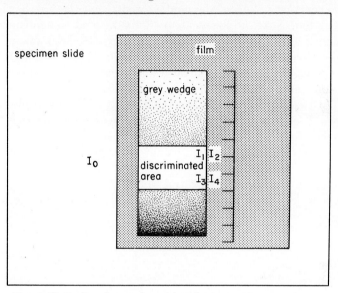

FIG. 9. Neutral wedge used as object for contrast measurements.

The usual definition of physical contrast will be used here, in which the photometrically measured intensities I_1 and I_2 of two adjacent image points are related as follows:

Contrast
$$K = \frac{I_2 - I_1}{I_1 + I_2}$$

Border cases

$$I_1 = 0 \qquad K = 1$$
$$I_2 = 0 \qquad K = -1$$
$$I_1 = I_2 \qquad K = 0$$

Contrast range $\qquad -1 \leqslant K \leqslant 1$

As shown in Fig. 9, a transparent specimen is used here to measure and demonstrate contrast.

A scale with graduations of $1/100$ mm is copied on a film and a neutral wedge is placed in the immediate vicinity of the scale. The length of the neutral wedge chosen is such that it exceeds the resolution of the optical detector. This film strip is mounted on a specimen support and covered with a cover glass. Next, the intensities are measured— with a microscope photometer of highest resolution set at the lowest magnification and at constant background intensity I_0—as a function of the local coordinates once each in the neutral wedge, in the adjacent film background, and, as a control, in a field without film. From these data the contrast values of the neutral wedge and the film background are calculated. Next, adjacent areas of the neutral wedge can be con- tinuously scanned photometrically with various detectors until one noisy signal can be clearly distinguished from the preceding one. The contrast values K for both neutral-wedge locations are taken from the calibration curve, their difference ΔK is formed, and the reciprocal value $N = 1/\Delta K$ is calculated. With that, the index of contrast resolution N of this arrangement will have been determined.

This measuring procedure can be demonstrated particularly well with quantitative television equipment (Fig. 10). After presetting the thresholds of discrimination, the discriminated range is directly indicated as a window at the neutral wedge. Now the values I_0 through I_4 shown in Fig. 9 are measured, from which the index of contrast resolution N is calculated.

$$K_1 = \frac{I_2 - I_1}{I_1 + I_2} \qquad\qquad K_2 = \frac{I_4 - I_3}{I_3 + I_4}$$

$$\Delta K = K_1 - K_2$$

$$N = 1/\Delta K = \text{number of possible steps of contrast.}$$

For visual observation, it is possible to determine photometrically the corresponding values of that point on the neutral wedge where the eye perceives the brightness of the wedge to be the same as that of the adjacent film background. By splitting a neutral wedge longitudinally and displacing both halves with respect to each other under a small slit until boundary areas of equal apparent brightness are adjoining, the same measurements can be performed at any position of the neutral wedge or the neutral-wedge steps. The detectors that were tested had the following threshold characteristics:

Eye $N = 10$ to 50

Plumbicon   Limits of resolution 25 to 30, usually around 10

Photocell   50 to 100

Photomultiplier   150 to 200

The contrast perception of the eye may vary widely and depends primarily on brightness conditions and the contrast and surface structure of adjacent areas on the object under observation.

The poor contrast resolution of television equipment (Fig. 10) is essentially due to the electronic scanning of the entire area of the microscopic image, resulting in the addition of all optical imaging errors and the full noise level of the microscope system to the electronic noise. In true microscopic photometry on the other hand, only the image at the centre of the field, which is sharply defined with minimum aberration, is measured by the photomultiplier (Fig. 8) with least error. This is in fact one of the significant advantages of microscopic photometry.

FIG. 10. Quantitative television microscope MICRO-VIDEOMAT with automatic unit.

Basic incremental steps in photometry range from $\frac{1}{2}$ μm up to several tens of μm while the measuring frequencies range from 50 to 100 Hz and up to several kHz in some exceptional cases. At the present time the optimum lies around 100 Hz.

In television microscopes, bandwidths range from 1 to 12 MHz, with the working frequencies usually somewhere between 4 and 6 MHz. According to C.C.I.R. standards, 50 half images per second are usually transmitted by the interlaced-scanning method, i.e. 25 pictures are covered per second. This exceptional speed and the high geometrical resolution are the real advantages of television systems.

By the coordinated use of instruments which permit the parallel application of various types of detectors it is possible to get the full benefit of the desirable features of these different detectors. An arrangement of this type is shown in Fig. 11. A photometer with a photomultiplier is mounted on a microscope that permits the use of many methods of microscopy with incident and transmitted light by a simple exchange of the optical elements for imaging and illumination. A plumbicon of a quantitative television microscope is additionally mounted on this system. An automatic 35 mm camera, controlled via a photomultiplier, is also built into the microscope. The scanning specimen stage which moves in incremental steps of 0·5 μm serves as timer for stereometry or positioning during photometry.

The binocular tube can be exchanged for a clip-on monocular tube

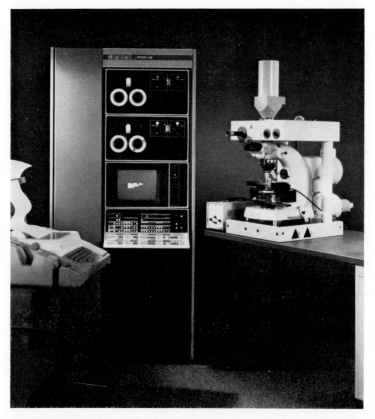

Fig. 11. Scanning microscope photometer SMP connected to quantitative television microscope MICRO-VIDEOMAT and PDP 12 process computer.

with an integrating eyepiece. If in addition the manual input for the linear analyzer is used (Fig. 7), it is possible to combine the instrument with a wide variety of electronic slide-in units and computer modules to form optimum arrangements of any desired degree of sophistication which allow the use of many visual, semi-automatic and automatic microscopic techniques of stereometry in the off- as well as on-line modes.

Expansion of the basic instrument is greatly facilitated by a rationally designed system of electronic slide-in units (Fig. 12) affording any level of data storage, selection and processing in on-line and off-line operations. The system includes the measuring amplifier (on the left) with the power-supply unit for the multiplier of the microscope photometer. Next to it is the digital display unit, which includes the analog-to-digital converter and which shows the measured value as decimal data with four digits.

The digital stage-control unit is illustrated second from the right in Fig. 12. With this unit the scanning stage can be programmed to move in a meander, comblike or rectangular pattern. The multiplication steps for the basic incremental motion of the stage and for the step sequences in x and y directions can be selected independently of each other. The entire system can also be controlled by a computer.

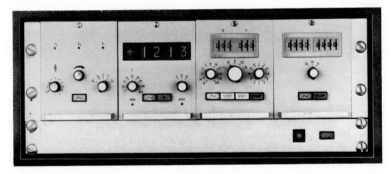

Fig. 12. Electronic slide-in system consisting of measuring amplifier, digital display unit, digital stage control unit and code converter.

Shown on the right is an encoder for the coding of the measured data in ASCII or Friden code and for the input of identifying auxiliary data. This makes it possible to transfer the analog measured data coming from the analog-to-digital converter to a punch- or magnetic tape for separate evaluation in a process computer.

There are several extensive programs available which permit practically any kind of recording and statistical processing of the measured data. These programs are suited for automatic measurement by means of photomultipliers and in conjunction with the process computers PDP 12 and WANG 700 as well as for the quantitative television microscope MICRO-VIDEOMAT used together with WANG computers of the 700 series. Data related to the basic stereometric characteristics thus become available rapidly and with a high degree of statistical accuracy.

IV. Evaluation of Measured Data and Samples

Statistical tasks are a major element of stereological measurement. First of all, a truly representative sample must be available for the measurement. Next, the particles of this sample must be statistically assessed. Finally, the measured data must fall within a pre-determined confidence range.

The problems of sampling and statistical verification of the data are identical to those encountered in other physical measuring techniques and will therefore be treated only briefly with regard to their general applicability in stereometry.

The evaluation of the statistically assessed particle population, however, is a different problem, for it is a task intrinsically peculiar to stereology and image analysis; as such, it constitutes the heart of this article.

A. Verification of the Measured Data

In examining the measured data one may proceed from the assumption that they approximate a normal distribution and that applicable standard equations can be used in the assessment. If, however, the evaluation is to be somewhat more critical, this assumption should not be made, and rather than taking normal distribution for granted, it should be subject to verification.

1. Standard Deviation and Estimation Formula

Assuming that the measured data approximate a normal distribution a meaningful estimation formula for planning the measurement may be set up based on the standard deviation s:

$$\text{Standard deviation } s = \sqrt{\frac{\Sigma(x-\bar{x})^2}{n-1}}$$

$\bar{x}$ = arithmetic mean of measured values

x = measured values

n = number of measurements.

Relative percentile error r_{Av}:

$$r_{Av} = \frac{s}{x} \times 100 = \frac{100}{\bar{x}} \sqrt{\frac{\Sigma(x-\bar{x})^2}{n-1}}$$

Estimation formula for number of measurements n which are assigned a relative percentile error r_{Av}:

$$n \approx \frac{10^4 \Sigma(x-\bar{x})^2}{\bar{x}^2 r_{Av}^2}$$

With this formula, only a few measurements are necessary to determine the sum value of the squared deviation $\Sigma(x-\bar{x})^2$ and to extrapolate with the corresponding mean value $\bar{x}$ (often still inaccurate) and the given r_{Av}^2 to n. This estimation formula can be applied in any measurement, such as number of points, intersections and area measurement, for instance as shown below.

Example: Estimation of the measuring positions n required for determining the particle numbers x with the help of a quantitative television microscope from 10 measuring positions if $r_{Av} = 10\%$.

Result: $\bar{x} = 37\cdot6$ particles/measuring position

$$\Sigma(x-\bar{x})^2 = 518\cdot2$$

$$n \approx \frac{10^4 \times 518\cdot2}{37\cdot6^2 \times 10^2} = 40 \text{ measuring positions}$$

2. *Graphic Control over the Mean Values*

During measurement, mean values are immediately formed from the preceding data, including those of the position that is in the process of being measured, and the values measured per position are entered on the ordinate against the number of measuring positions R_n. As can be seen from Fig. 13, these mean values converge toward a boundary value, and the measurement can therefore be terminated in a controlled manner. A distinction must be made between two limiting cases:

(a) The measured values are concentrated in one measuring position by way of statistical projection. Under these conditions the deviation values correspond to the azimuthal inhomogeneities of the object. The curve will converge toward the mean of the measuring positions (Fig. 13, left).

This statement is also valid for an ideally representative object measured in different positions.

(b) The object is systematically scanned at various points. If the mean values converge toward a boundary value, it means that the object is additionally representative. The deviations are due to the statistical inhomogeneities of the sample and the "azimuthal differences" of the positions in question (Fig. 13, right).

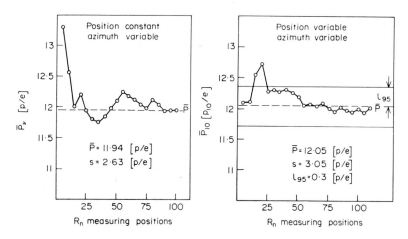

Fig. 13. Graphite in spheroidal graphite iron. Volume measurement. Statistical verification. Measurements with integrating disk II (points/eyepiece position = p/e).

3. Verification of Normal Distribution

The purpose is to test whether the measured values approximate a normal distribution. This requires that a sufficient number of independent measuring positions is taken, which usually means at least 100 positions.

For verification, the measured values per measuring position are subdivided into 10 to 15 classes, and the frequency of assignments or cumulative frequencies of the measured values are counted against the measuring record. The frequency percentages f are then entered on the ordinate (Fig. 14, left), while the class centers of the measured values per position are entered on the abscissa. A more convenient presentation is to plot the cumulative-frequency percentages and the measured values per position on probability paper (Fig. 14, right). If in doing so the measured values can be approximated by a straight line, they approach a normal distribution. This normal distribution is unequivocally fixed by the arithmetic mean $\bar{x}$ and the standard deviation s; these characteristic values of the population can be derived from the sum frequencies F_{16}, F_{50} and F_{84} with the corresponding abscissa values x_{16}, x_{50} and x_{84} as follows:

Arithmetic mean $\bar{x} = x_{50}$

Standard deviation $s = x_{84} - x_{50} = x_{50} - x_{16}$

$$= \frac{x_{84} - x_{16}}{2}$$

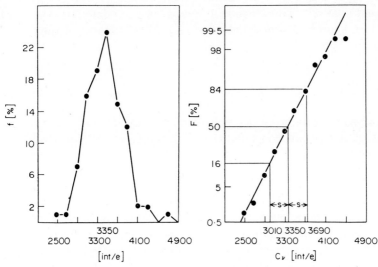

FIG. 14. Graphite in soft iron. Specific surface. Statistical verification. Measurements with MICRO-VIDEOMAT.

B. *Representativity of the Sample*

The cases discussed under Section IV A involved samples which had a uniform local makeup, i.e. the object was sufficiently representative. Under these conditions, the measurements could be performed at any point of the object, but a direct verification and control of this representation was not possible.

In the present section an attempt will be made to derive—through rational planning of the examination rather than through additional measurements—a mathematical statement concerning the representativity of the sample. For this purpose, an identical number of independent measuring positions ν will be determined at various points of the object, and their mean values $\bar{x}_\nu$ and, possibly, their standard deviations s_ν will be calculated. The mean values $\bar{x}_\nu$ will be considered a new population with normal distribution for which the arithmetic mean $\bar{x}$ and the standard deviation $s = \sqrt{(\bar{x}_\nu - \bar{x})^2 / N - 1}$ will be calculated The value $(N-1)$ in this equation will be called the variant, of which

N represents the number of measuring fields in which the measurements are made. From these values, the l_{95}-limit is derived in the following manner:

$$l_{95} = t_{95}s/\sqrt{N-1},$$

where t_{95} is a factor of probability theory assigned the confidence coefficient "95%". This "Student factor" t_{95} is related to the variant $N-1$ and can be found tabulated in handbooks. Some of the t_{95} values are given below.

$N-1$	2	3	4	5	9	16	25	31	64	100
t_{95}	4·30	3·18	2·78	2·57	2·21	2·12	2·06	2·03	2·00	1·99

On the basis of these values the statement can be made that the mean value of the population falls with a certainty of 95% within the confidence range

$$x \pm l_{95} = \bar{x} \pm t_{95}s/\sqrt{N-1}.$$

Example: Five adjacent fractional fields on a polished specimen were measured with an integrating plate having 100 measuring points. In each field, 25 independent, continuously linked measuring positions were taken up and the hits were counted with reference to the phase. The results were as follows:

$$N = 5 \qquad\qquad t_{95} = 2·78$$
$$\bar{x}_v[\%] = 12·28,\ 12·12,\ 11·62,\ 11·94,\ 12·08$$
$$\bar{x}[\%] = 12·01$$
$$s[\%] = 0·50$$
$$l_{95}[\%] = t_{95}s/\sqrt{4} = 0·70.$$

Result: The mean of the area or volume fraction that is to be determined lies with a certainty of 95% within the range $\bar{x} \pm l_{95}$, *i.e.* 11·31–12·71.

If it is accepted that an object whose confidence limits deviate $\pm 5\%$ can be considered representative, the specimen subject to this test meets this criterion.

V. STEREOMETRIC CHARACTERISTICS

In this section the characteristic values of stereometric analysis, the major relevant problem definitions, and the accuracy of the measurement will be discussed.

A. *The Number of Particles*

In many cases, and especially when mean values are to be calculated, it is necessary to know the number of particles contained in a sample. In visual counting, all particles within the measuring field are counted directly. Particles intersected by the border line of the measuring field are given half weight in the count.

The same counting criteria apply in visual linear analysis. As pointed out in Section III B, the interval between any two adjacent lines must be chosen to be greater than the diameter of the largest particle in the population. Under these conditions, any convex particle will not be intersected more than twice. Points of contact with the measuring line count once. The number of particles is computed from half the number of points of intersection.

Special counting criteria are required for systems with line patterns whose grid constant is significantly smaller than the object diameter. This is the case with the scanning microscope photometer (Figs 8 and 11) and with quantitative television microscopes (Fig. 10).

Since scanning photometers are usually coupled to process computers working in the on-line mode, all of the measured data can be stored in the computer and subsequently processed according to any program, i.e. for any desired measuring criteria. This will apply particularly in case of boundary value problems.

When working with quantitative television microscopes, clear-cut counting criteria must be established for concave-convex transitions. In addition, the border line of the measuring field must be correctly statistically averaged. One may count, for example, all particles whose major portion falls within the border line of the measuring field. A rectangular measuring field may include the particles that are intersected by two borders of equivalent weight, while the particles of the other border lines will not be counted. The effects of the border line can furthermore be largely reduced through judicious adjustment of the microscope magnification.

Results of measurements of this type are shown in Fig. 15, in this case obtained on chromium points and working with the MICRO-VIDEOMAT quantitative television microscope. The statistical verifications refer to counts without correction (index O) and with correction (index K). As discussed in Section IV B, the following characteristic data result:

$$\bar{x}_0 = 37{\cdot}5 \text{ particles/measuring field}$$

$$s_0 = 2{\cdot}76 \text{ particles/measuring field}$$

$$l_{0;95} = 2.08 \text{ particles/measuring field}$$
$$\bar{x}_K = 32.5 \text{ particles/measuring field}$$
$$s_K = 2.35 \text{ particles/measuring field}$$
$$l_{K;95} = 1.77 \text{ particles/measuring field}$$

These diagrams establish at the same time the percentile measuring errors usually incurred in this type of statistical counting. As a rule, values $(s/\bar{x}) \times 100$ of 10% are attained after 30 measurements if the samples are halfway representative, and even with a large number of measuring positions this value can rarely be reduced to less than 5%.

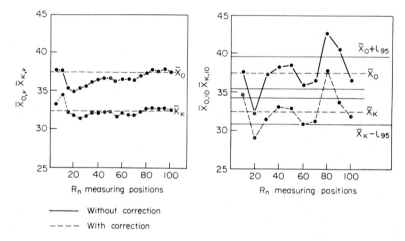

Fig. 15. Chromium points. Determination of number. Statistical verification. Measurements with MICRO-VIDEOMAT.

B. *The Number of Intersections*

According to Sections I 1 and I 2, the following applies if a grid with a grid constant "a" and a total length L is superposed on an object (L_v, S_v, V, A):

$$L_v = \frac{\pi}{2} a C_v = S_v \frac{A}{V} = \frac{S_v}{t}$$

$$\frac{S_v}{V} = \frac{L_v}{A} = K \frac{a C_v}{A} = K \frac{C_v}{L}$$

$$K = 2 = \text{isotropic object}$$

$$K = \frac{\pi}{2} = \text{oriented object}$$

From these formulae the following may be inferred:

1. The length L_v of any curve in the object plane can be determined from the number of intersections C_v of this curve with the lines of a grid of grid constant "a". According to the formula, the length L_v can also be allowed to stand for surface S_v of the corresponding phase v per unit of sample thickness t.

2. The specific surface S_v/V, i.e. the surface S_v of phase v per volumetric unit of the sample, can be computed from the number of intersecting points C_v of the grid lines with the phase boundaries if the grid constant "a" of the grid and the projection surface A corresponding to the sample volume V (or, which is identical, to the length $L = A/a$ of the measuring line) are given.

3. If the sample volume V is known, S_v can additionally be derived absolutely from S_v/V.

The statistical factors $\pi/2$ or 2 apply only if the number of intersections C_v that is used is azimuthally well averaged. A mere parallel shifting during the measurement will not suffice: the object must be rotated statistically through different azimuths. The reason for this can be explained by reference to the simple geometry of a square, where the number of intersections in the diagonal length is greater by $\sqrt{2} \times 100 = 141\%$ compared with the side of the square. These anisotropic effects—which, as the example shows, also occur on isometric curves—can be eliminated only through statistical azimuthal averaging.

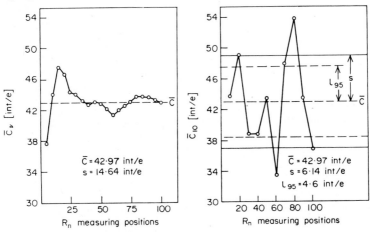

Fig. 16. Vascular cell bundle, white beech. Length measurement. Statistical verification. Measurements with Integrating eyepiece II.

The statistical controls applied to the results of measurements on vascular-bundle cells of a white beech are given in Fig. 16. The measurements were performed with the integrating eyepiece. The averaged values of the numbers of intersections $\overline{C}$ (or of chord groupings $\overline{C}_{10}$) are entered against the number of counting positions R_n. The statistical data and measured results given below were derived from this information.

$$N = 10 \qquad\qquad t_{95} = 2\cdot21$$

$$\overline{C} = 42\cdot97 \text{ intersections/eyepiece positions}$$

$$s_v = 14\cdot6 \text{ intersections/eyepiece positions}$$

$$s = .6\cdot1 \text{ intersections/eyepiece positions}$$

$$l_{95} = 4\cdot6 \text{ intersections/eyepiece positions}$$

Total circumference L_v of the vascular bundles measured per measuring position:

$$L_v = \frac{\pi}{2} a \overline{C} = \frac{\pi}{2} 48\cdot8 \times 42\cdot97 = 3295 \ \mu\mathrm{m}$$

Specific surface S_v/V of the vascular bundles per measuring field:

$$S_v/V = \frac{\pi}{2} C_v/L = \frac{\pi}{2} \frac{42\cdot97}{4888} = 0\cdot014 \ \mu\mathrm{m}^{-1}$$

By counting in addition the number of cross-sections of the vascular bundles, one could also calculate such data as mean cross-sections of vascular bundles and mean surfaces.

According to Fig. 16 (left), the averages $\overline{C}_v$ become gradually centered on the nominal value $\overline{C}$ after about 30 to 40 measuring positions. Measurements on test distances, conducted independently, have shown that the averages will approximate the nominal values to within 1 to 1·5% after about 30 to 50 measuring positions. Further improvement of results like these by increasing the measuring statistics is usually not possible due to the limited representativity of the object.

C. Measuring the Area

In Section III A it was shown that the following statement applies to area and volume percentages A_v° and V_v° of a phase v if they were determined by means of area, linear or point analysis:

$$A_v^\circ = V_v^\circ = \frac{a_v}{\Sigma a_v} \times 100 = \frac{l_v}{\Sigma l_v} \times 100 = \frac{p_v}{\Sigma p_v} \times 100.$$

With the corresponding specific weights γ_v, it is possible to derive from this the weight percentages G_v°:

$$G_v^\circ = \frac{\gamma_v V_v^\circ}{\Sigma \gamma_v V_v} \times 100$$

The areas a_v are directly determined if the linear analysis is performed with a very small grid constant, as is the case in quantitative television microscopy. The fractional lengths l_v corresponding to the measuring length $L = \Sigma l_v$ are obtained directly by visual linear analysis. The

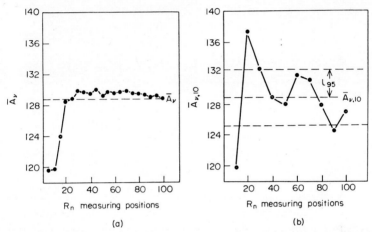

Fig. 17. Graphite in spheroidal graphite iron. Volume measurements with MICRO-VIDEOMAT.

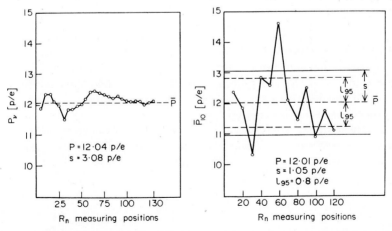

Fig. 18. Graphite in spheroidal graphite iron. Volume measurements with integrating disk II (points /eyepiece position = p/e).

points p_ν corresponding to phase ν are determined through the point patterns of the integration plates in the integrating eyepieces, while the total number of points $P = \Sigma p_\nu$ is fixed by the point pattern of the integrating plate. The statistical controls for the results of measurements on a spheroidal graphite iron are shown in Figs 17 and 18.

The graphite portion in Fig. 17 was measured with a television microscope, the one in Fig. 18 with an integrating plate. The measuring positions of the two illustrations are not identical. The results were:

$$\text{MICRO-VIDEOMAT} \quad V_\nu^\circ = (12\cdot8\pm0.2)\%$$
$$G_C^\circ = 4\cdot0\% \text{ graphite portion}$$
$$G_{Fe}^\circ = 96\cdot0\% \text{ iron portion}$$
$$s = 0\cdot5\%$$
$$l_{95} = 0\cdot4\%$$
$$\text{Integrating eyepiece} \quad V_\nu^\circ = 12\cdot02\%$$
$$G_C^\circ = 3\cdot7\% \text{ graphite portion}$$
$$G_{Fe}^\circ = 96\cdot3\% \text{ iron portion}$$
$$s_\nu = 3\cdot1\%$$
$$s = 1\cdot0\%$$
$$l_{95} = 0\cdot8\%.$$

Here, too, the averages become in both cases gradually centered on the limiting values. As can be seen in Fig. 17(b) the sample measurements may fall off as the counting positions are increased, which means that true representativity can no longer be presumed. Generally, the empirical rules described in Section III A apply here too.

D. *Contiguity*

In published work there have been various references to the advantages arising from the determination of contiguity, contact areas and similar characteristics of phases in the sample. Since thus far there is a lack of meaningful experimental data on the subject, problems of this nature will not be treated here.

Moreover, linear analyzers (Fig. 7) and phase calculators (Fig. 8) of the type described in Section III, when used in conjunction with the proper software, offer sufficient flexibility to handle any problem of this type in an optimum fashion.

E. *Direction and Form Factors*

The directional orientation of phase components often has a decisive bearing on the mechanical, electrical, magnetic, dilatational and thermal characteristics of a sample. Such anisotropic orientation of phases can be expressed in a number of ways.

1. *Directional Factors*

The various azimuths assigned to the projection lengths of a particle can be determined with the help of grids of small grid constants via the number of intersections C_v. As shown in Fig. 19, these data may be entered, with the zero point suppressed, as a function of the azimuthal angle. This clearly identifies the geometrical anisotropy of the particle. The following is an example of a magnitude defining the directional factor k:

$$k = \frac{C_{max}}{C_{min}} \times 100 = \frac{244 \cdot 9}{299 \cdot 3} \times 100 = 81 \cdot 8\%.$$

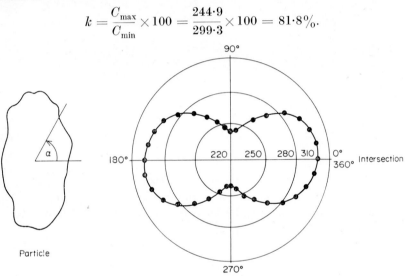

FIG. 19. Number of intersections of a particle as a function of azimuthal angle. MICRO-VIDEOMAT.

The projection lengths of a particle population can be determined in the same manner, as is shown with measurements on the graphite of a spheroidal graphite iron presented in Fig. 20. The visual impression that there is practically no directional dependence in the sample is confirmed by the left diagram. However, a closer examination, shown in the diagram on the right with suppressed zero point, indicates that there is a slight anisotropy. Extreme projection lengths were measured for 10° and 190°, and for 70° and 310°. According to the definition given above, a directional factor of the following magnitude exists:

$$k = \frac{C_{min}}{C_{max}} \times 100 = \frac{1200}{1250} \times 100 \approx 96\%.$$

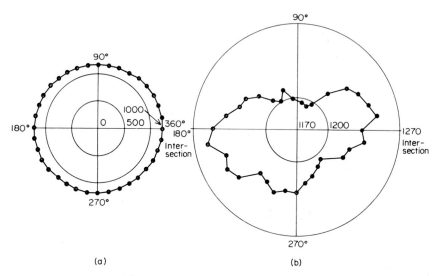

Fig. 20. Graphite in spheroidal graphite iron. Intersections as a function of azimuthal angle. Measured with MICRO-VIDEOMAT.

2. Form Factors

Depending on personal choice and experience, a wide range of characteristics can be defined and described as form factors. These characteristics can generally be measured with any point-line pattern or with television microscopes.

The simplest definition relates the circumference L_v of the particles to the measured phase area A_v.

$$k = \frac{L_v}{A_v} \, \mu m^{-1}$$

Example: Mean number of particle intersections $\bar{C}_v$ determined with the MICRO-VIDEOMAT from 50 measuring positions.

$$\bar{C}_v = 277{\cdot}2 \text{ intersections/measuring field}$$

$$a = 0{\cdot}539 \; \mu m/\text{line} = \text{grid constant television line}$$

$$L_v = \frac{\pi}{2} a \bar{C}_v = 234{\cdot}7 \; \mu m$$

$$A_v = 18{\cdot}7\% \text{ equal to } A_v = 4{\cdot}77 \times 10^3 \; \mu m^2$$

$$k = \frac{L_v}{A_v} = \frac{234{\cdot}7}{4{\cdot}77 \times 10^3} = 0{\cdot}049 \; \mu m^{-1}.$$

This value approximates closely the form factor $k_K = 0{\cdot}034\ \mu\mathrm{m}^{-1}$ calculated from equivalent radii, i.e. the particle had a nearly isometric form.

To this category also belong the values defined by Saltykov (1958), Smith and Guttmann (1953) and Ministr (1971), which can all be derived from basic measured characteristics, such as number, intersections and areas.

Spatial characteristics can be included in the definition analogously to the form factors given above, and they are also derived from basic measured characteristics; but they differ from the definitions given thus far in that they involve numbers representing surface and spatial dimensions clearly different in their order of magnitude.

Such magnitudes are, for example:

The relation of a surface of an equivalent sphere to the equivalent volume of the sphere computed from the area fraction.

The relation of an equivalent sphere derived from the specific surface to a sphere determined from the area fraction of the phase.

These form factors have the disadvantage that there is no direct correlation between the statistical projection with which C_v must be measured and the azimuth of preferred orientation of the object.

F. *Characteristic Values of Particle Populations*

The structure of phase populations making up an object is of crucial importance when assessing such physical and chemical characteristics as strength, electrical and magnetic properties, dilatation, thermal properties, absorption, color, sintering properties, packing density and growth processes. Depending on the available time and accuracy requirements, various characteristic values may be used which will define the population more or less thoroughly.

1. *Partial Characterization of the Population*

The measuring methods discussed here require only a moderate effort, as a consequence of which the resulting particle data are of mediocre quality, that is, in no case do they describe the population completely.

(a) *Area A_v and number of particles n_v*

From the measured area $A_v\ \mu\mathrm{m}^2$ and the number of particles n_v, a mean particle area a_v can be calculated:

$$a_v = A_v/n_v\ \mu\mathrm{m}^2$$

From this value a mean equivalent diameter d'_v is derived:

$$d'_v = 2\sqrt{\frac{\overline{a_v}}{\pi}}\ \mu m$$

Since the particle population was statistically intersected in height, this diameter d'_v must be multiplied by the statistical factor $3\pi/8 \approx 1\cdot178$ in order to obtain the corresponding mean diameter of the sphere d_v.

$$d_v = \frac{3\pi}{8}d'_v = \frac{3\pi}{4}\sqrt{\frac{\overline{a_v}}{\pi}}\ \mu m$$

Example: The mean cross-section of the vascular bundle of a white beech is to be measured with an integrating eyepiece.

$$n_v = 41\cdot6 \text{ vascular bundle cells per eyepiece setting}$$
$$A_v^\circ = 13\cdot75\%$$
$$A_v = 3\cdot274\times10^4\ \mu m^2$$
$$a_v = A_v/n_v = 7\cdot87\times10^2\ \mu m^2$$
$$d'_v = 2\sqrt{\frac{\overline{a_v}}{\pi}} = 31\cdot7\ \mu m$$

(b) *Number of intersections C_v and particles n_v*

From $\bar{C}_v$ and n_v it is possible to compute a mean circumference l_v and from this in turn a diameter d'_v in the object plane. When multiplied by $3\pi/8$, this will yield the corresponding mean diameter of the sphere d_v.

$$L_v = \frac{\pi}{2}aC_v\ \mu m = \text{sum of phase boundaries}$$

$$l_v = L_v/n_v\ \mu m = \text{circumference per particle}$$

$$d'_v = \frac{L_v}{\pi n_v}\ \mu m = \text{circumference-equivalent diameter}$$

$$d_v = \frac{3\pi}{8}\frac{L_v}{\pi n_v} = \frac{3\pi}{16}\frac{aC_v}{n_v}\mu m.$$

Example: The mean diameter of graphite particles in a polished specimen is to be determined by means of a television microscope.

$$a = 0\cdot847\ \mu m/\text{line}$$
$$\bar{C}_v = 1029 \text{ intersections/measuring field}$$
$$n_v = 28\cdot5 \text{ particles/measuring field}$$
$$d_v = \frac{3\pi}{16}\frac{a\bar{C}_v}{n_v} = 18\cdot0\ \mu m.$$

(c) *Determination of mean particle size by the diameter method*

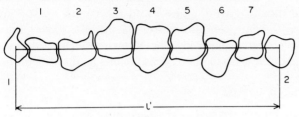

FIG. 21. The diameter method.

A measuring line of known length l' is superposed on the particle population. Particles intersected by the measuring line count half $(= n_K)$, all other particles count full $(= n_G)$.

Number of particles $\qquad\qquad\qquad n_v = n_G + \tfrac{1}{2}n_K$

Measured mean diameter $\qquad\qquad d''_v = \dfrac{l'}{n_v}\,\mu\text{m}$

Mean diameter in object plane $\qquad d'_v = \dfrac{3\pi}{8}d''_v$

Mean equivalent diameter of sphere $\qquad d_v = \dfrac{3\pi}{8}d'_v$

$$d_v = \left(\frac{3\pi}{8}\right)^2 \frac{l'}{n_v}\,\mu\text{m}$$

Example: Measuring the mean particle diameter d of soft iron with the integrating eyepiece.

$$l' = 467\ \mu\text{m}$$
$$n_v = 10{\cdot}87\ \text{particles/measuring position}$$
$$d_v = \left(\frac{3\pi}{8}\right)^2 \frac{l'}{n_v} = 59{\cdot}6\ \mu\text{m}.$$

With the number of particles n_v, this measuring method simultaneously establishes C_v and thus the specific surface S_v/V.

$$C_v = 2n_v$$
$$\frac{S_v}{V} = 2 \times \frac{C_v}{l'} = \frac{4n_v}{l'}$$

Using the figures given above

$$\frac{S_v}{V} = \frac{4 \times 10{\cdot}87}{467}\,\mu\text{m}$$
$$= 0{\cdot}093\ \mu\text{m}^{-1}.$$

The diameter method is particularly advantageous for television microscopy. By means of the electrical apertures, the measuring field is narrowed down to a few lines n and the length l'. The intersections per line $C_v = C_n/n$ are computed after the intersections C_n in the measuring field have been measured. The known length l' of the measuring field can again be used in the computations as described above.

(d) The circle method

A circle of known area A_K is superimposed on the object. Particles intersected by the circumference are counted as half $(= n_K)$ while particles within the circle are counted full $(= n_G)$.

Number of particles $\qquad\qquad n_v = n_G + \tfrac{1}{2} n_K$

Area per particle $\qquad\qquad a_v = A_K/n_v\ \mu\text{m}^2$

Mean equivalent diameter of circle $\qquad d'_v = 2\sqrt{\dfrac{a_v}{\pi}}\ \mu\text{m}$

Mean equivalent diameter of sphere $\qquad d_v = \dfrac{3\pi}{4}\sqrt{\dfrac{a_v}{\pi}}\ \mu\text{m}$

Example: The mean equivalent sphere diameter of soft-iron particles in a polished specimen is to be determined with the integrating eyepiece.

$$D = 253\ \mu\text{m} = \text{diameter}$$
$$n_v = 24{\cdot}7\ \text{particles/circular area}$$
$$A_v = \pi D^2/4 = 5{\cdot}02726 \times 10^4\ \mu\text{m}^2$$
$$a_v = A_v/n_v = 2035{\cdot}3\ \mu\text{m}^2$$
$$d_v = \frac{3\pi}{4}\sqrt{\frac{a_v}{\pi}} = 60{\cdot}0\ \mu\text{m}.$$

(e) Comparative images

Comparative images are, up to a point, suitable for the evaluation of populations. In this method, the microscopic image is compared under defined conditions, either in the eyepiece or on a projection screen, with series of standardized images and matched to the one that fits best. The known characteristic data of the standard image are then used to evaluate the microscopic image.

There are differences in the quality of these standard images. In the most basic design, monodisperse systems, such as the honeycomb net at the left of Fig. 22, are linked in the image. The next higher system makes use of theoretically constructed populations for which in each case a median value and a standard deviation are established. Finally for special cases there are comparative images available in the form of typical replicas obtained under defined conditions and intended for empirical application (Fig. 22, right); when using these images, the working conditions under which they were obtained must be strictly adhered to.

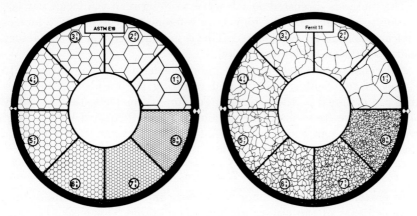

FIG. 22. Standard series. Projection disks ASTM E 19–46 and Steel-Iron test sheet 1510–61, standard series for ferrite grain size.

The mean grain size of successive images is usually classified in a geometrical series. Most often the modulus of this series is $\sqrt{2}$. In accordance with ASTM standards, the image series are designed in such a manner that at $100\times$ total magnification,

$$Z_N = 2^{N-1}$$

particles are arranged within a square inch. N is called the ASTM or grain-size number, and depending on the averaging, the number N is rounded off to tenth, half or full numbers. The ASTM number N defines the characteristic values of the comparative image. The following is applicable for the object space:

Mean grain area $\qquad a_N = \dfrac{0 \cdot 062}{Z_N} \, mm^2/grain$

Mean number of grains $\qquad m_N = \dfrac{1}{a_N} = \dfrac{Z_N}{0 \cdot 062} \, grain/mm^2$

Mean square equivalent length $\qquad l_N = 0 \cdot 249 \times 2^{(1-N)/2} \, mm/grain^{\frac{1}{2}}$.

6

Example: $N = 3 \cdot 5$ $Z_N = 2^{2 \cdot 5} = 5 \cdot 65$ particles

$$a_N = 0 \cdot 011 \ \text{mm}^2/\text{grain}$$

$$m_N = 91 \ \text{grain}/\text{mm}^2$$

$$l_N = 0 \cdot 10 \ \text{mm}/\text{grain}^{\frac{1}{2}}.$$

2. *Full Characterization of the Population*

The methods discussed so far serve to determine the mean particle size or to characterize the object by reference to comparative images that are more or less well suited. This is not sufficient for a satisfactory characterization of the population.

Full characterization requires subdivision of the population into classes of sufficient specificity and counting the number of particles that are assigned to these classes. To simplify matters, the frequency or cumulative frequency distributions are then identified by means of ordinary two-parameter, easy-to-integrate approximation functions that are kept as simple as possible.

(a) *General Considerations and Empirical Values*

In practice it has been found that linear and logarithmic-equidistant arrangements of the classes are most favourable. This means that the class limits x_n and x_{n-1} and the class centres x_n and x_{n-1} are arranged in either arithmetic or geometrical series.

Arithmetic or linear-equidistant arrangement:

Definition of the series: $x_n - x_{n-1} = \varDelta_A$

$$x_n = x_{n-1} + \varDelta_A$$

Class width $\varDelta_A = \dfrac{x_{\max} - x_{\min}}{n}$

Number of classes $n = \dfrac{x_{\max} - x_{\min}}{\varDelta_A}$

Class centres $\bar{x}_n = \dfrac{x_{n-1} + x_n}{2}$

$$\bar{x}_n = \bar{x}_{n-1} + \varDelta_A.$$

Geometric or logarithmic-equidistant arrangement:
Definition of the series:

$$\dfrac{x_n}{x_{n-1}} = \varDelta_G \quad \text{or} \quad \log x_n - \log x_{n-1} = \log \varDelta_G$$

$$x_n = x_{n-1} \times \varDelta_G \qquad \log x_n = \log x_{n-1} + \log \varDelta_G$$

Class width

$$\Delta_G = \sqrt[n]{\frac{x_{\max}}{x_{\min}}} \qquad \log \Delta_G = \frac{1}{n} \log \frac{x_{\max}}{x_{\min}}$$

Number of classes

$$n = \frac{\log x_{\max} - \log x_{\min}}{\log \Delta_G}$$

Class centres

$$\bar{x}_n = \sqrt{x_{n-1} \times x_n} \qquad \log \bar{x}_n = \tfrac{1}{2}(\log x_{n-1} + \log x_n)$$
$$\bar{x}_n = \bar{x}_{n-1} \times \Delta_G \qquad \log \bar{x}_n = \log \bar{x}_{n-1} + \log \Delta_G.$$

An arithmetical arrangement is preferred if there is no wide spread in the particle population and if the population is to be described in terms of the normal distribution curve. The normal distribution is unambiguously identified by the arithmetic mean $\bar{x}$ and the standard deviation s of the population. In the cumulative frequency representation (Fig. 29) these values can be taken directly from the probability graph if they are plotted from the cumulative frequency values F_{16}, F_{50} and F_{84} and the corresponding abscissae x_{16}, x_{50} and x_{84}. These are related as follows:

$$\bar{x} = x_{50}$$
$$s = x_{84} - x_{50} = x_{50} - x_{16} = \tfrac{1}{2}(x_{84} - x_{16})$$

Logarithmic-equidistant arrangements should always be used if there is an extensive scale of characteristics and if the specific or absolute surface corresponding to the particle population is to be computed. Approximation functions requiring a logarithmic-equidistant sub-division are usually easy to integrate. Important functions to which this applies are:

The logarithmic normal distribution with the parameters median value $\bar{x}_{50}$ and standard deviation s. Analogous to the normal distribution, both values can be taken from the log probability paper plot (Fig. 30). The following relationships hold:

$$\log s = \log x_{84} - \log \bar{x}_{50} = \log \bar{x}_{50} - \log x_{16}$$

$$\text{or } s = \frac{x_{84}}{x_{50}} = \frac{\bar{x}_{50}}{x_{16}} = \sqrt{\frac{x_{84}}{x_{16}}}$$

$$\bar{x}_{50} = \sqrt{x_{16} \times x_{84}}.$$

In addition, this approximation function yields convenient terms in the area and volume transformation and, among other things, usually describes growth processes well.

The Rosin-Rammler-Sperling (RRS) distribution equation is frequently used for the analysis of particulate samples obtained by the process of sieving (see Rosin and Rammler, 1933; Herdan, 1960). This can be written in the form

$$R = 100 \exp{-(x/x')^n}$$

R is the percentage of particles with a diameter greater than x (i.e. the fraction retained by the sieve). x is the linear aperture of a sieve on which $1/e$ or 36.8% of the sample is retained. n is the "distribution criterion" which indicates the range of sizes present; if n were infinite all the particles would be of equal size. This relationship can be written in the form

$$\log \log \frac{100}{R} = n \log x - n \log x'$$

A special double logarithmic paper is available for plotting in this form, (German DIN 4190) which also allows the specific surface to be read off directly. The RRS function is particularly useful for studying populations obtained by grinding and pulverizing, e.g. coals, cement, ores, dyes, soil and flour.

It has been found that a subdivision into about ten classes is required for describing a population with sufficient accuracy. Since a sample consists of various particle populations, it is usually safe to allow for 20 to 30 classes per analysis.

A visual count of 1000 to 1500 particles is sufficient for filling the classes. For automatic particle-size analysis (PSA) this counting rate should be considerably increased since counting criteria are usually less certain than during visual measurement.

For an unequivocal determination and description of the particle population it is advisable to calculate the cumulative frequency values and enter them in the corresponding graph. This process requires less work and is much more reliable than an evaluation via frequency curves.

(b) *Instruments and Measuring Methods*

Instruments and measuring methods must be distinguished as follows:

(*a*) Plans for a class structure must be clearly established prior to the measurement. Only one class structure is possible, and this structure cannot be varied subsequent to the measuring process.

(b) The measured values can be simultaneously assigned to various class structures, but no variation is possible subsequent to the measurement.

(c) The conditions stated under (b) apply. Additionally, the measured values are available at any time, particularly for other class structures.

Instrumental arrangements meeting the criteria of (b) and (c) are very flexible and efficient but require as a rule the use of process computers. The entire problem can thus be conveniently handled in terms of software; if there are any limitations at all, they are only set by the storage capacity of the computer.

A relatively simple (but not very accurate) way of evaluating particle populations is visually by means of circle systems arranged in the projection plane or in an eyepiece. Such a system, with logarithmic-equidistant division and the modulus $\Delta_G = \sqrt{2}$, is shown in Fig. 23.

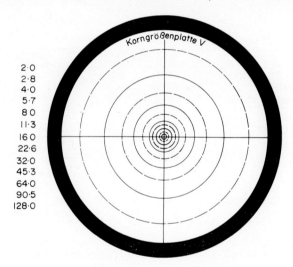

FIG. 23. Grain size disk with logarithmic-equidistant division. Modulus $\Delta_G = \sqrt{2}$.

The results of measurements on a diamond powder are shown in Fig. 24; the counting was done with the help of circle systems having linear- and logarithmic-equidistant divisions. In spite of the relatively large number of 1300 particles that were measured, the population is in both cases difficult to determine because the number of classes (4 and 6) is insufficient for good differentiation.

Often the range of characteristics of an object exceeds the measuring range of an instrument. If this is the case, macroscopic, microscopic or submicroscopic photographs may be of help. The TGZ 3 Particle-Size Analyzer (Fig. 25) is an instrument designed for this purpose; it is used to measure the area-equivalent circle of a photograph and assign it to one of 48 possible classes. The class division can be established in advance to be either linear- or logarithmic-equidistant. There is a choice of recording either the frequency or cumulative frequency values.

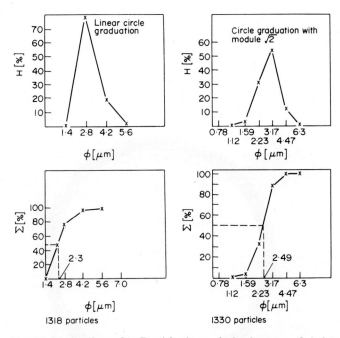

FIG. 24. Diamond powder. Particle-size analysis via group of circles.

When used with an analog-to-digital converter, an encoder and a hole punch, the TGZ 3 Automatic is suitable for operation in the off-line mode, in which case each value standardized by the number 1000 is stored and will be available for further processing in a computer (see also 3. *Comparison of particle populations* below).

The diagrams in Fig. 26 represent the results of measurements performed with TGZ 3 on the diamond samples shown in Fig. 24. As can be seen, these results approximate a normal distribution as well as a log-normal distribution. The characteristic values of this curve are:

$$\bar{x} = 3\!\cdot\!07 \ \mu\mathrm{m} \qquad s_A = 0\!\cdot\!8 \ \mu\mathrm{m}$$

$$\bar{x}_{50} = 3\!\cdot\!04 \ \mu\mathrm{m} \qquad s_G = 1\!\cdot\!29 \ \mu\mathrm{m}$$

Fig. 25. TGZ 3 particle-size analyzer-Automatic.

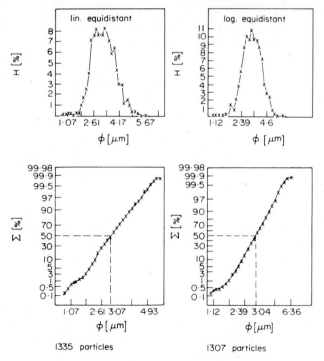

1335 particles   1307 particles

Fig. 26. Diamond powder. PSA with TGZ 3.

As pointed out in 3, both linear analyzers (Fig. 7) and phase computers (Fig. 8) are excellently suited for PSA. The instruments in question are universally applicable and their performance is limited only by the capacity of the computer. The soft-ware makes it possible to handle practically any number of classes, class divisions and derived characteristics of the populations.

Quantitative television microscopes (Figs 10 and 11) can be used similarly for visual as well as automatic PSA. When determining the length of particles that are not evenly convex, care must be taken that the electronic criteria of such equipment will not cause measuring errors. Furthermore, special tests must be made to determine whether such systems will give meaningful, reliable results in PSA with logarithmic-equidistant subdivision. Comparative measurements of this type can be performed with TGZ 3. In conventional samples, the moduli Δ_G of the geometrical series lie around 1·1 to 1·3. Results of measurements performed with the MICRO-VIDEOMAT (Figs 10, 11) on a bronze sample are shown in Fig. 27. The characteristic values of the measurement and of the log-normal distribution are:

$$x_{min} = 3 \text{ Scaleline} = 3 \text{ Sl} \qquad x_{max} = 80 \text{ Sl} \qquad \Delta_G = 1·18$$
$$x_{50} = 23·4 \text{ Sl} = 3·5 \text{ } \mu m$$
$$x_{16} = 15·7 \text{ Sl} \qquad\qquad\qquad x_{84} = 34·7 \text{ Sl} \qquad s = 1·48 \text{ Sl}$$

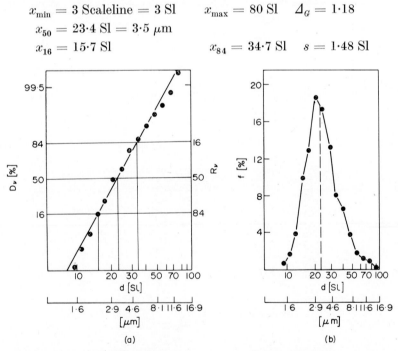

FIG. 27. Bronze. PSA with log-equidistant division by means of MICRO-VIDEOMAT (Scaleline = Sl).

3. Comparison of Particle Populations

Depending on the measuring method that is used, a PSA involves the recording of particle numbers (TGZ 3, MICRO-VIDEOMAT, etc.), area sizes or volume/weight ratios. These number, area and volume statistics cannot be compared immediately and must first be transformed by means of moment theory.

A problem of this type will be illustrated by the program STEREOM, which is designed for the evaluation of data obtained with the TGZ 3 Automatic (Fig. 25). The computer used is a PDP 12.

With this program, measured values can be transformed into number, area and volume statistics; linear- or logarithmic-equidistant class widths can be preselected and any class numbers in the range below 999 can be called up. These values are available as frequency- and cumulative-frequency numbers. All data is printed out and can be graphically verified on a monitor. By selecting in advance a scale with either linear, logarithmic, double-logarithmic or Gauss-integral division both for the abscissa and the ordinate it is possible to test the

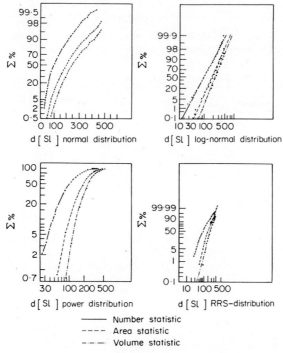

FIG. 28. Dunite. PSA with TGZ 3 Automatic. Evaluated according to STEREOM program on PDP 12 process computer. (Scaleline = Sl.)

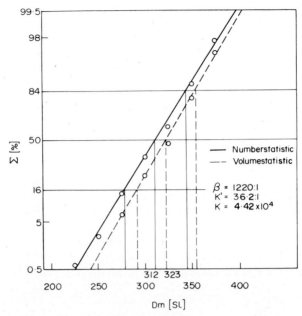

Fig. 29. Frog blood. PSA with TGZ 3 Automatic. Evaluation according to STEREOM
program on PDP 12 process computer. Normal distribution (Scaleline = Sl).

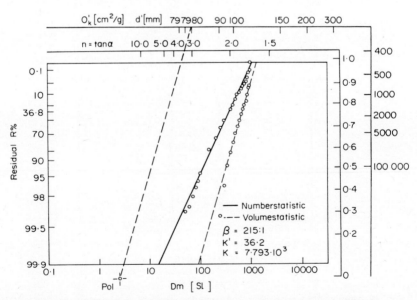

Fig. 30. Soft iron. PSA with TGZ 3 Automatic. Evaluation with PDP 12 process
computer according to STEREOM program. Log-normal distribution. (Scaleline = Sl.)

measured data at the monitor with any approximation function. Figure 28 shows the verification sequence at the monitor of a process computer. The data are those of a polished dunite specimen measured with the TGZ 3 Automatic. According to these results, the measured values of all statistics are best approximated by a log-normal distribution.

By a similar analysis, the measured data on frog blood shown in Fig. 29 can be optimally characterized by a normal distribution. By the same token, the measured values of soft iron shown in Fig. 30 approximate an RRS curve. In all the cases shown here the difference between the various statistics is clearly apparent. As described in (a) *General Considerations and Empirical Values* above, the characteristic values, and particularly the specific surface, can be read from the diagrams or calculated by means of the appropriate transformation equations.

VI. Concluding Remarks

The limitations, possibilities and the measuring accuracy of stereometric analyses are described by means of examples. Image analysis proper, i.e. the correlation of physical data with local coordinates, has only been briefly discussed. The present state of the art of microscopic analytical techniques is represented by the instruments shown in Figs. 8, 10 and 11. These instruments feature linear detectors of high sensitivity, stage positioning in basic increments of $\frac{1}{2}$ μm within an area of 25×75 mm², and computer compatibility. Figure 31 shows a problem that is typical of the subject discussed here.*

A chromosome was measured with the scanning microscope photometer (Fig. 11) operated in the on-line mode with a PDP 12 computer. The absorption values were printed out via a plotter as a function of the local coordinate. In this method, all of the measured values are stored in the computer and can thus be called up at any time and according to any criteria. This makes the entire contents of the image instantly available.

At various points of this paper the limitations of the instruments have been discussed. In many cases it is necessary to adapt the specimen to the measuring conditions by means of appropriate preparatory techniques; in fact, in most cases, mastery of the preparation problems is really a prerequisite for the measurement proper and therefore just as important.

Contrast can frequently be improved by means of such microscopic

* Example by courtesy of Dr. Zimmer, Microscopy Department, Carl Zeiss, Oberkochen, West Germany.

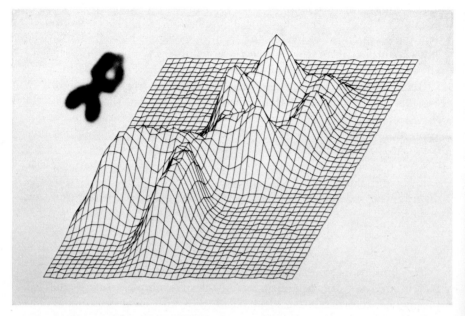

Fig. 31. Human chromosome. Absorption values measured with scanning microscope photometer in on-line mode with PDP 12 process computer.

techniques as good field illumination, dark field, fluorescence and interference methods (phase contrast, two-beam and differential interference, polarization). Specimens furthermore can be adapted to the measuring conditions through staining, etching, embedding, etc. Steps like these make it almost always possible to adapt an object in an optimum manner to the measuring method, which in the end means accurate results achieved within reasonable time and at an acceptable cost.

REFERENCES

General

The literature on stereology and related topics is growing rapidly. Comprehensive references may be found in the following:

De Hoff, R. T. and Rhines, E. N. (1968). Editors "Quantitative Microscopy", McGraw-Hill, New York.
Underwood, E. E. (1969). "Quantitative Stereology", Addison Wesley, Reading, Mass., U.S.A.
Microscope (1971), **19**, part 1. Papers on image analysis with bibliography.
J. Microscopy (1972), **95**, parts 1 and 2 contain papers given at the 3rd International Congress for Stereology. These have also been printed as a book

"Stereology 3" (Weibel, E. R., Meek, G., Ralph, B., Echlin, P. and Ross, R., eds.), published for The Royal Microscopical Society by Blackwell Scientific Publications, Oxford.

Text references

Herdan, G. (1960). "Small Particle Statistics", 2nd Ed., Butterworths, London.

Ministr, Z. (1971). *Prakt. Mettallogr.* **8**, 344, 407.

Rosin, P. and Rammler, E. (1933). *J. Inst. Fuel* **7**, 29.

Saltykov, S. A. (1958). "Stereometric Metallurgy" (Russian), 2nd Ed., Metallurgizdot.

Smith, C. S. and Guttmann, L. (1953). *Trans. Am. Inst. Met. Eng.* **197**, 81.

The Fourier Transform of an Electron Micrograph—First Order and Second Order Theory of Image Formation

HAROLD P. ERICKSON*

Medical Research Council, Laboratory of Molecular Biology, Hills Road, Cambridge, England

I. INTRODUCTION

THE effects of defocusing and aberrations in the electron microscope are displayed much more simply and directly in the Fourier transform of the image than in the image itself. In this paper the theory of image formation is presented in a form that is applicable to a specimen treated as a continuous two-dimensional distribution of mass density, and expressions are derived relating the Fourier transform of the image to the Fourier transform of the object density. In a related experimental study (Erickson and Klug, 1970) the general validity of the theory has been confirmed for conventional electron microscopy of a typical biological specimen. Some aspects of the theory presented here are largely a restatement of existing work on image formation, brought

* Present address: Department of Anatomy, Duke University Medical Center, Durham, N.C. 27710, U.S.A.

together here to give a unified basis for discussing the experimental results. Other aspects of the theory have been developed in much greater detail than has hitherto been attempted in order to explain a number of significant deviations from the simple theory that were found in the experimental study and are of practical interest in conventional microscopy and in image processing systems. The potential application of this theory to compensate for spherical aberration and extend the resolution of the microscope is also discussed.

Image formation is frequently explained in terms of the production of contrast, which can be attributed to two different mechanisms. Amplitude contrast is traditionally attributed to the removal from the electron beam of electrons that have been scattered outside the objective aperture. Phase contrast is produced by interference between the unscattered electron wave and the electron wave that is coherently scattered within the objective aperture. The contribution to the image from each of these mechanisms is best described by the wave theory of image formation, which is treated in various texts for light optical imaging (see, e.g. Born and Wolf, 1964). A number of specific applications of the theory to electron microscopy have been given. The imaging of single atoms by phase contrast was first discussed by Scherzer (1949). More recent treatments include that of Hanszen and Morgenstern (1965), and Hanszen (1967, 1971), where amplitude and phase contrast are discussed in terms of the modulation transfer function of the electron lens; the treatment of phase contrast by Heidenreich (1964, 1967), that of Lenz (1965), the detailed calculations of the imaging of single atoms by Eisenhandler and Siegel (1966a), Reimer (1966, 1969), and Niehrs (1969).

A. *Definitions and Outline of the Theory of Image Formation*

The two functions that are of central importance in this presentation are the object density function and its Fourier transform. The object is assumed to be thin enough so that the variation in focus through the specimen is negligible. The effect of object thickness and the validity of this assumption is discussed later. The object can then be specified by a two dimensional function, $\sigma(x^o, y^o)$, defined as *the projected density, expressed in atoms per unit area, at object plane coordinates* (x^o, y^o). The object transform is the two dimensional Fourier transform of this function,

$$T^o(\alpha, \phi) = \iint \sigma(x^o, y^o) \exp\left[\frac{-2\pi i}{\lambda}(x^o\alpha \cos \phi + y^o\alpha \sin \phi)\right] dx^o dy^o. \quad (1)$$

The transform is expressed in circular coordinates: α (radial) and ϕ

(azimuthal). The reciprocal radial coordinate is specified in the integral as α/λ, anticipating later physical interpretation where α will be the (dimensionless) angle of scattering from the object to the diffraction plane, and λ the electron wavelength. Because $\sigma(x^o, y^o)$ is a real function, the transform obeys the symmetry relationship

$$T^o(\alpha, \phi) = T^{o*}(\alpha, \phi+\pi). \tag{2}$$

The first problem in describing the process of image formation is to specify the electron wave in the object in terms of $\sigma(x^o, y^o)$. It is assumed that the object is illuminated by a monochromatic plane wave of electrons (corrections for the effects of chromatic aberration and partial coherence are treated later). This incident wave is modulated on passing through the specimen to give the electron wave in the object plane, $\psi^o_{tot}(x^o, y^o)$. Since actual absorption of electrons is negligible for the thin specimens normally examined in biological and high resolution microscopy, the object is a pure phase object, and modulates the phase but not the amplitude of the incident wave. Assuming the incident wave to be of unit amplitude, the object wave can be written

$$\psi^o_{tot}(x^o, y^o) = \exp[i\delta(x^o, y^o)] = \exp[i\psi^o_{ph}(x^o, y^o)]. \tag{3}$$

The phase shift, $\delta(x^o, y^o)$, is written here as a wave function, $\psi^o_{ph}(x^o, y^o)$, because, in the approximation used in the derivations, it is equivalent to the scattered wave in the object plane. This function is closely related to object mass density, $\sigma(x^o, y^o)$, as shown in Part 1, following equation 8c.

The subsequent process of image formation is outlined in Fig. 1. The object wave gives rise, by the Huygens-Fresnel construction, to a wave in the diffraction or back focal plane of the microscope, $\psi^d(f\alpha, \phi)$, which is proportional to the Fourier transform of the object wave. This wave is expressed, for convenience in the derivation, in circular coordinates in the diffraction plane: ρ is the radial coordinate in the diffraction plane, but is written here as the product $\rho = f\alpha$, where f is the focal length of the lens and α is the scattering angle from the object plane; ϕ is the azimuthal coordinate.

The effect of spherical aberration, defocusing, and the objective aperture are accounted for in the wave theory of image formation as a modification of the wave in the diffraction plane. Spherical aberration and defocusing are accounted for as a phase shift, dependent on the radial coordinate, $\rho = f\alpha$, in the diffraction plane. The amount of the phase shift in radians, is (Scherzer, 1949)

$$\chi(\alpha) = \frac{2\pi}{\lambda}\left(-C_s\frac{\alpha^4}{4}+\Delta f\frac{\alpha^2}{2}\right). \tag{4}$$

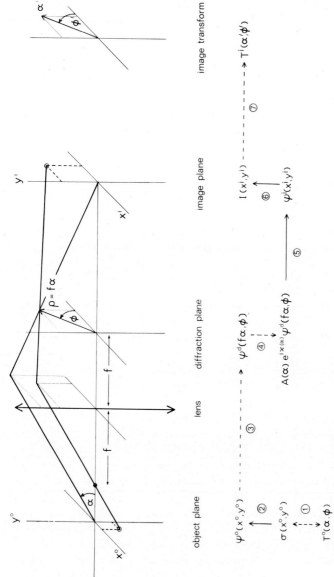

FIG. 1. Outline of the process of image formation. (1) $\sigma(x^o, y^o)$ is the two dimensional projected object density at object plane coordinates x^o, y^o. $T^o(\alpha, \phi)$, the object transform, is the Fourier transform of $\sigma(x^o, y^o)$, in circular coordinates; α is the radial coordinate or scattering angle, and ϕ is the azimuth. (2) The illuminating plane wave of electrons is modulated by passing through the object, giving the wave in the object plane. (3) The electron wave in the object plane gives rise to the wave in the diffraction plane by the Huygens-Fresnel construction or Fourier Transform. (4) The wave in the diffraction plane is modified by the aberration and aperture functions. (5) This modified wave gives rise to the wave in the image plane by the second Huygens-Fresnel construction or Fourier transform. (6) The intensity of this wave gives the recorded image. (7) The transform of the micrograph is the Fourier transform of this intensity function.

C_s is the coefficient of spherical aberration and Δf is the deviation from Gaussian focus (Δf is positive for a weaker or underfocused lens). The effect of the objective aperture can be accounted for by an aperture function, $A(\alpha)$, which is zero over those parts of the diffraction plane obstructed by the objective aperture and unity otherwise. The modified wave in the diffraction plane is then

$$\psi^{d'}(f\alpha, \phi) = \psi^d(f\alpha, \phi)A(\alpha) \exp [i\chi(\alpha)]. \tag{5}$$

This modified wave in the diffraction plane gives rise to the electron wave in the image plane, $\psi^i(x^i, y^i)$, by a second Huygens-Fresnel construction, or Fourier transformation. The recorded or visualized image is given by the intensity of this wave (not by the wave itself), $I(x^i, y^i) = |\psi^i(x^i, y^i)|^2$. With proper photographic processing the optical density of the micrograph is directly proportional to the electron intensity (Valentine, 1965). The transform of the image, which is the central point of this presentation, is therefore the transform of this intensity function. It is expressed in the circular coordinates, α and ϕ.

B. *Approximations Useful for Simplified Derivation and Physical Interpretation*

The theoretical image of a single atom, or a small group of atoms, can be calculated exactly by the wave theory of image formation if the scattering properties of the atom are known. The wave in the diffraction plane scattered from a single atom is simply proportional to the scattering factor, $f(\alpha)$. The image intensity is derived from this wave as outlined above. For this exact calculation it is necessary to use the complex scattering factor, which has a real part and a smaller imaginary part. The effects of amplitude contrast, generated by the aperture function, are primarily derived from the imaginary part of $f(\alpha)$. This approach has been used by Reimer (1969) for making numerical calculations of the image of single atoms or small groups of atoms.

The exact derivation has two drawbacks. In the first place, it does not give an analytical expression for the image or image transform in terms of the electron optical parameters, but gives only a single numerical answer for a given set of values of these parameters. For physical interpretation and for general application of the theory the analytical expression is obviously desirable. In the second place, the theory cannot be readily applied to specimens that are more complicated than a simple arrangement of a few atoms. Consequently the results cannot be directly applied to problems of conventional microscopy.

With the use of some approximations the theory can be developed to give analytical expressions for the image that are applicable to a wide range of specimens. The development is based on the assumption that only a small fraction of the incident electrons are scattered by the object. This approximation is valid for many applications of electron microscopy, especially of biological specimens. Numerical evaluations relevant to this point have been tabulated by Dupouy (1967), based on the data of Burge and Smith (1962). In a 75 kV beam passing through a mass density equivalent to a 50 Å thickness of carbon, a typical density for a specimen detail, about 10% of the electrons are scattered outside a normal aperture, and a further 10% are coherently, or elastically, scattered within the aperture. In this case ψ_{ph}^{o} is small compared to unity and the development of the theory of image formation can be simplified by expanding the exponential in the expression for the object wave

$$\psi_{tot}^{o}(x^{o}, y^{o}) = \exp\left[i\psi_{ph}^{o}(x^{o}, y^{o})\right] \simeq 1 + i\psi_{ph}^{o}(x^{o}, y^{o}) - \tfrac{1}{2}[\psi_{ph}^{o}(x^{o}, y^{o})]^{2} + \ldots$$

$$(6)$$

Higher order terms in the expansion will be small compared to the lower order ones and can be ignored. In Part 1 the simplest treatment is presented, where only the first order term is kept. Additional assumptions are introduced that allow the theory to be developed in terms of the concepts of amplitude and phase contrast. In Part 2 the second order terms are included in the derivation and the object is treated as a pure phase object. Image properties identified with phase and amplitude contrast arise naturally in this more rigorous derivation, and are discussed in comparison with the simpler first order theory.

In the wave theory of image formation phase contrast is identified with the imaginary part of the scattered electron wave and amplitude contrast with the real part. If the image formation is treated by an exact theory, as by Reimer (1969), it is important to use the exact, complex scattering factor. The real scattered wave then comes from the imaginary part of the scattering factor. In the derivations presented here, based on first order or second order approximations, it is appropriate to use the purely real, Born approximation scattering factor. The approximation involved here, in expanding the exponential of the object wave and ignoring higher order terms is equivalent to that involved in the Born approximation, where only single scattering events are considered.

In the first order theory the effects of amplitude contrast are described by introducing the real scattered wave *a posteriori*, as an extra term in the derivation. In the second order theory the second order term in the expansion of the object wave is itself real, and amplitude contrast arises from this. In both of these derivations it would be redundant and inappropriate to include the imaginary part of the atomic scattering factor since the effects of amplitude contrast, or of the real scattered wave, are already accounted for.

II. PART 1. FIRST ORDER APPROXIMATION—LINEAR THEORY OF PHASE AND AMPLITUDE CONTRAST IMAGE FORMATION

In this derivation the wave in the object plane is approximated by

$$\psi^o_{tot}(x^o, y^o) = \exp\left[i\psi^o_{ph}(x^o, y^o)\right] \simeq 1 + i\psi^o_{ph}(x^o, y^o). \tag{7}$$

The right hand side of this expression is treated as two waves. The real term of unit amplitude is the unscattered or background wave, a plane wave of unit amplitude, identical to the incident electron wave. The imaginary function $i\psi^o_{ph}(x^o, y^o)$ represents the scattered electron wave. The phase contrast image is produced by the interference of these two waves after each has gone through the imaging system.

A. The Phase Contrast Image

The form of $\psi^o_{ph}(x^o, y^o)$ and its relation to $\sigma(x^o, y^o)$ is derived most directly in terms of the scattered wave produced by a single atom in the diffraction plane of the microscope. For an atom at object coordinates (x^o, y^o) the scattered wave in the diffraction plane is given by the Huygens-Fresnel construction (see also Eisenhandler and Siegel (1966a))

$$\psi^d_{atm}(f\alpha, \phi) = \frac{i}{f} f(\alpha) \exp\left[\frac{-2\pi i}{\lambda}(x^o \alpha \cos \phi + y^o \alpha \sin \phi)\right]. \tag{8a}$$

$f(\alpha)$ is the atomic scattering factor for elastic scattering, normally given in units of Å. (There should be no confusion between $f(\alpha)$ and the focal length f.) The imaginary i here indicates that this scattered wave is 90° out of phase with the unscattered wave. It arises from the derivation of electron scattering in the Born approximation, in which the scattered electron wave $if(\alpha)$, is purely imaginary ($f(\alpha)$ is real) and the unit unscattered wave purely real. An additional factor of $-i$, which is common to the Huygens-Fresnel construction of each of the waves, and which cancels in the subsequent construction from the diffraction plane to the image plane, is ignored in this derivation. Inelastic scattering will be largely incoherent and should therefore contribute little to phase contrast. Its contribution to the phase contrast image will be ignored, but it is of course included in the total cross section, S_t, used in the specification of the amplitude wave (equation 13a).

The total scattered wave in the diffraction plane is obtained by summing the contributions from all atoms in the object. It is assumed for simplicity that the specimen is composed of similar atoms, so that $f(\alpha)$ is the same for all atoms. Replacing the summation over discrete atoms by integration over the continuous density function, $\sigma(x^o, y^o)$, the expression for the scattered wave in the diffraction plane is obtained

$$\psi^d_{\text{ph}}(f\alpha, \phi) = \frac{i}{f} f(\alpha) \iint \sigma(x^o, y^o) \exp\left[\frac{-2\pi i}{\lambda} (x^o \alpha \cos \phi + y^o \alpha \sin \phi)\right] dx^o \, dy^o$$

(8b)

The integral in this expression is equal to the object transform, equation 1, where the physical interpretation of α and λ in equation 1 as the scattering angle and wavelength is now specified. Then

$$\psi^d_{\text{ph}}(f\alpha, \phi) = \frac{i}{f} f(\alpha) \, T^o(\alpha, \phi).$$

(8c)

This wave in the diffraction plane can be considered to have arisen from the scattered wave in the object plane, $i\psi^o_{\text{ph}}(x^o, y^o)$, by the Huygens-Fresnel construction. The waves in the diffraction plane and object plane are therefore related to each other by Fourier transformation, and $i\psi^o_{\text{ph}}(x^o, y^o)$ can be specified as proportional to the inverse Fourier transform of $\psi^d_{\text{ph}}(f\alpha, \phi)$. $\psi^d_{\text{ph}}(f\alpha, \phi)$ is proportional to the product of the object transform and $f(\alpha)$ (equation 8c). $\psi^o_{\text{ph}}(x^o, y^o)$ is, therefore, proportional to the convolution of the object density, $\sigma(x^o, y^o)$, with the transform of $f(\alpha)$. If the atoms making up the object were point scatterers, $f(\alpha)$ would be constant, and $\psi^o_{\text{ph}}(x^o, y^o)$, which is interpreted either as the phase shift suffered by the wave in passing through the object (equation 3), or as the amplitude of the scattered wave in the object plane (equation 7), would be directly proportional to the object density, $\sigma(x^o, y^o)$.

The wave in the diffraction plane is modified by the aberration function and aperture function to give

$$\psi^{d'}_{\text{ph}}(f\alpha, \phi) = \psi^d_{\text{ph}}(f\alpha, \phi) \, A(\alpha) \exp[i\chi(\alpha)].$$

(8d)

The scattered wave in the image plane is then generated from this wave by the second Huygens-Fresnel construction.

$$\psi^i_{\text{ph}}(x^i, y^i) = \frac{1}{L_i\lambda} \int_{-\pi}^{\pi} \int_0^{\infty} \psi^{d'}_{\text{ph}}(f\alpha, \phi) \exp\left[\frac{-2\pi i}{\lambda} (x^i \alpha \cos \phi + y^i \alpha \sin \phi)\right]$$

$$(f\alpha)d(f\alpha)d\phi \qquad (9a)$$

L_i is the distance from the lens to the image plane. In normal conditions the magnification is large and the distance from the lens to the object plane is approximately f, the focal length. The magnification is then $M = L_i/f$. The reduced image plane coordinates, x^i, y^i, used here are scaled by dividing the actual image plane coordinates by M, so that they are the same magnitude as the conjugate object plane coordinates, x^o, y^o. Substituting for $\psi_{ph}^{d'}(f\alpha, \phi)$, the scattered wave in the image plane is

$$\psi_{ph}^i(x^i, y^i) = \frac{1}{M}\frac{i}{\lambda}\int_{-\pi}^{\pi}\int_0^{\infty} T^o(\alpha, \phi)\, A(\alpha)\, f(\alpha)\, \exp\left[i\chi(\alpha)\right]\times$$

$$\exp\left[\frac{-2\pi i}{\lambda}(x^i\alpha\,\cos\phi + y^i\alpha\,\sin\phi)\right]\alpha\,d\alpha\,d\phi. \qquad (9b)$$

The unit background wave is focused at the centre of the diffraction plane, $\alpha = 0$, and is not affected by the aberrations or aperture. It therefore gives rise to a plane wave in the image plane of amplitude $1/M$. The total wave is the sum of the unscattered wave and the scattered wave in the image plane, $\dfrac{1}{M} + \psi_{ph}^i(x^i, y^i)$. The phase contrast image is given by the intensity of this wave:

$$I_{ph}(x^i, y^i) = \left|\frac{1}{M} + \psi_{ph}^i(x^i, y^i)\right|^2 \qquad (10a)$$

$$= \left(\frac{1}{M} + \psi_{ph}^i\right)\left(\frac{1}{M} + \psi_{ph}^{i*}\right) \qquad (10b)$$

$$= \frac{1}{M^2} + \frac{1}{M}(\psi_{ph}^i + \psi_{ph}^{i*}) + |\psi_{ph}^i|^2. \qquad (10c)$$

In the first order approximation the quadratic term $|\psi_{ph}^i|^2$ is negligible. in comparison to the others. Then

$$I_{ph}(x^i, y^i) = \frac{1}{M^2} + \frac{1}{M}[\psi_{ph}^i(x^i, y^i) + \psi_{ph}^{i*}(x^i, y^i)]. \qquad (10d)$$

Writing this out in full,

$$I_{ph}(x^i, y^i) = \frac{1}{M^2} + \frac{i}{M^2\lambda}\int_{-\pi}^{\pi}\int_0^{\infty} T^o(\alpha, \phi)\, A(\alpha)f(\alpha)\, \exp\left[+i\chi(\alpha)\right]\times$$

$$\exp\left[\frac{-2\pi i}{\lambda}(x^i\alpha\,\cos\phi + y^i\alpha\,\sin\phi)\right]\alpha\,d\alpha\,d\phi$$

$$-\frac{i}{M^2\lambda}\int_{-\pi}^{\pi}\int_0^{\infty} T^{o*}(\alpha, \phi)A(\alpha)f(\alpha)\, \exp\left[-i\chi(\alpha)\right]\times$$

$$\exp\left[\frac{+2\pi i}{\lambda}(x^i\alpha\,\cos\phi + y^ia\,\sin\phi)\right]\alpha\,d\alpha\,d\phi \qquad (10e)$$

If the variable in the second integral is changed to $\phi' = \phi + \pi$, then $T^{o*}(\alpha, \phi') = T^o(\alpha, \phi)$ (equation 2), $\cos\phi' = -\cos\phi$, $\sin\phi' = -\sin\phi$, and the two integrals can be combined to give

$$I_{ph}(x^i, y^i) = \frac{1}{M^2} + \frac{i}{M^2\lambda} \int_{-\pi}^{\pi} \int_0^{\infty} T^o(\alpha, \phi)A(\alpha)f(\alpha)\{\exp[i\chi(\alpha)]$$

$$-\exp[-i\chi(a)]\} \exp\left[\frac{-2\pi i}{\lambda}(x^i\alpha\cos\phi + y^i\alpha\sin\phi)\right]\alpha d\alpha d\phi. \quad (10f)$$

Setting $\{\exp[i\chi(\alpha)] - \exp[-i\chi(\alpha)]\} = 2i\sin\chi(\alpha)$, the expression for the phase contrast image is reduced to

$$I_{ph}(x^i, y^i) = \frac{1}{M^2} - \frac{2}{M^2\lambda} \int_{-\pi}^{\pi} \int_0^{\infty} T^o(\alpha, \phi)A(\alpha)f(\alpha)\sin\chi(\alpha) \times$$

$$\exp\left[\frac{-2\pi i}{\lambda}(x^i\alpha\cos\phi + y^i\alpha\sin\phi)\right]\alpha d\alpha d\phi \quad (10g)$$

An important aspect of this manipulation is that $\chi(\alpha)$ appears in equation 10g as an amplitude modulation, $\sin\chi(\alpha)$, rather than as a phase modulation, $\exp[i\chi(\alpha)]$. This results because $\chi(\alpha)$ is independent of ϕ, and would hold more generally so long as the aberration and aperture functions have twofold symmetry, i.e. are equal at azimuthal values ϕ and $\phi + \pi$.

The phase contrast image thus consists of a constant background intensity, $1/M^2$, minus the Fourier transform of $[T^o(\alpha, \phi)A(\alpha)f(\alpha) \sin\chi(\alpha)]$. Except for the background intensity the image is proportional to the Fourier transform of the object transform, $T^o(\alpha, \phi)$, multiplied by the three factors. The image intensity is thus related to the object density by a double Fourier transform, modified at each step, and the interpretation is not simple. A very direct interpretation can, however, be obtained by taking the Fourier transform of the image intensity and relating this to the Fourier transform of the object density. For convenience the image transform will be defined as the inverse transform of the image contrast, $[I(x^i, y^i) - I_{av}]/I_{av}$, where I_{av} is the average image intensity, $1/M^2$. The image transform is then

$$T^i(\alpha', \phi') = \frac{M^2}{S} \iint \left[I(x^i, y^i) - \frac{1}{M^2}\right] \exp\left[\frac{+2\pi i}{\lambda}(x^i\alpha'\cos\phi' +\right.$$

$$\left. y^i\alpha'\sin\phi')\right] dx^i dy^i, \quad (11a)$$

where the integration is over the area S. Writing this in full for the case of phase contrast image intensity,

$$T^i_{ph}(\alpha', \phi') = -\frac{2}{S\lambda} \iiint_{-\pi}^{\pi} \int_0^{\infty} T^o(\alpha, \phi)A(\alpha)f(\alpha)\sin\chi(\alpha) \times$$

$$\exp\left\{\frac{-2\pi i}{\lambda}[x^i(\alpha\cos\phi - \alpha'\cos\phi') + y^i(\alpha\sin\phi - \alpha'\sin\phi')]\right\}\alpha d\alpha d\phi\, dx^i dy^i \quad (11b)$$

If the area is large enough the integral over x^i and y^i will tend to zero except when the terms in the exponential are zero, i.e. unless $\alpha' = \alpha$ and $\phi' = \phi$. In this case the expression reduces to

$$T^i_{ph}(\alpha, \phi) = -T^o(\alpha, \phi)A(\alpha)\frac{2}{\lambda}f(\alpha)\sin\chi(\alpha). \qquad (11c)$$

If the average background intensity had not been subtracted out before taking the transform there would be an additional zero order term corresponding to the transform of this constant intensity over the area of the image included in the transform (a delta function if the area is infinite).

The interpretation of the image in terms of the Fourier transform is simple and direct because each of the factors in equation 11c, $A(\alpha)$, $f(\alpha)$ and $\sin\chi(\alpha)$, is a real number, each is a function only of the spatial frequency, α, and each appears as a simple multiplying factor. The image transform, $T^i(\alpha, \phi)$, is thus the same as the object transform, $T^o(\alpha, \phi)$, in that it has the same Fourier components, with the same phases. It differs only in that the amplitudes of the components are modulated by the transfer function.

If $A(\alpha)$, $f(\alpha)$, and $\sin\chi(\alpha)$ were unity for all α the image transform would be identical to the object transform and the imaging system would be perfect. In fact, however, $A(\alpha)$ is zero for all $\alpha > \alpha_o$, where α_o is the angle of the objective aperture. Fourier components of spatial frequency greater than α_o/λ are thus missing from the image transform or, in other words, the resolution of the image is limited to α_o/λ. $f(\alpha)$ is a slowly varying, monotonically decreasing function of α, which has the effect of reducing the amplitude of higher resolution Fourier components. The most important factor of the three is $\sin\chi(\alpha)$, which varies from plus one to minus one. Neglecting the small modulation by $f(\alpha)$, and assuming the Fourier components of interest fall inside the objective aperture, one can see that the Fourier components of the object transform generally contribute to the image transform with a reduced amplitude, proportional to the value of $\sin\chi(\alpha)$. Object details of corresponding spacings are thus said to be imaged with a contrast proportional to $\sin\chi(\alpha)$. The physical significance is best discussed with reference to the graphs of $-\sin\chi(\alpha)$ in Fig. 2.

At $\Delta f = 0$, Fig. 2(a), $\chi(\alpha)$ is determined solely by spherical aberration which is significant only at higher spatial frequencies. $\sin\chi(\alpha)$ is thus zero for $\alpha/\lambda < 0.1$ Å^{-1}, and lower resolution components of the object transform do not contribute to the in-focus phase contrast image. Higher resolution components contribute with varying positive and negative contrast, as discussed below.

The optimum defocusing for high resolution phase contrast microscopy is approximately 900 Å under focus in the assumed operating conditions (see caption), Fig. 2(b). $-\mathrm{Sin}\,\chi(\alpha)$ is then close to $-1\cdot0$ over a large range of spatial frequencies, for values of α/λ between $0\cdot1$ Å^{-1} and $0\cdot23$ Å^{-1}. The negative sign which appears in equation 11c

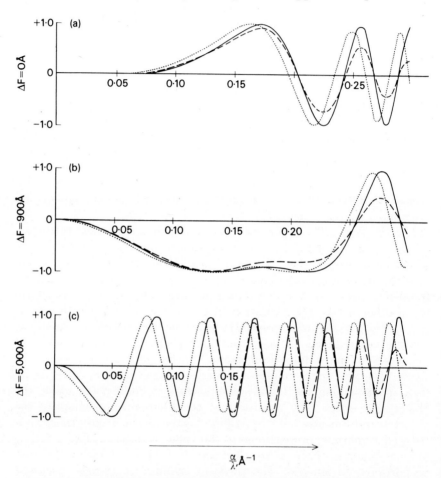

FIG. 2. The phase contrast transfer function, $-\sin\chi(\alpha)$, plotted as a function of α/λ, in Å^{-1}, for $\lambda = 0\cdot042$ Å, $C_s = 1\cdot3$ mm, and for the indicated values of Δf. A negative value of this function indicates that the corresponding region of the object transform is contributing to the image with normal or "dark" contrast, i.e. there is a subtraction from the background electron intensity over regions of high mass density. The solid curves are for pure phase contrast. The dashed curves are corrected for the effects of chromatic aberration with normal electrical instabilities, by averaging over a range of Δf of ± 200 Å. The dotted curves are corrected for the effects of the partial coherence of the electron source, assuming a 100 μ diameter condenser aperture.

and which is included in the graphs in Fig. 2, indicates a decrease in electron intensity over areas of high mass density, the condition of normal or "dark" contrast. The image transform is thus identical with the object transform over this region and corresponding details are being imaged with maximum or "true" phase contrast. If $\sin \chi(\alpha) = 1$ for all α the microscope would be a perfect phase contrast microscope. Actually for values of α/λ less than 0·1 Å^{-1} and greater than 0·23 Å^{-1}, $\sin \chi(\alpha)$ is less than unity. Corresponding components of the object transform will contribute to the image with reduced contrast. If the amplitudes of the significant Fourier components are changed relative to one another by only a small amount there will be no serious image artifacts. Normally a range of higher resolution components are imaged with maximum contrast, while lower resolution components are reduced to about one-third or one-half. Even with this reduction, the low resolution components are generally much stronger, and the result is essentially a relative enhancement of the weak high resolution details, giving a sharpening of edges and contours. In many cases this is a desirable effect. Of course if the low resolution components are reduced excessively, say by a factor of ten, so that the high and low resolution components are comparable in amplitude, the image would be dominated by spurious high resolution details.

Apart from this, serious artifacts and distortions in the image will only occur if the phases of Fourier components are changed. This type of artifact occurs at higher resolution where $\sin \chi(\alpha)$ goes through zero and changes sign, e.g. for $\alpha/\lambda > 0·26$ Å^{-1} in Fig. 2(b). This sign change corresponds to a phase change of 180° for the corresponding Fourier components. These will contribute to the image but because of the sign change the contrast will be reversed, i.e. image details corresponding to this reciprocal spacing will be black where they should be white. It is in this sense that the valid optical resolution of the microscope is limited by spherical aberration to about 4·5 Å ($\alpha/\lambda = 0·23$ Å^{-1}). At higher resolution the object details are being imaged with alternating reversed and normal contrast, and Fourier components near the zeros of the transfer function are missing.

Point-to-point resolution is not directly limited by the spherical aberration but rather by mechanical and electrical instabilities. Image details of about 2 Å resolution can, in fact, be recorded in favourable circumstances. These are, of course, subject to the artifacts of contrast reversal due to the spherical aberration, and are not within what is referred to here as the valid optical resolution.

At larger Δf the peak of normal phase contrast becomes sharper and moves to lower values of α/λ. At 5000 Å under focus, Fig. 2(c), spacings between 50 Å and 20 Å, $\alpha/\lambda = 0.02$ to 0.05 Å^{-1}, will be imaged with enhanced phase contrast, and artifacts will occur for resolutions beyond 15 Å, $\alpha/\lambda > 0.07$ Å^{-1}. This is a particularly useful condition for conventional biological microscopy, where one is frequently interested in imaging details between 100 and 20 Å with high contrast and is not concerned about artifacts at higher resolutions. The use of underfocus contrast enhancement in biological microscopy has been discussed in detail in connection with the experimental investigation (Erickson and Klug, 1970).

B. *The Amplitude Contrast Image*

The first order expression for the image transform, equation 11c, arises from the interference between the imaginary scattered wave and the unscattered or background wave. It therefore corresponds to the phase contrast image. One might expect that the modification of the wave in the diffraction plane by the aperture function would account for the loss of electrons scattered outside the aperture and that the effects of amplitude contrast should arise naturally. This is, in fact, the case when second order terms are included in the expansion of the object wave and in the subsequent derivation, as outlined in Part 2. Amplitude contrast does not arise when only the first order is included in the derivation.

To describe the effects of amplitude contrast by the simple first order theory, an extra term can be introduced *a posteriori* to account for the loss of electrons. The electrons are actually lost only when they hit the objective aperture in the diffraction plane, but in this derivation the loss will be treated as if it occurred in the object plane. For this treatment it is necessary to assume that the fraction of electrons scattered outside the objective aperture, from any point or small area of the object, is simply proportional to the mass density at that point. The loss is then equivalent to the electrons having been absorbed by the object, and can be accounted for as a reduction in the intensity of the electron wave in the object plane. In fact, because of diffraction effects, the distribution of electrons in the diffraction plane will be affected by the local arrangement of atoms around the object point and by extended periodicities in the object. For the present treatment it is assumed that these diffraction effects do not alter significantly the fraction of electrons scattered outside the aperture from that expected for a single atom. This is a reasonably good approximation for treating the imaging of low and medium resolution details, say to 20 Å or 10 Å resolution, in an object in which the atomic arrangement is largely amorphous and independent of the low resolution structure. The validity of this approximation and a more rigorous description of amplitude contrast will be discussed in Part 2.

The object wave is therefore written

$$\psi_{tot}^o(x^o, y^o) = B(x^o, y^o) \exp[i\psi_{ph}^o(x^o, y^o)], \tag{12a}$$

where $B(x^o, y^o)$ is a real function describing the amplitude variation of the wave. The amplitude is the square root of the electron intensity, which can be written in terms of the expressions of Burge and Smith (1962) as a product of scattering cross-section and object mass density:

$$B(x^o, y^o) = [I(x^o, y^o)]^{\frac{1}{2}} = \left\{ \exp\left[-S_t \frac{A}{N_o} \sigma(x^o, y^o) \right] \right\}^{\frac{1}{2}} =$$
$$\exp\left[-\frac{1}{2} S_t \frac{A}{N_o} \sigma(x^o, y^o) \right]. \tag{12b}$$

S_t is the total (including elastic and inelastic scattering) cross-section per gram of matter for scattering outside a given objective aperture. A is the atomic weight (not to be confused with the aperture function, $A(\alpha)$), N_o is Avogadro's number, and $\sigma(x^o, y^o)$ is the object density expressed in atoms per unit area. Defining

$$\psi_{amp}^o(x^o, y^o) = -\tfrac{1}{2} S_t \frac{A}{N_o} \sigma(x^o, y^o), \tag{13a}$$

the object wave can be written

$$\psi_{tot}^o(x^o, y^o) = \exp[\psi_{amp}^o(x^o, y^o)] \exp[i\psi_{ph}^o(x^o, y^o)] \tag{13b}$$

This expression is now simplified, assuming ψ_{amp} and ψ_{ph} are small compared to the unit unscattered wave, by expanding both exponentials and keeping only first order terms.

$$\psi_{tot}^o = (1 + \psi_{amp}^o + \tfrac{1}{2}[\psi_{amp}^o]^2 + \ldots)(1 + i\psi_{ph}^o - \tfrac{1}{2}[\psi_{ph}^o]^2 + \ldots) \tag{13c}$$

$$\psi_{tot}^o(x^o, y^o) \cong 1 + \psi_{amp}^o(x^o, y^o) + i\psi_{ph}^o(x^o, y^o) \tag{13d}$$

The expression for the wave in the object plane, equation 13d, now has three components: the plane wave of unit amplitude corresponding to the unscattered electron wave; the real scattered wave, $\psi_{amp}^o(x^o, y^o)$, corresponding to the contribution from amplitude contrast; and the imaginary scattered wave, $i\psi_{ph}^o(x^o, y^o)$, corresponding to the contribution from phase contrast. (Both ψ_{amp}^o and ψ_{ph}^o are real functions.)

In the first order theory the only significant interactions of these three waves in producing the image intensity will be that of each of the scattered waves with the unscattered wave. It is appropriate then to consider independently the imaging of $1 + \psi_{amp}^o(x^o, y^o)$ and $1 +$

$i\psi^o_{\mathrm{ph}}(x^o, y^o)$. The latter has already been shown to give the phase contrast image, equation 11c. The corresponding derivation for the imaging of $1+\psi^o_{\mathrm{amp}}$ will give the transform of the amplitude contrast image.

The real scattered wave in the object plane, $\psi^o_{\mathrm{amp}}(x^o, y^o)$, is already specified in equation 13a. This wave gives rise to the wave in the diffraction plane by the Huygens-Fresnel construction

$$\psi^d_{\mathrm{amp}}(\alpha, \phi) = \frac{1}{f\lambda} \iint \psi^o_{\mathrm{amp}}(x^o, y^o) \exp\left[\frac{-2\pi i}{\lambda}(x^o\alpha\cos\phi + y^o\alpha\sin\phi)\right] dx^o dy^o$$
(14a)

$$\psi^d_{\mathrm{amp}}(f\alpha, \phi) = \frac{1}{f\lambda}\left(-\tfrac{1}{2}S_t\frac{A}{N_o}\right) T^o(\alpha, \phi)$$
(14b)

It may be expected that image contrast, particularly that from poorly localized events of inelastic scattering, will depend on the spatial frequency or size of object details, i.e. on the reciprocal coordinate α/λ. An additional factor, similar to the atomic scattering factor, could be included here to account for this, but since it cannot generally be specified theoretically it will be ignored in this derivation.

The wave ψ^d_{amp} will be modified by the aberration phase factor and the aperture function and give rise to the scattered amplitude wave in the image plane. The amplitude contrast image intensity will be determined from the sum or interference of this and the unscattered wave, as in the case of phase contrast. The essential difference between this case and that of the phase contrast imaging is that here the scattered wave is not multiplied by the imaginary i. Consequently the aberration factor $\chi(\alpha)$ appears finally in the expression for image intensity as $\cos\chi(\alpha)$ rather than as $\sin\chi(\alpha)$. The transform of the amplitude contrast image intensity is

$$T^i_{\mathrm{amp}}(\alpha, \phi) = -T^o(\alpha, \phi)A(\alpha)\frac{S_t}{\lambda^2}\frac{A}{N_o}\cos\chi(\alpha).$$
(15)

C. The Total Image—Amplitude and Phase Contrast

The amplitude and phase contrast contributions to the image will add independently in the first order approximation, so that the transform of the total image can be written, from equations 11c and 15,

$$T^i_{\mathrm{tot}}(\alpha, \phi) = -2T^o(\alpha, \phi)A(\alpha)\left\{\frac{f(\alpha)}{\lambda}\sin\chi(\alpha) + \left[\frac{S_t}{2N_o\lambda^2}A\right]\cos\chi(\alpha)\right\}$$ (16a)

The maximum possible contribution from amplitude contrast (where

$\cos \chi(\alpha) = 1$) relative to that from phase contrast (where $\sin \chi(\alpha) = 1$) is given by the factor $Q(\alpha)$ where

$$Q(\alpha) = \frac{S_t A}{2N_o \lambda f(\alpha)} \qquad (16b)$$

The actual contributions from the two to any particular image will, of course, depend on the value of $\chi(\alpha)$

$$T^i_{tot}(\alpha, \phi) = -T^o(\alpha, \phi) 2A(\alpha) \frac{f(\alpha)}{\lambda} [\sin \chi(\alpha) + Q(\alpha) \cos \chi(\alpha)] \qquad (16c)$$

We can estimate the magnitude of $Q(\alpha)$ by setting $S_t = 1 \cdot 2 \times 10^5$ cm^2 gm^{-1}, a value taken from Burge and Smith (1962, Fig. 5) that is approximately correct for all elements at 75 kV when a given small objective aperture is used in the microscope. Then $Q(\alpha) = 0 \cdot 023 A/f(\alpha)$, taking $\lambda = 0 \cdot 042$ Å and with $f(\alpha)$ in Å, and thus depends on the atomic number and scattering factor of the element of which the object is composed. Using values of $f(\alpha)$ tabulated by Ibers et al. (1962) (at $\alpha/\lambda = 0 \cdot 1$ Å^{-1}), Q is $0 \cdot 12$ for carbon; $0 \cdot 19$ for iron; $0 \cdot 30$ for xenon; and $0 \cdot 39$ for uranium. In practice these figures might be somewhat lower if a larger objective aperture is used, or if the resolution dependence of amplitude contrast is considered.

Because of the theoretical uncertainties the most direct approach to determining $Q(\alpha)$ has been experimental measurement. In the associated experimental study (Erickson and Klug, 1970) $Q(\alpha)$ was determined for a typical negatively stained specimen (where the image is largely that of the heavy metal stain, uranium) by measuring the changes in the image transform as a function of defocusing. $Q(\alpha)$ was found to be about $0 \cdot 4$ at very low spatial frequencies, $\alpha/\lambda < 0 \cdot 02$ Å^{-1}, dropping to less than $0 \cdot 1$ for $\alpha/\lambda > 0 \cdot 05$ Å^{-1}. These findings are consistent with the values predicted above, but show that amplitude contrast is most important at low resolutions. Equation 16b predicts that the amplitude contrast should increase slightly at higher resolution, as $f(\alpha)$ decreases. The experimental finding indicates that the resolution dependence of amplitude contrast suggested above is probably important.

Since $Q(\alpha)$ is generally small, the transfer function can be written alternatively as

$$[\sin \chi(\alpha) + Q(\alpha) \cos \chi(\alpha)] = N(\alpha) \sin [\chi(\alpha) + \Phi(\alpha)]. \qquad (16d)$$

The effect of a small fraction of amplitude contrast is here treated as an additional phase shift, $\Phi(\alpha) = \tan^{-1} Q(\alpha)$, in the phase contrast transfer function. $N(\alpha)$ is a normalizing factor, $N(\alpha) = 1/\cos \Phi(\alpha)$, which is generally close to unity. The zeros and peaks of the transfer functions plotted in Fig. 2 are accordingly shifted to the left, and the curve does not go to zero as α/λ goes to zero.

Finally it should be noted that the large variation in $Q(\alpha)$ expected between light and heavy elements (0·1 for carbon, 0·4 for uranium) should provide a useful tool for element discrimination in electron microscope images. For example a frequently encountered problem is that of distinguishing the image of a thin layer of stain from the granular structure of a supporting carbon film. In this case the in-focus micrograph provides a significant discrimination (at medium and low resolution) between the heavy metal stain and the carbon film. In the in-focus image, phase contrast is negligible ($\sin \chi(\alpha) = 0$) and amplitude contrast maximum ($\cos \chi(\alpha) = 1$) out to 15 Å resolution, $\alpha/\lambda = 0\cdot07$ Å^{-1} (cf. Fig. 2(a)). Since $Q(\alpha)$ is much larger for the stain than for the carbon film, a given mass thickness of stain will contribute to the in-focus, amplitude contrast image with four times as much contrast as the same mass thickness of carbon. In a moderately underfocused image, in which the contribution from phase contrast is important, the stain and carbon film will contribute more or less equally to the image. Thus the in-focus, amplitude contrast image gives a better signal (stain) to noise ratio than the underfocused image. This can be understood as the basis for the concept, widely applied in biological microscopy, that the in-focus image is a valid or "true" image and that the structures seen in an underfocused image are artifacts. In fact both the in-focus and the moderately underfocused images are valid, but the unwanted image of the carbon film granularity contributes with relatively greater contrast in the underfocused image. In a more sophisticated approach to element discrimination two or more micrographs at different defocusing could be compared and combined through the image transforms. A complete separation of the superimposed images of heavy and light elements should be possible in favourable cases.

D. *The Effect of Specimen Thickness*

The object can be treated as a two-dimensional projected density function only if it is thin enough so that all parts of the specimen are essentially at the same level of focus. To account for finite thickness an additional defocusing phase shift, exp $i(\pi/\lambda)z^o\alpha^2$, would have to be included at the diffraction plane to account for the difference in focus of the different object planes at distance z^o from the centre of the specimen (cf. Heidenreich, 1967 or Cowley and Moodie, 1957). The phase shift depends on the scattering angle, α, as well as on the z^o coordinate in the object. For a given specimen thickness the phase shift will be small enough to be ignored out to a certain value of the reciprocal coordinate, α/λ. For example, the phase shift, $(\pi/\lambda)z^o\alpha^2$, will be less than $\pi/10$ to a resolution corresponding to $\alpha/\lambda = 0 \cdot 1$ Å^{-1} (i.e. 10 Å resolution) if $|z^o| < 230$ Å; and to $\alpha/\lambda = 0 \cdot 3$ Å^{-1} (3 Å resolution) if $|z^o| < 21$ Å. In the microscopy of biological specimens one is generally interested in resolution down to 20 or 10 Å. Since these specimens are normally from 100 to 500 Å thick, the thickness will not introduce defocusing artifacts except for resolutions beyond 10 Å. Specimens used for high resolution microscopy are normally less than 50 Å thick. This will have negligible effect to 3 Å resolution. Thus it is generally valid to treat the object as a two-dimensional function giving the projected density in a single object plane.

E. *Chromatic Aberration*

Fluctuations in high voltage and lens current cause a change in the focal length of the objective lens which is equivalent to a variation in the defocusing, Δf. The magnitude of the average variation is

$$\delta f = C_c \left[\left\{ \frac{\Delta V}{V} \right\}^2 + \left\{ 2 \frac{\Delta I}{I} \right\}^2 \right]^{\frac{1}{2}} \tag{17a}$$

(Haine, 1961). For a modern microscope (Philips EM 300) $C_c = 1 \cdot 3$ mm and the voltage and lens current supplies are regulated so that the average values of both $(\Delta V/V)$ and $2(\Delta I/I)$ are about 5×10^{-6}. The expected variation in Δf is then

$$\delta f = C_c \sqrt{2} \times 5 \times 10^{-6} \simeq 100 \text{ Å.} \tag{17b}$$

Thus as the image is being recorded the actual value of Δf is varying between $\Delta f + \delta f$ and $\Delta f - \delta f$, and the micrograph is really the sum of images with the different Δf's. Considering for simplicity the case of pure phase contrast, the factor $\sin \chi(\alpha) = \sin 2\pi/\lambda[-C_s\alpha^4/4 + (\Delta f)\alpha^2/2]$ should be replaced by

$$\int_{-\delta f}^{+\delta f} \sin \frac{2\pi}{\lambda} \left\{ -C_s \frac{\alpha^4}{4} + (\Delta f + \delta) \frac{\alpha^2}{2} \right\} d\delta. \tag{17c}$$

In Fig. 2, the dashed curves show the corrected phase contrast transfer functions for $\delta f = 200$ Å, twice the value given above. The effect is negligible at low resolution but the amplitudes of the higher resolution peaks in the transfer function are reduced. At very high resolution the transfer function goes to zero, and details at these resolutions will not be imaged. These instabilities thus set a limit to the point-to-point resolution of the microscope.

7

F. *Partial Coherence*

The incident illumination in the electron microscope is not perfectly parallel, since it comes to the specimen through a condenser aperture of finite size. The image discussed so far assumes coherent illumination, i.e. a single plane wave coming from the centre of the aperture and travelling parallel to the optic axis. Superimposed on this image will be images produced by electron waves originating from other points in the aperture and therefore at an angle to the optic axis. The summation of these independent images has been treated in detail by Hopkins (1953) for light optical systems in terms of the theory of partial coherence. His general expressions, equations 17 and 18, can be adapted to the first order theory being developed here by ignoring all interactions except those involving a zero order term. The angular aperture of the objective is many times greater than that of the condenser system so its role in the effects of partial coherence will be negligible. The phase shift $\chi(\alpha)$, due to spherical aberration and defocusing, is the only important parameter. When Hopkins' expressions are adapted to this case it is seen that the effects of partial coherence are accounted for by replacing $\exp\left[i\chi(\alpha)\right]$, the phase shift of the wave in the diffraction plane, by

$$\int \gamma(\beta) \exp\left\{i[\chi(\alpha+\beta)-\chi(\beta)]\right\}dA. \qquad (18a)$$

β is the angle at which the illumination is incident upon the specimen and the integration is over all β in the area of the effective source of illumination. $\gamma(\beta)$ gives the intensity distribution over this effective source.

The exit pupil of the illumination system is the second condenser aperture, of 100 to 300 μ diameter, located about 130 mm away from the specimen. For normal conditions of microscopy this aperture is essentially uniformly illuminated with incoherent illumination, and can therefore be treated as the effective source of illumination. The essential criterion here is that the size of a coherently illuminated area in this aperture be small compared to the size of the aperture. Normally the condenser system is focused at or close to "cross-over", meaning that a demagnified image of the filament is focused on the specimen, giving an illuminated area of 1 to 10 μ diameter. The size of the coherent area in the exit pupil is determined by the angle, α', which this illuminated area subtends at the exit pupil, $d_{coh} = (0 \cdot 16\lambda)/\alpha'$ (Born and Wolf, 1964, Section 10.5.1). If the illuminated area is 1·3 μ, α' is 10^{-5} radians, and d_{coh} is 0·06μ. As this is much smaller than the size of the aperture, 100 μ, the second condenser aperture can be considered to be incoherently illuminated and thus constitutes the effective source. The illumination of this aperture is essentially uniform, so $\gamma(\beta) = 1$. Equation 18a then becomes

$$\int_0^{\beta_{\max}} \exp\{i[\chi(\alpha+\beta)-\chi(\beta)]\}d\beta \tag{18b}$$

where $\beta_{\max}$ is the half angle subtended by the condenser aperture at the object plane. When expression 18b is used for the aberration phase factor in the derivation of the phase contrast image, the factor $\sin \chi(\alpha)$ in the final expressions is replaced by

$$\int_0^{\beta_{\max}} \sin[\chi(\alpha+\beta)-\chi(\beta)]d\beta. \tag{18c}$$

With a 100 μ diameter condenser aperture, located 130 mm above the specimen, $\beta_{\max}$ is $3\cdot85\times10^{-4}$ radians. Dividing by $\lambda = 0\cdot042$ Å to express it in units of spatial frequency, $\beta_{\max}/\lambda = 0\cdot009$ Å^{-1}, or one can say that the transverse coherence length is 110 Å. The corrected phase contrast transfer functions for this case are shown by the dotted curves in Fig. 2. The predominant effect is to shift all features of the curves toward the origin, and this is significant at both low and high resolution. The amplitudes of the peaks are reduced only at very high resolutions. The partial coherence thus does not normally affect the resolution of the microscope, but does cause a significant shift in the peaks and zeros of the transfer functions.

III. PART 2. SECOND ORDER APPROXIMATION—GENERATION OF AMPLITUDE CONTRAST AND SECOND ORDER EFFECTS IN THE IMAGE OF A PURE PHASE OBJECT

In Part 1 the theory of image formation has been treated in a first-order or linear approximation, ignoring all second order terms in the derivation. In order to account for amplitude contrast it was necessary to postulate an artificial absorption of electrons in the specimen corresponding to the loss of electrons scattered outside the objective aperture. In this section the process of image formation will be outlined more rigorously, treating the object as a pure phase object and including all second order terms in the derivation. Amplitude contrast arises naturally in this second order theory from the interaction of the aperture function with the second order terms. The validity of the assumptions invoked in the previous derivation can be examined by comparing the expression for amplitude contrast in Part 1 with that derived here. Additional second order effects, due to the $|\psi^i|^2$ term in the expression for image intensity (equation 10c), and to the quadratic term in the expansion of the object wave, are also determined. These can be important in many cases of practical interest where a large fraction of the incident electrons are scattered by the object and the linear approximations are less accurate.

For simplicity this derivation will be outlined in one dimension; the extension to two dimensions will be obvious by comparison with the previous treatment. Since the object is treated here as a pure phase object, the wave in the object plane will be

$$\psi^o_{tot}(x^o) = \exp\left[i\psi^o_{ph}(x^o)\right]. \tag{19a}$$

This expression is expanded as before, keeping both first and second order terms

$$\psi^o_{tot}(x^o) = \exp\left[i\psi^o_{ph}(x^o)\right] \cong 1 + i\psi^o_{ph}(x^o) - \tfrac{1}{2}[\psi^o_{ph}(x^o)]^2. \tag{19b}$$

For the development of the theory one needs to relate each of these terms to the object density and to determine the Fourier transform of the total object wave. $T^o(\alpha)$ is the one dimensional transform of the object density, $\sigma(x^o)$,

$$T^o(\alpha) = \int \sigma(x^o) \exp\left[\frac{-2\pi i}{\lambda} x^o\alpha\right] dx^o. \tag{20a}$$

The transform of $[\psi^o_{ph}(x^o)]^2$ will be designated $T^o_{II}(\alpha)$. The convolution theorem states that the transform of the product of two functions is the convolution of their transforms, so the transform of $[\psi^o_{ph}(x^o)]^2$ will be the convolution of $T^o(\alpha)f(\alpha)$ with itself.

$$T^o_{II}(\alpha) = \int T^o(\gamma)f(\gamma)T^{o*}(\gamma-\alpha)f(\gamma-\alpha)d\gamma. \tag{20b}$$

The transform of the unit background wave will be a delta function, $\delta(\alpha)$. The Fourier transform of the total object wave, $\psi^o_{tot}(x^o)$, keeping first and second order terms and dropping all higher order terms as in 19b, is designated $U(\alpha)$.

$$U(\alpha) = \int \psi^o_{tot}(x^o) \exp\left[\frac{-2\pi i}{\lambda} x^o\alpha\right] dx^o = \delta(\alpha) + iT^o(\alpha)f(\alpha) - \frac{1}{2} T^o_{II}(\alpha) \tag{20c}$$

Except for constants of proportionality in the Huygens-Fresnel construction, which will not be carried through this derivation, the wave in the diffraction plane is proportional to the transform of the wave in the object plane,

$$\psi^d_{tot}(f\alpha) = U(\alpha). \tag{21}$$

This wave is modified by the aberration phase factor, $\exp\left[i\chi(\alpha)\right]$, and the aperture function, $A(\alpha)$, and the modified wave gives rise, by the second Huygens-Fresnel construction, to the wave in the image plane

$$\psi_{\text{tot}}^i(x^i) = \int U(\alpha)A(\alpha) \exp\left[i\chi(\alpha)\right] \exp\left[\frac{-2\pi i}{\lambda} x^i \alpha\right] d\alpha. \qquad (22)$$

$\psi_{\text{tot}}^i(x^i)$ is the total wave in the image plane, and includes the unscattered or background wave. The image intensity will be

$$I_{\text{tot}}(x^i) = |\psi_{\text{tot}}^i(x^i)|^2 = \psi_{\text{tot}}^i(x^i)\psi_{\text{tot}}^{i*}(x^i). \qquad (23\text{a})$$

Using the convolution theorem, the transform of the image intensity can be written

$$T_{\text{tot}}^i(\beta) = \int_{-\infty}^{\infty} U(\alpha)U^*(\alpha-\beta)A(\alpha)A(\alpha-\beta) \exp\{i[\chi(\alpha)-\chi(\alpha-\beta)]\}d\alpha. \qquad (23\text{b})$$

This gives the image transform in terms of the transform of the object wave, $U(\alpha)$. For further interpretation it is necessary to express the image transform in terms of the transform of the object density, $T^o(\alpha)$. Using equation 20c, the product $U(\alpha)U^*(\alpha-\beta)$ can be written

$$U(\alpha)U^*(\alpha-\beta) \cong \delta(\alpha)\delta(\alpha-\beta)-i\delta(\alpha)T^{o*}(\alpha-\beta)f(\alpha-\beta)+$$
$$i\delta(\alpha-\beta)T^o(\alpha)f(\alpha)-1/2\delta(\alpha)T_{II}^{o*}(\alpha-\beta)-1/2\delta(\alpha-\beta)T_{II}^o(\alpha)+$$
$$T^o(\alpha)f(\alpha)T^{o*}(\alpha-\beta)f(\alpha-\beta), \qquad (24)$$

where terms higher than second order have been dropped. In the integration over α, those terms containing a delta function give a single value. The result is further simplified by the symmetry relationships

$$T^o(\alpha) = T^{o*}(-\alpha); \quad T_{II}^o(\alpha) = T_{II}^{o*}(-\alpha); \quad \chi(\alpha) = \chi(-\alpha). \qquad (25)$$

With these substitutions and simplifications, equation 23b is reduced to

$$T_{\text{tot}}^i(\beta) = \delta(\beta)-T^o(\beta)2A(\beta)f(\beta)\sin\chi(\beta)-T_{II}^o(\beta)A(\beta)\cos\chi(\beta)$$
$$+\int_{-\infty}^{\infty} T^o(\alpha)f(\alpha)T^{o*}(\alpha-\beta)f(\alpha-\beta)A(\alpha)A(\alpha-\beta) \exp\{i[\chi(\alpha)-\chi(\alpha-\beta)]\}d\alpha. \qquad (26)$$

Using equation 20b to write $T_{II}^o(\beta)$ in terms of $T^o(\alpha)$,

$$T_{\text{tot}}^i(\beta) = \delta(\beta)-T^o(\beta)2A(\beta)f(\beta)\sin\chi(\beta)$$
$$-\left[\int_{-\infty}^{\infty} T^o(\alpha)f(\alpha)T^{o*}(\alpha-\beta)f(\alpha-\beta)d\alpha\right]A(\beta)\cos\chi(\beta)$$
$$+\int_{-\infty}^{\infty} T^o(\alpha)f(\alpha)T^{o*}(\alpha-\beta)f(\alpha-\beta)A(\alpha)A(\alpha-\beta) \exp\{i[\chi(\alpha)-\chi(\alpha-\beta)]\}d\alpha. \qquad (27)$$

The integrals are further simplified by changing the variable of integration to $\alpha' = \alpha-\beta/2$, and by replacing the aperture functions,

$A(\alpha'-\beta/2)A(\alpha'+\beta/2)$, in the second integral by specific limits on the integration, $\pm(\alpha_o-\beta/2)$, where α_o is the aperture angle.

$$T^i_{tot}(\beta) = \delta(\beta) - T^o(\beta)2A(\beta)f(\beta)\sin\chi(\beta)$$

$$-\left[\int_{-\infty}^{\infty} T^o(\alpha'+\beta/2)f(\alpha'+\beta/2)T^{o*}(\alpha'-\beta/2)f(\alpha'-\beta/2)d\alpha'\right]A(\beta)\cos\chi(\beta)$$

$$+\int_{-(\alpha_o-\beta/2)}^{+(\alpha_o-\beta/2)} T^o(\alpha'+\beta/2)f(\alpha'+\beta/2)T^{o*}(\alpha'-\beta/2)f(\alpha'-\beta/2)\times$$

$$\exp\{+i[\chi(\alpha'+\beta/2)-\chi(\alpha'-\beta/2)]\}d\alpha' \tag{28}$$

Each of the integrals can be separated into two parts, one with α' negative and one with α' positive, which can be combined using the symmetry relations. The result can be written

$$T^i_{tot}(\beta) = \delta(\beta) - T^o(\beta)2A(\beta)f(\beta)\sin\chi(\beta)$$

$$-\left[\int_0^{\infty} T^o(\alpha'+\beta/2)f(\alpha'+\beta/2)T^{o*}(\alpha'-\beta/2)f(\alpha'-\beta/2)d\alpha'\right]2A(\beta)\cos\chi(\beta)$$

$$+\int_0^{\alpha_o-\beta/2} T^o(\alpha'+\beta/2)f(\alpha'+\beta/2)T^{o*}(\alpha'-\beta/2)f(\alpha'-\beta/2)\times$$

$$2\cos[\chi(\alpha'+\beta/2)-\chi(\alpha'-\beta/2)]d\alpha'. \tag{29}$$

The integration of the first integral is over all space, for all α from zero to infinity. To separate the effects due to scattering outside the aperture (which will be identified with amplitude contrast) from interactions occurring within the aperture (which will be associated with phase contrast), it is convenient to separate this integral into two parts. The integration outside the aperture, $\alpha > \alpha_o$, is written as a separate term. The integration inside the aperture, $\alpha < \alpha_o$, is combined with the last term in equation 29, which has the same range of integration. It is also convenient to change the variable of integration from α' back to α to express the convolution integrals in the conventional form.

$$T^i_{tot}(\beta) = \delta(\beta) - T^o(\beta)2A(\beta)f(\beta)\sin\chi(\beta) \qquad\qquad T^i_{ph}(\beta)$$

$$-\left[\int_{\alpha_o}^{\infty} T^o(\alpha)f(\alpha)T^{o*}(\alpha-\beta)f(\alpha-\beta)d\alpha\right]2A(\beta)\cos\chi(\beta) \quad T^i_{amp}(\beta)$$

$$+\int_{\beta/2}^{\alpha_o} T^o(\alpha)f(\alpha)T^{o*}(\alpha-\beta)f(\alpha-\beta)\times$$
$$2\{-A(\beta)\cos\chi(\beta)+\cos[\chi(\beta)-\chi(\alpha-\beta)]\}d\alpha \qquad T^i_{II}(\beta)$$

$$\tag{30}$$

The first line of equation 30, designated $T^i_{ph}(\beta)$, is essentially identical to the expression derived in Part 1 for the first order phase contrast image, equation 11c. The $\delta(\beta)$ term is the transform of the average background intensity (unity here) that was subtracted out in the previous derivation of the image transform, equation 11a. The second term, designated $T^i_{amp}(\beta)$, is readily identified with amplitude contrast. The amplitude contrast image can be defined operationally as that obtained in an aberration-free system (i.e. $\chi(\alpha) \equiv 0$ for all α) with a finite objective aperture. $T^i_{amp}(\beta)$ depends as expected on the size of the objective aperture, and if $\chi(\alpha) \equiv 0$, all other terms in equation 30 are zero. $T^i_{amp}(\beta)$ thus describes completely the transform of the amplitude contrast image. The third term in equation 30 describes second order interactions within the objective aperture. In the absence of an objective aperture, $\alpha_o \rightarrow \infty$, the amplitude contrast term disappears, leaving $T^i_{II}(\beta)$ and the phase contrast term. $T^i_{II}(\beta)$ can thus be considered a correction to the first order phase contrast image due to the second order terms included in this derivation.

A. *Amplitude Contrast*

The amplitude contrast term, $T^i_{amp}(\beta)$, can be traced back through the derivation and shown to arise from the imaging of the quadratic term in the expansion of the object wave, $[\psi^o_{ph}(x^o)]^2$ in equation 19b. It comprises that part of this term that falls outside the objective aperture, the part that passes through the aperture being included in term $T^i_{II}(\beta)$. Since the second order interaction described by the convolution integral has occurred at the object plane the subsequent modification by the transfer function involves only the image transform coordinate (β), and does not depend on the coordinate α of the convolution integral. The modulation of this term by $\cos \chi(\beta)A(\beta)$ is identical to that in the first order derivation. Also, the term depends as expected on the size of the objective aperture, disappearing as the aperture becomes large. This dependence was included implicitly in the scattering cross section S_t in the previous derivation. The difference between the first order and second order derivations is that the first order term was simply proportional to the object transform, while that derived here is proportional to the convolution integral. If the integration were over all space the convolution integral would be equal to the transform of $[\sigma(x)]^2$ (convoluted with the transform of $f(\alpha)$), implying that the amplitude contrast is proportional to the square of the object density, instead of being directly proportional to $\sigma(x)$ as in the first order derivation. The following discussion shows that this conclusion is in fact valid for a wide class of objects even when the integration is only over the range $\alpha > \alpha_o$.

Since the range of integration in $T^i_{amp}(\beta)$ is over $\alpha > \alpha_o$ it is the high resolution or atomic structure of the object that generates the amplitude contrast. In conventional microscopy, however, it is generally the lower resolution details that one is interested in imaging. Especially with biological specimens only lower resolution details seem to be preserved during specimen preparation and observation. There are generally no significant Fourier components in the image corresponding to resolutions beyond 20 Å, or occasionally 10 Å. In this case one is interested in the contribution to the image of Fourier components that lie well within the objective aperture (α_o normally corresponds to a resolution of about 5 Å). The important point here is to show how the high resolution atomic structure, which produces the scattering outside the objective aperture, generates an amplitude contrast contribution for the low resolution Fourier components.

The simplest model object would be one described by a single cosine wave whose transform would then have only one low resolution Fourier component. This would not give rise to amplitude contrast because the object transform is zero outside the objective aperture and the convolution integral would consequently be zero. If the object consists of a single high resolution component there will be a trivial reduction in the average electron intensity over the image but no significant amplitude contrast, since the Fourier component is cut off by the aperture function, $A(\beta)$. Furthermore, if the high and low resolution components are simply added there will still be no amplitude contrast generated. The simplest model object that demonstrates the production of amplitude contrast is the two component system illustrated in Fig. 3. Here the high resolution atomic structure is represented by a high frequency cosine wave, where f_2 is significantly greater than α_o. The low resolution structure, which one is interested in imaging, is represented by a low frequency cosine wave, where f_1 is much less than α_o. The important feature of this model is that the low frequency wave is assumed to be a variation in the thickness of the object and thus appears as a modulation or multiplier of the amplitude of the underlying high resolution structure. This is a realistic model of most objects for which the low resolution structure is indeed a variation in the thickness or density of the atomic structure.

The object density of this model is thus written

$$\sigma(x) = a[1+\cos 2\pi f_2 x][1+b\cos 2\pi f_1 x]$$
$$= a\{1+\cos 2\pi f_2 x+b\cos 2\pi f_1 x+b\cos 2\pi f_2 x\cos 2\pi f_1 x\}$$
$$= a\{1+\cos 2\pi f_2 x+b\cos 2\pi f_1 x+\frac{b}{2}[\cos 2\pi(f_1+f_2)x+\cos 2\pi(f_1-f_2)x]\}.$$

$$(31)$$

(a) OBJECT

$$\sigma(x) = a\big[1 + \cos 2\pi f_2 x\big]\ \big[1 + b \cos 2\pi f_1 x\big]$$

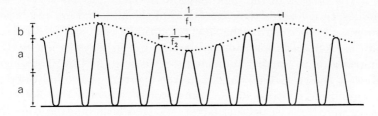

(b) OBJECT TRANSFORM, $T^0(\alpha)$

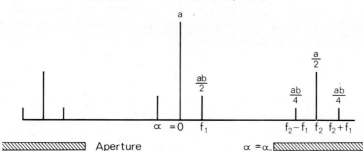

(c) AMPLITUDE CONTRAST IMAGE TRANSFORM.

$$-2 \int_{\alpha_o}^{\infty} T^0(\alpha)\, T^0(\alpha - \beta)\, d\alpha$$

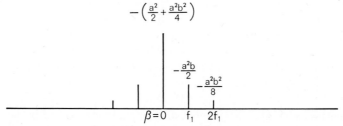

FIG. 3. The generation of amplitude contrast from a two component model object. The object density, $\sigma(x)$, is the solid curve plotted in (a). It consists of a high frequency cosine wave of frequency f_2, representing the atomic structure, modulated by a low frequency cosine wave of frequency f_1, the dotted curve. The object transform is shown in (b), with the objective aperture drawn below it to show what parts of the transform are cut off by the aperture. The low resolution transform of the amplitude contrast image is shown in (c). It is essentially the transform of the square of the low resolution object density.

From the last line of equation 31 it is seen that the object transform has components at $\alpha = \pm f_1$, $\pm f_2$, $\pm(f_1+f_2)$, and $\pm(f_1-f_2)$. Since the object is the *product* of the high and low frequency cosine waves, the total object transform is the *convolution* of the high and low resolution components. Consequently the low resolution transform is repeated around the high resolution components and in this way the low resolution information is "carried" outside the objective aperture. The object transform is shown in Fig. 3(b), where the aperture is also indicated.

The amplitude contrast image transform is shown in Fig. 3(c). For simplicity the atomic scattering factor, $f(\alpha)$, has been omitted from the convolution integral and the modulation by the transfer function ignored. The zero order component in the image transform shows the trivial reduction in the average background intensity. The two significant components are those at $\beta = f_1$ and $2f_1$. The amplitude contrast image corresponding to this transform is

$$I_{amp}(x) = I_{av} - a^2[b \cos 2\pi f_1 x + \frac{b^2}{4} \cos 2\pi(2f_1)x] \qquad (32a)$$

$$= I'_{av} - \frac{a^2}{2}[1 + b \cos 2\pi f_1 x]^2. \qquad (32b)$$

Thus the low resolution amplitude contrast image is proportional to the square of the low resolution object density function.

The faithfulness with which the amplitude contrast image represents the original object density depends on how similar the density function is to its square. This is best analyzed in terms of equation 32a, where the difference between the function and its square appears as a single extra Fourier component. The "true" image corresponds to the Fourier component of amplitude b at $\beta = f_1$; the extra component, which represents the aberrant image because it has twice the "true" frequency, is of amplitude $b^2/4$. Since the object density is always positive, b must be less than one, and in most cases, where the low resolution variation in thickness of the object is small compared to the total thickness, b will be much less than one. Consequently, the cosine wave with double frequency will always appear with less than 1/4 the amplitude of the cosine wave with true frequency, and in most cases, will be negligible. This is equivalent to saying that, although the amplitude contrast image is really proportional to the square of the object density, equation 32b, the square of the object density is very similar to the object density itself and usually the difference between the two is negligible.

The two component model system discussed above is the simplest example for demonstrating the generation of amplitude contrast. A generalized derivation is presented below that is applicable to problems of conventional microscopy where one is interested in the amplitude contrast of lower resolution images that have no significant Fourier components beyond 20 or 15 Å resolution. The essential requirement is that the object density can be separated into a low resolution density function, $\sigma_L(x)$, and a high resolution density function $\sigma_H(x)$. The Fourier transform, $T_L(\alpha)$, of $\sigma_L(x)$ has components only for $\alpha \ll \alpha_o$, well within the aperture. The Fourier transform, $T_H(\alpha)$, of $\sigma_H(x)$ has components only for $\alpha > \alpha_o$, outside the aperture. The low resolution density must be assumed to modulate the thickness or density of the underlying high resolution structure. The total object density is then the product of the high and low resolution density functions, and the object transform is the convolution of the high and low resolution transforms.

$$\sigma(x) = \sigma_L(x)\sigma_H(x) \tag{33a}$$

$$T^o(\alpha) = \int_{-\infty}^{\infty} T_L(\gamma)T_H^*(\gamma - \alpha)d\gamma \tag{33b}$$

By substituting equation 33b into the expression for $T^i_{amp}(\beta)$,

$$T^i_{amp}(\beta) = \cos \chi(\beta)A(\beta)\int_{\alpha_o}^{\infty} T^o(\alpha)f(\alpha)T^{o*}(\alpha - \beta)f(\alpha - \beta)d\alpha \tag{34a}$$

$$= \cos \chi(\beta)A(\beta)\int_{\alpha_o}^{\infty} \left[\int_{-\infty}^{\infty} T_L(\gamma_1)T_H^*(\gamma_1 - \alpha)d\gamma_1\right]f(\alpha) \times$$

$$\left[\int_{-\infty}^{\infty} T_L^*(\gamma_2)T_H(\gamma_2 - \alpha + \beta)d\gamma_2\right]f(\alpha - \beta)d\alpha \tag{34b}$$

$$= \cos \chi(\beta)A(\beta)\int_{-\infty}^{\infty}\int_{-\infty}^{\infty} T_L(\gamma_1)T_L^*(\gamma_2) \times$$

$$\left[\int_{\alpha_o}^{\infty} T_H^*(\gamma_1 - \alpha)T_H(\gamma_2 - \alpha + \beta)f(\alpha)f(\alpha - \beta)d\alpha\right]d\gamma_1 d\gamma_2. \tag{34c}$$

In the rearrangement shown in equation 34c it is seen that the integration over α involves only the high resolution transform. This integral, and the entire expression, can be simplified and reduced by invoking some realistic assumptions about the nature of the high resolution structure. Specifically the high resolution transform, $T_H(\alpha)$, will be assumed to be composed of a large number of components, for varying α, with similar amplitudes but rapidly varying and unrelated phases. The integrand, $T_H^*(\gamma_1 - \alpha)T_H(\gamma_2 - \alpha + \beta)$, will, for general values of γ_1 and

γ_2, be of the same nature, and the integral over α, being essentially the sum of a large number of equal terms with random phases, will tend toward zero. This integral will have a non-zero value only when $\gamma_2 = \gamma_1 - \beta$. The integral over α will then have a positive value,

$$S'_t = \int_{\alpha_o}^{\infty} T_H^*(\gamma_1 - \alpha) T_H(\gamma_1 - \alpha) f(\alpha) f(\alpha - \beta) d\alpha$$

$$= \int_{\alpha_o}^{\infty} |T_H(\gamma_1 - \alpha)|^2 f(\alpha) f(\alpha - \beta) d\alpha$$

$$\sim \int_{\alpha_o}^{\infty} |T_H(\alpha)|^2 [f(\alpha)]^2 d\alpha. \tag{34d}$$

In the last line γ and β have been treated as negligible in comparison to α since they are confined to low resolution and are therefore much smaller than α, which is always greater than α_o.

The integral has been designated S'_t because it is equivalent to the atomic cross section, S_t in equation 15, used in the first order derivation. Ignoring inelastic scattering and constants of dimensionality and proportionality, S_t involves only the atomic scattering factor,

$$S_t = \int_{\alpha_o}^{\infty} [f(\alpha)]^2 d\alpha.$$

The cross section derived here, S'_t, involves in addition the power spectrum of the high resolution atomic structure.

With this simplification (setting $\gamma_2 = \gamma_1 - \beta$), the amplitude contrast transform is

$$T^i_{\mathrm{amp}}(\beta) = \cos \chi(\beta) A(\beta) S'_t \int_{-\infty}^{\infty} T_L(\gamma_1) T_L^*(\gamma_1 - \beta) d\gamma_1. \tag{34e}$$

The convolution integral in equation 34e is proportional to the transform of $[\sigma_L(x)]^2$. In this generalized derivation, as in that of the two component model, the amplitude contrast image is proportional to the square of the low resolution object density (modulated by the amplitude contrast transfer function). As argued above in connection with the model example, the difference between the object density and its square is generally small and unimportant.

Even if the difference is negligible, it is somewhat surprising that the amplitude contrast image appears to be proportional to the square of the object density. Amplitude contrast has generally been considered to represent the object density faithfully, and a linear relationship between amplitude contrast and mass density has been demonstrated experimentally for several types of specimens, mostly involving large and relatively thick specimen details (Bahr and Zeitler, 1965). The quadratic relationship appears in this derivation because the real scattered wave, from which the amplitude contrast is derived, is proportional to the *intensity* of electrons scattered outside the aperture, $[\psi^o_{\mathrm{ph}}(x^o)]^2$ in equation 19b, rather than to the *amplitude* of the corresponding electron wave. The amplitude of the electron wave is proportional to $\sigma(x^o)$ so the intensity, and consequently the real scattered wave, is proportional to $[\sigma(x^o)]^2$. It should be emphasized that this is not a rigorous derivation, but still depends on the assumption that only a small fraction of electrons are scattered and that terms higher than second order are negligible. With thicker specimens, where the relationship between amplitude contrast and mass density is known to be linear, rather than quadratic, this approximation will no longer be valid and higher order terms will be important. In this case the simpler derivation of the first order theory of amplitude contrast, where the linear relationship is assumed and built in, will be preferable.

Amplitude contrast can also be generated in the absence of an objective aperture. In this case the term $T^i_{\mathrm{amp}}(\beta)$ is zero ($\alpha_o \to \infty$) and the effect is due to term $T^i_{II}(\beta)$, equation 30. In a perfect imaging system the two cosine factors in the brackets of this term cancel each other, but in a real system the combined effect of spherical aberration and fluctuations in lens current and voltage (chromatic aberrations) will cause $\cos[\chi(\alpha)-\chi(\alpha-\beta)]$ to average to zero at large values of the integration variable, α. For large α the phase shifts, $[\chi(\alpha)-\chi(\alpha-\beta)]$, will be changing rapidly with the small variations in the focal length caused by the chromatic aberrations. When this variation is about π radians or more the *average* value of $\cos[\chi(\alpha)-\chi(\alpha-\beta)]$ will be zero. The approximate value of α for which this obtains can be designated as the effective aperture, α'_o. The integration from α'_o to infinity will then involve only the convolution integral and the term $A(\beta)\cos\chi(\beta)$, and will be identical to the term $T^i_{\mathrm{amp}}(\beta)$. The integration from $\beta/2$ to α'_o will constitute the normal second order phase contrast term discussed below.

B. *Second Order Effects in the Phase Contrast Image*

The term $T^i_{II}(\beta)$, equation 30, describes the second order corrections to the linear expression for phase contrast. It can be written as the sum of two terms, each having a distinct physical basis.

$$T^i_{II}(\beta) = -2\cos\chi(\beta)A(\beta)\int_{\beta/2}^{\alpha_o} T^o(\alpha)f(\alpha)T^{o*}(\alpha-\beta)f(\alpha-\beta)d\alpha \qquad (35a)$$

$$+2\int_{\beta/2}^{\alpha_o} T^o(\alpha)f(\alpha)T^{o*}(\alpha-\beta)f(\alpha-\beta)\cos[\chi(\alpha)-\chi(\alpha-\beta)]d\alpha \qquad (35b)$$

The first term, 35a, can be traced back through the derivation and shown to arise from the $-1/2[\psi_{ph}^o(x)]^2$ term in the expansion of the object wave, equation 19b. It includes specifically that part of the transform of this term that passes through the objective aperture. The part that falls outside the aperture generates the amplitude contrast term $T_{amp}^i(\beta)$. This term therefore describes second order effects in the generation of the object wave, i.e. in the scattering of electrons by the specimen. This can be related to multiple scattering effects by interpreting the convolution integral in terms of scattering within the specimen. For this physical interpretation each Fourier component, $iT^o(\alpha)f(\alpha)$, of the primary scattered wave is treated as a new plane wave of illumination. Each of these components is scattered again by the object, giving rise to a secondary scattered wave whose transform at the coordinate β is proportional to the object transform, T^o, centered at α, the angle of the secondary illuminating wave, instead of at zero, i.e. to $iT^o(\beta-\alpha)f(\beta-\alpha) = iT^{o*}(\alpha-\beta)f(\alpha-\beta)$. The transform at coordinate β of the secondary scattered wave is proportional to the product of this secondary scattered component and the primary component generating it, $-T(\alpha)f(\alpha)T^{o*}(\alpha-\beta)f(\alpha-\beta)$. The sum, or integral over α, of the contributions from all the secondary scattered waves gives the total second order correction to the object wave Fourier component at β. This is subsequently modified by the aberration and aperture functions as a real (amplitude) wave.

The second term of $T_{II}^i(\beta)$, equation 35b, can be identified as the transform of the term $|\psi_{ph}^i(x^i)|^2$ in the expression for the image intensity, equation 10c, which was ignored in the first order derivation. It describes the second order interaction of Fourier components in the image plane, as equation 35a described those in the object plane. The aberration function here involves the coordinate α of the integration since the individual components are modified by the aberration function before reaching the image plane and before the interaction described by the convolution integral.

Both terms in equation 35 involve the convolution integral, $\int T^o(\alpha)T^{o*}(\alpha-\beta)d\alpha$, (ignoring the scattering factor $f(\alpha)$) and the second order effects will be significant only if this integral is large. For most cases the object transform will have many components of approximately equal amplitude but unrelated phases. The integral will then be essentially the sum of a large number of terms with random phases and will tend toward zero. The second order effects can become important when the object transform has only a few very strong components, as would be the case for a periodic object with high contrast. For example, if there are two strong components, at α_1 and α_2, the product of these, $T^o(\alpha_1)T^{o*}(\alpha_2)$, will make a strong contribution to $T^i_{II}(\beta)$ at $\beta = \alpha_1 + \alpha_2$. If these are the only strong components whose indices sum to equal β, the integral will be dominated by this product and the second order effect at $\beta = \alpha_1 + \alpha_2$ will be proportional to

$$T^i_{II}(\alpha_1 + \alpha_2) = -T^o(\alpha_1)T^{o*}(\alpha_2)f(\alpha_1)f(\alpha_2) \times$$
$$\{\cos \chi(\alpha_1 + \alpha_2) - \cos [\chi(\alpha_1) - \chi(\alpha_2)]\}. \tag{36}$$

The potential magnitude of the second order effect at $\beta = \alpha_1 + \alpha_2$ depends on the magnitude of the product, $T^o(\alpha_1)T^{o*}(\alpha_2)$, relative to that of the first order transform component, $T^o(\alpha_1 + \alpha_2)$. The actual magnitude of the effect observed in a particular image transform depends also on the aberration phase shift. The two cosine factors in the brackets in equation 36, which derive from terms 35a and 35b respectively, are of opposite sign and will partially cancel each other if the phase shifts, $\chi(\alpha_1)$, $\chi(\alpha_2)$ and $\chi(\alpha_1 + \alpha_2)$, are small, as for lower resolution details close to focus. In this case the second order effects, although potentially significant, may be negligible in comparison to the first order component. At greater defocusing the phase shifts, and the differences between them, become larger and the actual magnitude of the second order effect increases. The second order effect will be especially prominent in the image transform near the zeros of the first order phase contrast transfer function, $\sin \chi(\beta)$. Here the actual magnitude of the first order component, $T^o(\beta) \sin \chi(\beta)$, is near zero, while that of the second order effect remains high.

In the experimental study of a focal series of negatively stained catalase crystals (Erickson and Klug, 1970), a significant deviation from the first order theory was observed at one component in the image transform. This deviation was attributed to second order effects because the second order interaction of two of the strongest Fourier components would be superimposed on the relatively weak first order component at this point in the transform. However, a quantitative study showed that the magnitude of the deviation and its variation with Δf did not agree with the prediction of equation 36. It is now felt that the deviation measured in that study was due to additional second order effects, unrelated to image formation, such as non-linearities in the photographic recording or analysis of the image. Further experimental work will be required before the practical importance of second order effects in conventional microscopy and image analysis are understood.

IV. Discussion—The Compensation of Defocusing and Spherical Aberration

The physical interpretation of the expressions relating the image transform to the object transform has been discussed briefly in connection with the derivation. A more detailed consideration of the implications for conventional electron microscopy, especially for the use of underfocus contrast enhancement in biological microscopy, is presented in connection with the experimental investigation of the image transform (Erickson and Klug, 1970). In this final section the implications of the theory presented here for high resolution microscopy will be discussed, especially the possibility of compensating for the effects of spherical aberration and extending the resolution of the microscope.

As already mentioned, the modern electron microscope is essentially a perfect phase contrast microscope out to 4·5 Å resolution, with a useful contribution from amplitude contrast at lower resolutions, when operated slightly under focus as in Fig. 2(b). For straightforward imaging there is therefore no need for special instrumental techniques or image processing except for resolutions beyond 4·5 Å. The extension of resolution beyond this limit is largely of academic interest at the present time: first, because with current specimen preparation techniques, especially for biological microscopy, there is generally little preservation of meaningful structural detail beyond about 20 Å resolution; and second, because a variety of secondary factors, such as instrumental instabilities and specimen damage during observation, make microscopy at these very high resolutions very unreliable and certainly not a routine technique. Nevertheless there is considerable interest for the future of electron microscopy, anticipating the development of superior specimen preparation and instrumental techniques, in extending the resolution to atomic or subatomic levels. It is with this in mind that some schemes for compensating the effects of spherical aberration are discussed here.

One of the earliest proposals was to install a zone plate aperture in the diffraction plane of the microscope (Hoppe, 1961). This would consist of a set of concentric rings designed to obstruct the electron wave over those regions of the transform corresponding to the reversed contrast zones. The artifacts from contrast reversal would thus be eliminated before the image is formed, but of course the corresponding zones of the object transform would be missing from the image. Theoretical calculations (Langer and Hoppe, 1967; Eisenhandler and Siegel, 1966b) have indicated a significant improvement in resolution and contrast for the imaging of atomic structures using such a zone plate. Practical implementation of the scheme has, however, been frustrated by the considerable experimental difficulties (Thon and Siegel, 1970).

In terms of the first order derivation of image formation presented here one can see that exactly equivalent results can be obtained by processing the image after it is obtained in the conventional way. One needs only to obtain the Fourier transform of a conventional electron micrograph and reconstruct the image after eliminating all parts of the transform in the reversed contrast zones. This can be done very simply by using an optical filtering system, in which an optical zone plate, the scaled equivalent of the electron zone plate, is placed in the diffraction plane of the optical imaging system. Such a system has been demonstrated experimentally by Thon and Siegel (1970). It can also be done by computer processing. This involves scanning the micrograph to convert the image to a two dimensional array of optical densities and calculating numerically the Fourier transform. The image is reconstructed by inverse Fourier transformation after setting the Fourier coefficients to zero over the reversed contrast zones.

With a computer processing system, however, one can go much further in reconstructing an improved image. Instead of simply eliminating the reversed contrast zones by setting the transform to zero, these can be corrected to normal contrast merely by changing the sign of the Fourier coefficients (or by changing the phase 180°). Then the information in these zones would not be lost in the reconstructed image. In addition one can increase the amplitudes of the transform where the transfer function is less than unity, reconstructing an image to which almost the whole transform is contributing with uniform maximum contrast. (The optical filtering system could also be adapted for this amplitude and phase compensation, but not so directly as the computer processing.) The only parts of the transform that would be missing from the reconstructed image are those near the zeros of the transfer function, for here the information is actually missing from the original image, not simply modified in amplitude. To obtain this information an additional micrograph at a slightly different defocusing would be needed. Such an approach has been proposed and outlined by P. Schiske (1968), where the general ideas of compensation of aberrations by image processing through the Fourier transform are implied. The compensation system has been demonstrated experimentally in the medium resolution range accessible with current techniques in our own experimental investigation of the imaging of catalase crystals (Erickson and Klug, 1970) and in a demonstration of image reconstruction by J. Frank et al. (1970).

These compensation schemes are all based on the first order derivation of image formation, where the compensation is achieved simply by dividing the image transform by the transfer function. If second order terms are important this simple reconstruction will no longer give a valid image. This will pose the most difficult problems in attempting to reconstruct the compensated image from a single micrograph, where the second order effects dominate the image transform near the zeros of the transfer function. It should be much less serious in reconstructing the image from a set of micrographs in a focal series, where each of the transform components can be determined from images where the transfer function is near a maximum for its spatial frequency. Second order effects were demonstrated in the experimental investigation of image formation at moderate resolution (Erickson and Klug, 1970). It will be necessary to evaluate their importance for each particular case whenever the extension to high resolution is undertaken.

ACKNOWLEDGEMENTS

I would like to thank Dr. A. Klug for numerous helpful discussions and advice throughout the development of this work and the preparation of the manuscript, and especially for suggesting the need to consider second order effects in explaining aspects of the experimental data. I would also like to thank the many people who have read the manuscript during preparation and offered valuable comments and criticism.

I acknowledge support from the U.S. National Cancer Institute, post-doctoral fellowship number 5F02 CA23445–02.

REFERENCES

Bahr, G. and Zeitler, E. (1965). *In* "Quantitative Electron Microscopy" (G. Bahr and E. Zeitler, eds.), Williams and Wilkins Co., Baltimore, p. 208.

Born, M. and Wolf, E. (1964). "Principles of Optics", 2nd Ed., Pergamon Press, Oxford.

Burge, R. E. and Smith, G. H. (1962). *Proc. Phys. Soc.* **79**, 673.

Cowley, J. M. and Moodie, A. F. (1957). *Acta Cryst.* **10**, 609.

Dupouy, G. (1967). *J. Electronmicrosc.* **16**, 5.

Eisenhandler, C. B. and Siegel, B. M. (1966a). *J. Appl. Phys.* **37**, 1613.

Eisenhandler, C. B. and Siegel, B. M. (1966b). *Appl. Phys. Lett.* **8**, 258.

Erickson, H. and Klug, A. (1970). *Phil. Trans. Roy. Soc. Lon.* (Discussion Meeting on Electron Microscopy) **B261**, 105 (1971). Also *Ber. Bunsenges. Phys. Chem.* **74**, 1129.

Frank, J., Bussler, P., Langer, R. and Hoppe, W. (1970). *Ber. Bunsenges. Phys. Chem.* **74**, 1105.

Haine, M. E. (1961). "The Electron Microscope," Interscience Publishers, New York.

Hanszen, K. J. and Morgenstern, B. (1965). *Z. Ange. Phys.* **19**, 215.

Hanszen, K. J. (1967). *Naturwissenschaften*, **54**, 125.

Hanszen, K. J. (1971). "Advances in Optical and Electron Microscopy," **4**, 1.

Heidenreich, R. D. (1967). *J. Electronmicrosc.* **16**, 23.

Heidenreich, R. D. (1964). "Fundamentals of Transmission Electron Microscopy," Interscience Publishers, New York.

Hopkins, H. H. (1953). *Proc. Roy. Soc.* **A217**, 408.

Hoppe, W. (1961). *Naturwissenschaften* **48**, 736.

Ibers, J. A., Templeton, D. H., Vainshtein, B. K., Bacon, G. E. and Lonsdale, K. (1962). *In* "International Tables for X-ray Crystallography", Vol. III, 201, Kynoch Press, Birmingham.

Langer, R. and Hoppe, W. (1967). *Optik (Stuttgart)* **24**, 471.

Lenz, F. (1965). *In* "Quantitative Electron Microscopy" (G. Bahr and E. Zeitler, eds.), Williams and Wilkins Co., Baltimore, p. 70.

Niehrs, H. (1969). *Optik (Stuttgart)* **30**, 273.

Reimer, L. (1966). *Z. Naturforsch.* **21a**, 1489.

Reimer, L. (1969). *Z. Naturforsch.* **24a**, 377.

Scherzer, O. (1949). *J. Appl. Phys.* **20**, 20.

Schiske, P. (1968). *In* "Electron Microscopy 1968" (D. S. Bocciarelli, ed.), Vol. II, Tipografia Poliglotta Vaticana, Rome.

Thon, F. and Siegel, B. M. (1970). *Ber. Bunsenges. Phys. Chem.* **74**, 1116.

Valentine, R. C. (1965). *In* "Quantitative Electron Microscopy" (G. Bahr and E. Zeitler, eds.), Williams and Wilkins Co., Baltimore, p. 596.

Superconducting Electron Lenses

D. F. HARDY*

Department of Applied Physics, Cornell University, Ithaca, New York, U.S.A.

1. INTRODUCTION

WHEN Kunzler (1961) produced the first high field, high current superconducting wire, the study of superconductivity rapidly shed its reputation for having little, if any, technological value. The development of a conductor which was capable of supporting current densities of the order of 10^5 A cm^{-2} could not fail to have a profound influence on many branches of applied physics and electrical engineering. The remarkable properties of the Type II "hard" superconductors have ensured them a lasting position in scientific research, in spite of the complex problems associated with the manufacture of the materials themselves and the need to maintain superconductors at temperatures within 20°K of absolute zero.

With the appearance of the first commercially manufactured superconducting wire on the market, many suggestions were made as to how it might be employed in the construction of electron microscope lenses. Laberrigue and Levinson (1964) pointed out that the use of superconducting wire coils as ironless lenses could well revolutionize high resolution and high voltage electron lens design. By the following year Levinson *et al.* (1965) and Fernández-Morán (1965) had constructed

* Present address: Department of Applied Physics, University of Hull, Hull, HU6 7RX, England.

helium cryostats in which the superconducting lenses could be tested and the latter had obtained very crude micrographs of a grid at very low magnifications.

It soon became clear that the task of converting the conventional objective lenses of the electron microscope to the superconducting type was a difficult one and the majority of workers in the field took the attitude that they would like to be sure of the advantages to be gained before they discarded the conventional iron lens. There then followed a period of intensive investigation of the magnetic field distributions generated by many different types of superconducting lenses. In each case it was only possible to measure the axial field distributions and so subsequent computer calculations could only yield information about the cardinal elements and third order aberrations. No information was obtained about possible departures from axial symmetry and the magnitude of axial astigmatism that might be expected, and it was not possible to estimate the deterioration of performance that might be brought about by vibrations in the liquid helium system.

Several promising lens designs emerged during this period, which fully justified the interest paid to them originally. With this reassurance several laboratories have now returned to the problem of incorporating their lenses in high resolution instruments. To the present, only one author has published results which show that resolutions comparable with those obtained with the best conventional lenses can be obtained with superconducting objective lenses. However, work is continuing in several laboratories and more results can be expected soon.

In this review we will begin by outlining some of the more important features of superconducting materials and their possible impact on lens design. We will then discuss the various approaches that have been taken by different researchers and try to assess the degree of success that has been achieved.

II. Superconducting Materials

A. General Properties

1. Type I superconductors

A number of metallic elements undergo a transition from the normal to the superconducting state if they are cooled to within several degrees of absolute zero. When the transition occurs any magnetic flux passing through the sample at the time is expelled (the Meissner effect) and the material then has zero resistance. Small currents will circulate in closed loops of superconducting wire without any perceptible decay for very long periods. The field generated by these current loops is thus extremely stable and if any attempt is made to change the strength of the field in the vicinity of the loop the circulating current will alter so as to maintain the magnetic flux through the loop constant.

If these characteristics could be maintained for high currents and high ambient magnetic fields then the advantages of superconductors in electron microscopy would be unassailable. Unfortunately the superconductivity of most of the metal elements is quenched by the presence of magnetic fields of only a few hundred oersteds. Lead, for example, is quenched by a field of 800 oersteds at temperatures close to absolute zero. When it became clear that no element had a critical field much higher than this it was a serious disappointment to those who had planned to build high field superconducting magnets.

2. *Type II superconductors*

Considerable interest was generated when it was discovered that some impure metal samples often displayed anomalous characteristics.

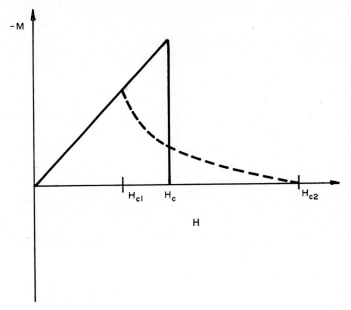

Fig. 1. The general form of the magnetization curves of Type I (full line) and Type II (broken line) superconductors.

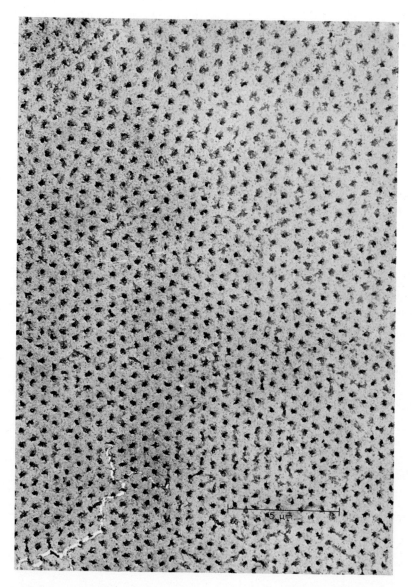

FIG. 2. Electron micrograph of a triangular array of flux vortices in a Pb–In Type II superconductor decorated with iron particles. (Reproduced with permission from Träuble and Essmann (1968).)

In these "dirty" superconductors the Meissner effect did not vanish dramatically at H_c but the field began to penetrate the superconductor gradually at H_{c1} ($< H_c$) and the diamagnetic moment continued to decrease slowly until it disappeared at H_{c2} ($> H_c$). The magnetization curve for these "Type II" superconductors is shown in Fig. 1. Although the Meissner effect was only partial between H_{c1} and H_{c2} the sample resistance was still zero in this region.

Abrikosov (1957) proposed an extensive theory to explain this phenomenon. He suggested that at fields above H_{c1} it became energetically favourable for the flux to penetrate the superconductor in a large number of microscopically small regions. The flux lines passed down filaments of normal material which were embedded in the superconducting matrix surrounded by a sheath of circulating current. In spite of the presence of these vortices the resistance of the bulk superconductor remained zero since a superconducting path through the material was still open. The theory was recently spectacularly verified by Träuble and Essmann (1968) who succeeded in decorating the vortices with iron particles which could be observed with an electron microscope. Figure 2 shows a typical vortex lattice prepared in this way.

B. *High Field, High Current Superconductors*

1. *Steady state properties*

Although the Type II superconductors displayed zero resistance at much higher magnetic field strengths than the Type I superconductors, it was found that they became resistive again when the current density in them exceeded a critical value. This phenomenon was in no way connected with any quenching of the superconductivity since it occurred well below the critical field of the superconductor concerned, but was found to be due to the motion of the flux vortices through the material.

The transport current through the superconductor exerts a force on the vortices. When the current density reaches the critical level the vortices are torn from the points where they have been temporarily pinned by imperfections in the matrix and move at right angles to the current vector, inducing a voltage across the sample as they move. Once torn from their pinning points the vortices soon reach a terminal velocity due to the action of other "viscous" forces about which little is currently known. This steady movement of flux through the conductor induces an e.m.f. tending to oppose the current flow and the superconductor appears to have become resistive.

Clearly this resistive effect arising from vortex flow is just as trouble-some as ohmic resistance, since it represents a flow of energy into the low temperature area which was precisely what had to be avoided. However, by loading the superconducting material with microscopic obstacles to the vortex flow the critical current density at which resist-ance appeared could be increased. These "pinning points", consisting of precipitates or tangles of dislocations, pinned the vortices or clusters of vortices along their length thus preventing flux motion for moderate fields and current densities.

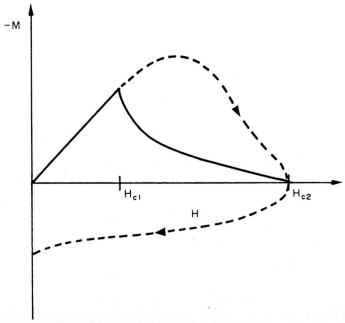

Fig. 3. A comparison of the magnetization curves of pinned (broken line) and un-pinned (full line) Type II superconductors.

It is thus the strength of the pinning points that determines the critical current density of a Type II superconductor and not H_{c2} or H_{c1}. The introduction of strong pinning points into a superconductor also has an influence on its magnetic properties. As the applied field is increased the penetration of the flux lines into the bulk will be initially prevented by the action of the pinning points, and when the applied field is reduced to zero again some magnetic flux will remain pinned in the specimen. The magnetization curve of such a superconductor, demonstrating this hysteresis, is given in Fig. 3.

2. *Instabilities*

The presence of the pinning points introduces one further difficulty—that of "flux jumps".

If, for any reason a vortex should suddenly become spontaneously unpinned it will be driven at right angles to the current flow until it encounters further resistance to its motion. As it moves through the superconductor energy is dissipated in the form of heat. The local heating of the superconductor then reduces the pinning strength of the pinning points in that region which allows further unpinning and the resultant avalanche of vortices is known as a flux jump. This avalanche can heat all of the sample above the transition temperature. These catastrophic effects generally only occur when the ambient magnetic field is altered.

The problem of flux jumps has been overcome as far as wire is concerned by the use of "filamentary" superconductors. These wires are finely subdivided into filaments, each several microns in diameter which are inherently stable against flux jumps since insufficient energy can be dissipated in the superconductor to start a flux avalanche.

On the other hand, thicker wires or even more massive pieces of superconducting materials need a more specialized approach. Many attempts have been made to ensure that the heat generated by an initial unpinning event is removed before the avalanche begins. This has been done by improving the thermal contact between the superconductor and the liquid helium bath either directly or by using a substrate of high thermal conductivity. Nevertheless great care must still be taken when increasing or decreasing the magnetic field in the vicinity of a bulk superconductor, which may limit the cycle time.

3. *Further comments*

This section was not intended to be a complete description of all Type II superconducting phenomena but to present a qualitative general outline of the characteristics of the superconducting materials that the electron lens designer is likely to encounter. Further information on this subject is given in a review article by Lowell (1965) on Type II superconductors which is a concise account of the development of the subject up to that date. Further points of interest to the electron lens designer may be found in a review of superconducting magnets by Chester (1967). A description of the latest work at the Rutherford Laboratory on filamentary superconducting composites is given in an article by Lewin *et al.* (1969).

Before moving on to discuss the application of superconductors to electron lens design we shall tabulate here some of the parameters of common Type II superconductors, some of which are available in commercial quantities (Table I).

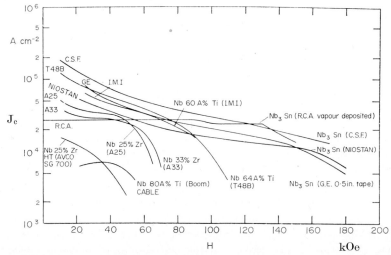

FIG. 4. Average critical current densities of some common superconducting wires when in solenoid form. (Reproduced with permission from Prior (1967).)

Figure 4 shows the variation with ambient field strength of the average current density which can be achieved in a solenoid with currently available types of superconducting wires. Allowance has been made for the space occupied by insulation, stabilizing layers and voids; the actual current density in the superconductor will, of course, reach higher levels than those indicated here.

TABLE I

Critical temperatures and upper critical fields of some common Type II super-conductors

Superconductors	T_c (°K)	H_{c2} at 4·2°K (kOe)
Nb_3Sn	18·1	225
V_3Si	16·8	225
$Nb_{0·75}Zr_{0·25}$	11·0	77
$Nb_{0·67}Zr_{0·33}$	10·8	83
$Nb_{0·4}Ti_{0·6}$	8·4	122
$Nb_{0·3}Ti_{0·7}$	7·0	110

III. The Design of Magnetic Electron Lenses

A. *General Principles*

1. *Limitations of conventional lenses*

Although the solenoid is the simplest form an electron lens can take, this element has found few applications in modern electron microscopy since it cannot be used to generate magnetic fields of the intensity and localized nature required for focusing electrons of energies exceeding more than several kiloelectronvolts.

Current densities in solenoid windings cannot be increased much above 300 A cm^{-2} without introducing serious problems caused by the heat dissipation. At this level of current density the fields generated by the coils fall far short of those required for an efficient electron microscope lens.

It is found necessary, then, to employ some kind of magnetic circuit to shape and intensify the magnetic field. The overall dimensions of the lens are still determined by the maximum permissible value of the current density in the lens windings but the axial extent of the focusing field is now determined entirely by the geometry of the iron circuit. The peak flux density on the axis can now be increased to about 18 kG at which point the iron polepieces begin to saturate. The existence of this upper limit for the magnetic flux density generated within an electron lens places certain restrictions on the dimensions and optical properties of that lens. Under these circumstances it becomes impossible to reduce the chromatic and spherical aberration coefficients below certain limits. These minimum values of C_c and C_s are proportional to the square root of the relativistically corrected accelerating voltage, and the dimensions of the pole pieces of the "optimum" lens vary in the same way.

We will now try to see how much is to be gained by raising the upper limit on the flux density. Let us assume that we have designed a "best" conventional lens for electrons of a specific beam voltage V*. The peak flux density (B_o) in the lens is the limiting flux density for the iron. Then the radius of curvature (ρ) of a ray at any particular point along its path will be related to the flux density there (B) by the well-known relation

$$B\rho \sin \theta / (V^*)^{\frac{1}{2}} = \text{constant}$$

where $V^* = V(1 + 0 \cdot 983 V \times 10^{-6})$ and θ is the angle between the tangent to the ray path and a local flux line. If we are now given a material which allows us to achieve peak flux densities of $B_o{}'$ ($> B_o$) what changes can we make in the lens design that will result in an improved performance?

We can get some idea of the improvements possible if we consider carrying out the following operations on the lens. First, we increase the magnitude of the flux density everywhere by the same factor so that the peak flux density is now B_o'. At the same time we scale down the linear dimensions of the lens pole pieces and the rays passing through the lens by some other factor and the ray radius of curvature becomes ρ'. It is clear that if these two operations are valid, that is to say, if the scaled down rays correspond to possible rays in the scaled-down lens, then the beam stiffness relationship must hold and thus

$$B'\rho' = B\rho$$

Since $B'/B = B_o'/B_o$, it follows that the appropriate geometrical scaling factor is simply

$$\sigma = \frac{\rho}{\rho'} = \frac{B_o{}'}{B_o}$$

We see that the increase in B_o has allowed us to construct a more compact electron lens with a shorter focal length. Moreover, since C_c and C_s both have dimensions of lengths the magnitude of these aberrations will have been reduced by a factor of σ.

Other geometrical aberration coefficients, such as those which describe the distortion, coma and third order astigmatism would be increased, so that there is little point in applying this scaling down procedure to any but objective lenses.

2. *Potential advantages of the use of superconducting materials*

The development of a new conducting material that is capable of supporting current densities far greater than it is possible to achieve with copper will clearly have an impact on many aspects of lens design. It is possible to identify two types of modifications that can be made. First, there are those design changes which will allow us to obtain higher resolution than can be achieved with conventional lenses and second, there are those modifications which make the microscope more convenient to operate.

The fundamental advantage of using superconductors in the construction of electron lenses is that it becomes possible to dispense with the iron circuit, which can lead to an improvement in optical performance as we outlined in the last section. It is this aspect of the lens design that will be emphasized in this review.

Many authors have pointed out other "operational" advantages in using superconducting lenses. At the most trivial level we see that it is possible to reduce the physical dimensions of the lens windings by a large factor. The need for a cryostat with multiple walls to isolate the lens thermally from its room temperature surroundings tends to cancel out the advantages of size reduction in all electron microscopes except those operating with beam voltages in excess of 1 MV.

Some electron microscopists may find it convenient to use low aberration superconducting lenses when examining specimens at low temperatures. In the past these studies have been carried out using a combination of a conventional objective lens and a liquid helium cold stage for the specimen. This combination has not been easy to achieve and compromises in the design have often led to a loss of resolution arising from mechanical instabilities or non-optimum lens geometry. It is natural to suggest that lens and specimen stage would be more compatible if they were both designed to operate at the same temperature.

Other advantages are the dramatic reduction of the microscope pressure in the vicinity of the specimen because of cryopumping at the cold surfaces, and the possibility of maintaining an ultrastable lens field by operating in a "persistent current" mode. Fernández-Morán (1966a,b) stresses the importance of the latter, but it is difficult to see how one can take advantage of the remarkable current stability since other mechanical and electrical instabilities will tend to mask any possible improvement.

In conclusion it must be admitted that these operational advantages do little to off-set the major disadvantage of superconducting lenses, which is the need to provide each lens with a sophisticated cryostat and helium supply system.

B. *Assessment of Objective Lens Designs*

With very few exceptions, superconducting lenses have been built and tested with the specific aim of overcoming the limitations of conventional lens designs. Unfortunately many designers content themselves with presenting limited details of the performance of experimental lenses without making any critical comparisons with the performance of comparable conventional lenses. The reviewer could calculate all the characteristics of the electron lenses in the literature if the B_z distribution along the optical axis were known, but this information is rarely presented in descriptions of lens designs, which makes a detailed comparison of different lenses difficult.

However, quite often results of lens flux density measurements are condensed into two parameters, the peak flux density on the axis B_o and the half width of the distribution at half height (d).

If it is assumed that the form of the flux density distribution is given by the Glaser model

$$B_z(z) = \frac{B_o}{1+\left(\dfrac{z}{d}\right)^2}$$

and we know the magnitude of the dimensionless number

$$k^2 = 0.022 \frac{B_o^2 d^2}{V^*}$$

(B_o in gauss, V^* in volts, d in centimetres)

then it is possible to calculate the corresponding values of the aberration coefficients and cardinal elements using the analytic expressions derived by Glaser (1952). The values of some of these parameters are given in Table II for a range of values of k^2. It must be admitted that the Glaser model (shown in Fig. 5) is often an unrealistic description of the flux density distribution of some lenses, but it does provide a reasonable means of comparing lens performances.

To simplify comparison even more we shall only compare lenses having identical k^2 values for the same beam voltage. For this purpose

TABLE II

The focal length f, the distance from the lens centre to the focus z_f, and aberration coefficients ($M = \infty$) for the Glaser model lens as a function of k^2, the Glaser parameter.

k^2	f/d	z_f/d	C_s/d	C_c/d
1·0	1·26	0·76	0·73	0·88
1·2	1·17	0·61	0·59	0·79
1·4	1·11	0·49	0·50	0·73
1·6	1·08	0·40	0·44	0·69
1·8	1·05	0·32	0·40	0·66
2·0	1·03	0·29	0·37	0·64
2·2	1·02	0·18	0·35	0·62
2·4	1·01	0·13	0·33	0·61
2·6	1·00	0·08	0·31	0·60
2·8	1·00	0·04	0·30	0·60
3·0	1·00	0·00	0·28	0·59

it is convenient to combine the measurements of d, B_o in a single quantity which we shall call the "electron optical power", P, of the lens which is given by

$$P = 0{\cdot}022B_o^2d^2.$$

Clearly the Glaser parameter is simply given by

$$k^2 = \frac{P}{V*}.$$

If two lenses have identical values of P then it follows that the lens with the smaller flux distribution halfwidth will have proportionately smaller aberration coefficients irrespective of the beam voltage.

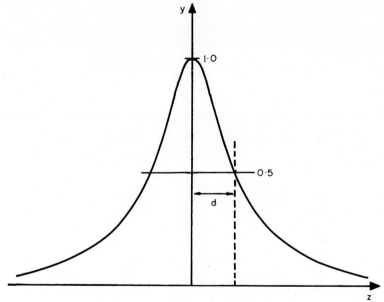

FIG. 5. The Glaser "bell" function $\dfrac{B_z(z)}{B_o} = \dfrac{1}{1+\left(\dfrac{z}{d}\right)^2}.$

In most cases we have chosen to compare each superconducting lens described in the following pages with a standard conventional iron lens having the same P value. Such a conventional lens would have its peak flux density fixed at 18 kG, whilst d is permitted to take any value. This comparison allows us to define a figure of merit,

$$\sigma = \frac{B_o}{B_{\text{lim}}}$$

where B_o is the maximum flux density achieved in the superconducting lens and B_{lim} is the maximum flux density achieved in the conventional lens, which we have taken to be 18 kG. The values of f, C_s, C_c of the superconducting lens are then always $1/\sigma$ times those of the conventional lens having the same P value.

The absolute value of P gives us a guide to the beam voltage for which the superconducting lens will be suited. On the whole it is most convenient to use an objective lens having a k^2 value lying between 1·5 and 3. If k^2 falls below 1·5 the important aberration coefficients become large and if k^2 lies above 3 the lens has multiple foci which can cause alignment difficulties. So, in all the discussion that follows we have assumed that the most "suitable" beam voltage for a particular pair of B_o, d values is that which makes $k^2 = 3$.

TABLE III

Focal length and aberration coefficients ($M = \infty$) of the optimum, flux density limited, Glaser model lens, ($k^2 = 2\cdot8$, $B_{lim} = 18$ kG) as a function of beam voltage

V(kV)	V^*(kV)	$f(\approx d)$(mm)	C_s(mm)	C_c(mm)
100	110	2·08	0·63	1·24
200	239	3·07	0·93	1·84
400	556	4·68	1·42	2·80
600	952	6·12	1·85	3·66
800	1 425	7·44	2·27	4·48
1 000	1 978	8·83	2·67	5·28
2 000	5 948	15·32	4·64	9·16
3 000	11 806	21·58	6·54	12·90
4 000	19 656	27·84	8·44	16·65

In certain cases it has not been possible to discover the exact values of B_o and d for a particular lens and in other cases the flux density distributions have been too unlike the Glaser model to allow the kind of comparison described above. On these occasions we can only compare the values of C_s, C_c, f quoted by the authors with those obtained for the optimum Glaser bell model lens, which has dimensions which have been chosen so that C_s is a minimum ($k^2 = 2\cdot8$, $B_o = 18$ kG). Table III gives the values of the cardinal elements and important aberration coefficients of the optimum Glaser lens for a range of beam voltages.

IV. Superconducting Electron Lenses

A. *Lenses without Pole Pieces*

1. *Simple solenoids*

The field distribution on the axis of a coil of rectangular section is given by the well-known expression (see, for example, Montgomery (1969)):

$$B_z(z) = \frac{2\pi}{10} \frac{I}{\eta} \left\{ G(x_1+z) + G(x_1-z) \right\}$$

where

$$G(u) = u \ln[\{y_2 + (y_2^2+u^2)^{\frac{1}{2}}\}/\{y_1 + (y_1^2+u^2)^{\frac{1}{2}}\}]$$

and the variables are defined as follows:

i—current density in A cm^{-2}
η—packing factor
$2x_1$—length of the solenoid in cm.
y_1—inner radius of the solenoid
y_2—outer radius.

Laberrigue and Severin (1967) have carried out a theoretical study of small coils of this type with a view to using them as strong objective lenses. It was found that if a class of solenoids all having the same inner radius was studied, a particular pair of values of x_1 and y_2 could be found which made $G(0)$ a maximum for each value of d, the distribution half-width. The results are shown in Fig. 6.

The flux densities marked on the vertical axes are those which would be measured at the centre of the coil if a current close to the critical value were passed through superconducting windings of various types. The authors of this work carried out the analysis assuming windings of three different early types of superconducting wire. Although new materials have become available since then it is a fair assumption that the range of critical currents has not altered much. Modern materials span a range between the values given for Supercon's A25 NbZr wire at the low end and General Electric's experimental Cryostrand at the high end.

It is seen that despite the large current-carrying capacity of the superconductor, it is still not quite possible to generate flux densities of the order of 18 kG while limiting the spread of the distribution to 3 mm. This is often achieved in the objective lens of a conventional commercial high resolution microscope.

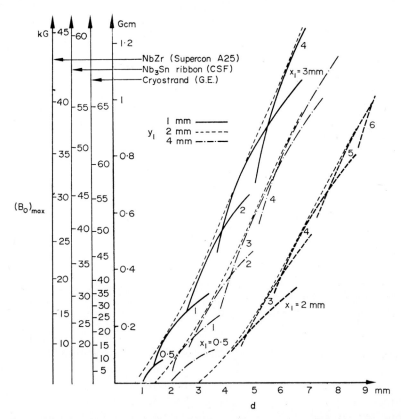

FIG. 6. The maximum attainable axial flux density B_o as a function of the flux density distribution halfwidth d, for simple solenoids of fixed internal diameter. (Reproduced from Laberrigue and Severin (1967) with permission.)

The variation of the quantity P with d is given in Fig. 7 for several different lens geometries. The region below the shaded line is that which can be covered by a conventional iron lens which saturates at about 20 kG. The NbZr solenoid is clearly not competing until very high P values are reached. The 2, 4 and 8 mm i.d. Cryostrand solenoids start to have an advantage when accelerating voltages reach about 100, 300 and 600 kV respectively. At an accelerating voltage of 1 MV, which corresponds to $V^* = 2 \cdot 10^6$ V, even the 8 mm bore solenoid has spherical and chromatic aberration coefficients which are a factor of two better than those of a conventional lens.

It is clear from this work and a similar piece of analysis by Der–Schwartz and Makarova (1968) that superconducting solenoids cannot be expected to give better resolution than conventional lenses in microscopes employing accelerating voltages of 100 kV or less. For higher voltages the gains may become considerable.

Merli (1968, 1970) has studied the possibility of using a sequence of superconducting coils to form an objective lens, the object plane of which lies outside the bore of the lens. A typical lens of this type would have $C_s = 2\cdot7$ mm, $C_c = 3\cdot4$ mm for a working distance of $3\cdot7$ mm.

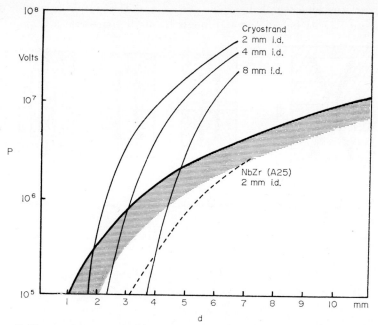

FIG. 7. The maximum attainable electron optical power P as a function of the flux density distribution halfwidth d for solenoid lenses of fixed internal diameter. (Full line—Cryostrand windings, broken line—A25 NbZr windings.) The corresponding curve for a conventional lens would be in the shaded region.

The major disadvantage of the solenoid lens is that it is difficult to construct since small winding errors can give rise to serious departures from rotational symmetry, which in turn causes axial astigmatism and other parasitic aberrations (Amboss and Jennings, 1970). Although techniques have been developed to overcome this problem for ironless electron lens coils wound with conventional conductors by Le Poole (1964), there has been little interest in applying these methods in the winding of superconducting lens coils. This is not surprising, as it might be expected that the extremely high currents flowing in the windings would demand a winding accuracy that might be difficult to achieve. No experimental work on these lenses has been reported.

2. Iron-shrouded solenoids

If the maximum flux density on the axis of a superconducting solenoid is of the order of 20 kG some enhancement can be achieved by shrouding the coil with iron. The flux density on the axis can then be considered to arise from two separate sources, the magnetization of the iron circuit and the solenoid itself. This type of lens is a hybrid, falling somewhere between the lens which has pole pieces and the simple solenoid, and consequently its behaviour is difficult to predict theoretically.

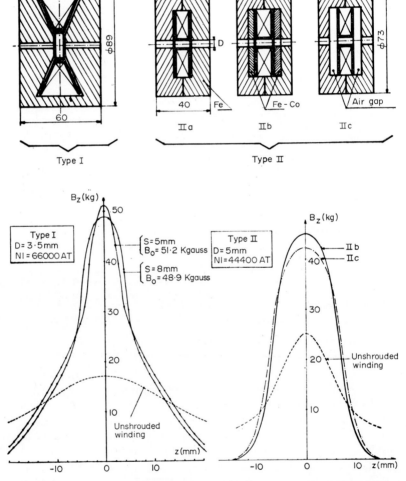

FIG. 8. Shrouded solenoid lenses. (Reproduced with permission from Genotel *et al.* (1967a).)

Some experimental lenses constructed by Genotel and co-workers (1967a) at the Collège de France are shown in Fig. 8. It is seen that there are no pole pieces and the windings are allowed to come as close to the axis as possible. To take full advantage of this configuration the dimensions of the coil should be chosen so that the current in the coil is approaching its critical value just as the iron nearest the centre of the lens is beginning to saturate. If the coil has too large a cross-section the iron will saturate and the value of d will increase rapidly with excitation. If the coil cross-sectional area is too small the current in the coil will reach its critical value before the flux density at the centre of the lens has risen high enough.

TABLE IV

Typical parameters for four types of shrouded solenoid lens

Type	B_o (kG)	d (mm)	P (volts)	V_3(MV)	σ
I	50·7	5·5	$1·69 \times 10^7$	1·8	2·8
IIa	42·6	7·6	$2·30 \times 10^7$	2·3	2·3
IIb	66·6	7·4	$5·34 \times 10^7$	3·7	3·7
IIc	50	11·6	$7·40 \times 10^7$	4·4	2·8

Figure 8 also shows the axial flux density distributions which were achieved using the lenses shown. Peak flux densities of up to 65 kG have been attained with a distribution half-width of only 7 mm. As an example, measurements of B_o and d for four typical lenses are given in Table IV. Also tabulated are V_3, the accelerating voltage for which the focal point would lie at the centre of the lens field (assuming that the distribution is described by the Glaser bell model) and σ, the figure-of-merit. The lenses described apparently would be suitable for operation in the 1–4 MV regime and have a figure of merit lying between 2 and 3. Ozasa et al. (1966, 1968) have constructed a shrouded lens with a figure of merit of approximately 2·5 which they propose to use as an alternative objective lens for the Hitachi 1 MV electron microscope.

Kitamura et al. (1966) have described several small lenses of the shrouded solenoid type which were designed to operate at lower voltages. They also experimented with ribbon windings (Fig. 9) and were able to achieve flux density distributions having a halfwidth of about 4 mm and a peak value of 40 kG. An analysis of their flux density measurements shows that although figures of merit of at least 2 were obtainable in lenses suitable for use with accelerating voltages of about 900 kV, σ had dropped to 1·2 for 200 kV lenses.

It had also been hoped that the presence of the iron circuit would in some way reduce the influence of winding errors on the symmetry of the magnetic flux distribution. It would be expected that only winding errors in a small section near the centre of the lens could give rise to asymmetries. Electron optical tests on lenses of this type in an electron microscope have been reported in two instances only. Fernández-Morán (1966a) found that his resolution was limited to about 50 Å, apparently by astigmatism, and Laberrigue *et al.* (1967) found that the astigmatism of their lens was many times worse than that of a conventional iron lens.

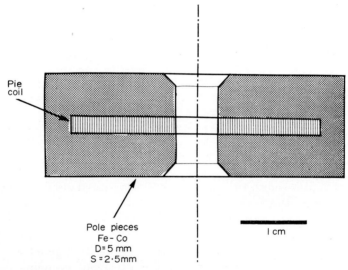

FIG. 9. A ribbon-wound shrouded solenoid ("pie coil") (After Schulhof (1967).)

3. *"Trapped flux" lenses*

If an external magnetic field is applied parallel to the axis of a long superconducting cylinder no flux lines will initially pass through the bore of the cylinder because of the "shielding" properties of the superconductor. If the flux density at the surface is increased penetration will occur progressively until flux lines have reached the inner surface of the cylinder. Provided external field was being increased at a very slow rate the bore of the cylinder would then slowly be filled with magnetic flux. In practice, the surge of flux through the material at the moment of breakthrough generates sufficient heat to drive the cylinder normal in a flux jump which equalizes the internal and external fields. If the external field continues to increase the process repeats itself and the internal field increases in steps. When the external field is reduced the same "stepping" phenomenon is observed.

This behaviour of superconducting cylinders was used by Kim *et al.* (1963) to demonstrate the validity of a "pinning point" model for a hard superconductor. A typical plot of internal flux density against external flux density is given in Fig. 10. It is seen that some flux remains "trapped" in the cylinder once the external field is removed. In other words, a persistent circulating current has been induced in the walls of the cylinder.

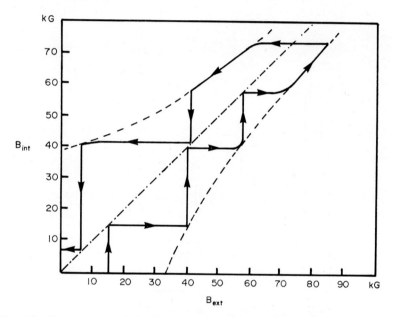

FIG. 10. The variation of the flux density inside a superconducting Nb₃Sn tube (diameter 0·84 cm, wall thickness 0·12 cm) as the external flux density is cycled. Stable states of the system do not exist beyong the "critical state" curves (broken lines). Here, the maximum possible trapped flux density is 40 kG, the maximum flux density that can be completely excluded is 35 kG. (Reproduced with permission from Kim *et al.* (1963).)

The magnitude of maximum trapped flux density that may be obtained can be calculated using the theory outlined by Kim but this is strictly only valid for superconducting cylinders with a high ratio of length to diameter, which is a geometry that is rarely required for electron lenses.

Boersch *et al.* (1966, 1966/67) have used flux trapped in a super-conducting cylinder for electron optical imaging. They placed the cylinder on the axis of a conventional iron lens and were able to trap some of the flux produced by it. Figure 11 shows a simple version of this type of lens. The niobium cylinder trapped flux up to a flux density of 700 G which gave a focal length of 27 mm at a beam voltage of 35 kV. A more sophisticated lens using NbZr cylinders (Fig. 12) achieved a focal length of 4·3 mm at 40 kV with a cylinder of length 3·5 mm, outside diameter 10 mm and inside diameter 3·5 mm.

Kawakatsu *et al.* (1968) used a stack of superconducting discs to trap flux generated by a superconducting coil. The discs were manufactured

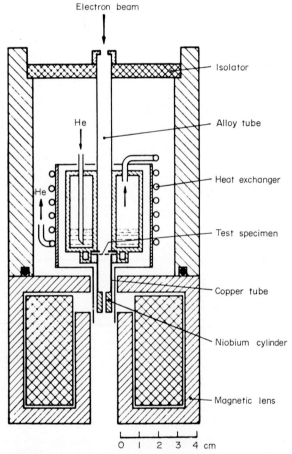

Fig. 11. A "trapped flux" lens with a conventional iron lens providing the external magnetic field. (Reproduced with permission from Boersch *et al.* (1966).)

from Nb$_3$Sn ribbon and a series of concentric rings were etched into the superconductor to ensure that the transport current flow was rotationally symmetric. The presence of a Hastelloy substrate and stabilizing layers of silver reduced the average critical current density of the stack but enhanced its stability against flux jumps as compared with a homogeneous cylinder of superconducting material.

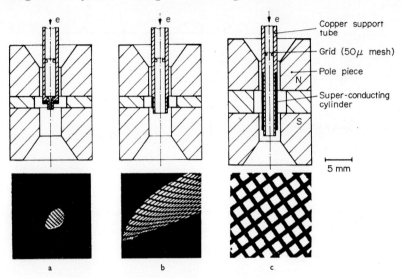

FIG. 12. A 50 μm mesh grid imaged with flux trapped in a superconducting cylinder. (Reproduced with permission from Boersch *et al.* (1966/67).)

The disc stack and the superconducting solenoid which generated the external field were both placed within the iron circuit (Fig. 13). The iron thus played a dual role in that it formed the pole pieces of the magnet that generated the external field and acted as a shrouding material for the disc stack itself. Peak trapped flux densities of the order of 25 kG were achieved and the corresponding distribution half-width was approximately 2 mm. A lens having these parameters would be suitable for operation with beam voltages of about 150 kV and would have a figure of merit of 1·3.

Optical tests were carried out in an electron microscope with the lens at low excitation and the astigmatism observed was not large in comparison with that generally encountered in conventional lenses. Similar work has been reported by Berjot *et al.* (1970).

The basic advantage of the trapped flux lens over the solenoid lens is that the superconducting cylinder can be made perfectly rotationally symmetric while the solenoid cannot be. However, if the trapped flux

lens is to be free of astigmatism the flux pinning points must be distributed evenly through the trapping cylinder. Little is known about
variations in pinning point density in a superconductor and so it is
impossible to predict how large the departures from rotational symmetry will be at high excitations.

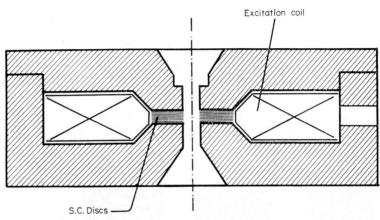

FIG. 13. "Trapped flux" lens using a stack of superconducting annuli to trap flux
produced by a superconducting coil. (Courtesy of Prof. B. M. Siegel, Cornell University.)

A major drawback in the use of these lenses is that it is difficult to
change their strength once the flux has been trapped. Kawakatsu *et al.*
(1968) described how they tried to focus their lenses by changing the
microscope accelerating voltage, which is clearly only feasible if the
microscope is very well-aligned, and by using an additional focusing
coil. Another disadvantage is that the overall dimensions of the lens
unit will tend to be somewhat greater than those of other types because
of the need to generate high fields external to the trapping cylinder
itself.

B. *Lenses with Pole Pieces*

1. *Iron pole pieces*

The superconducting lens design which is the least technically
demanding is one which incorporates a superconducting coil in a conventional iron circuit. Levinson *et al.* (1965) have designed and built
an elegant liquid helium cryostat which can be used to cool the windings
of a lens while the iron circuit remains at room temperature. The work
of Bonhomme and Laberrigue (1969) demonstrated that the electrical
and mechanical stability of a lens of this type were good enough to
allow the attainment of a resolution which was comparable with that

of a good conventional lens. While this achievement did not represent any advance in electron optical quality, it was a step towards integrating cryogenic equipment, with all its sources of vibration and electrical disturbance, into a high resolution microscope without degrading the quality of its performance.

Trinquier and Balladore (1968, 1970) have built and tested a lens with superconducting windings and an iron circuit (Fig. 14). During tests the complete lens was immersed in the liquid helium bath. It was designed to be operated as a "saturated" lens and flux densities of 36 kG are obtained with a total of 64 000 ampere-turns excitation. No figures were given for the distribution halfwidth but, operating with a 3 MV beam voltage, $f = 9\cdot8$ mm, $C_s = 4\cdot5$ mm and $C_c = 6\cdot6$ mm. (The corresponding figures for an optimum Glaser type distribution limited to a maximum axial flux density of 18 kG are $f = 21$ mm, $C_s = 6\cdot5$ mm and $C_c = 12\cdot9$ mm.)

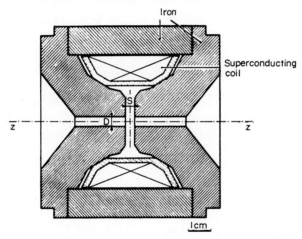

FIG. 14. Superconducting lens with iron pole pieces for operation under conditions of magnetic saturation. (Reproduced with permission from Trinquier and Balladore (1968).)

Trinquier *et al.* (1969) have also experimented with superconducting cylinders placed within the bore of the lens to reduce the width of the flux density distribution.

2. Rare earth metal pole pieces

Bonjour and Septier (1967a,b, 1968) have pioneered the use of the rare earth metals holmium and dysprosium as pole piece materials in electron microscopy. These elements have higher saturation flux densities than iron or even cobalt steel but they only become ferro-magnetic at very low temperatures. Details of their magnetic properties are listed in Table V.

TABLE V

Properties of high saturation ferromagnetic materials

Material	T_c (°K)	$B_s–H$ (kG)
Holmium	20	31
Dysprosium	85	29
Cobalt steel $(Fe_{0.5}Co_{0.5})$	—	24
Iron	1043	22

It seemed natural then that these materials should be used in a super-conducting lens. Simple pole pieces taking the form of truncated cones were constructed and tested. Figure 15 shows a typical lens with dysprosium pole pieces and its flux density distribution. The yoke of the magnetic circuit was made from cobalt steel. Although the perme-ability of dysprosium is not very high at high flux densities ($\mu \sim 5$ when $B = 30$ kG) it is sufficient to raise the peak flux density far above the level that could be achieved with iron pole pieces.

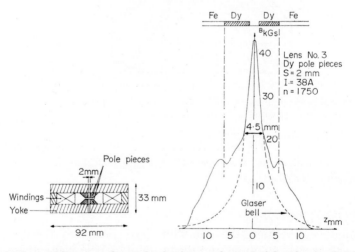

FIG. 15. Lens with rare earth metal pole pieces and a typical flux density distribution curve. (Reproduced with permission from Bonjour and Septier (1967a).)

The secondary peaks in the distribution occur at points on the axis near the dysprosium-cobalt steel interface and could be caused either by a small gap in the magnetic circuit or simply by the permeability mis-match. In either case the effect could be reduced by careful design. It is clearly difficult to estimate the performance of the lens in terms of the Glaser model. Bonjour (1969) proposed a model for the distribution which consisted of a central bell-shaped function

$$B_z = \frac{B_1}{1+\left|\dfrac{z}{d}\right|^n} + B_2$$

with a triangular "wing" on either side. He calculated the cardinal elements and important aberration coefficients for a lens with holmium pole pieces (D = 2 mm, S = 1–8 mm, B_o = 35–60 kG) over a range of beam voltages between 1 and 4 MV. Table VI shows the best values for C_s for four beam voltages (and corresponding values of C_c, f) as taken from the published graphs.

TABLE VI

Electron optical parameters of optimally excited electron lenses with rare earth pole pieces. (S = 5 mm, D = 2 mm, holmium)

V(MV)	B_o(kG)	C_s(mm)	C_c (mm)	f (mm)
1	40	1·2	2·3	3·6
2	50	1·8	3·2	5·2
3	60	2·4	4·4	7·0
4	60	2·7	4·5	7·2

Comparing these figures with those given in Table II for a conventional lens it is found that in the range 1–4 MV the Bonjour/Septier lens can achieve values of C_s, C_c and f which are smaller by a factor which lies between 2 and 3. (This is only slightly less than the figure of merit of an optimum Glaser-type lens which has the same peak flux density value.)

No electron optical tests have been carried out to date but work is going ahead with an ion optical test system (Bonjour, 1970). There is a possibility that the strong anisotropy of the rare earth metal crystal structure may cause some asymmetry about the optical axis but at the present moment there is no evidence to support or deny this.

The fabrication of the pole pieces themselves appears to present no serious problems although holmium and dysprosium are very soft and liable to deterioration if exposed to the atmosphere for long periods.

3. *Diamagnetic "flux shields"*

In this section we will discuss those lenses in which superconducting materials are used as "flux shields" to shape the flux density distribution. In all the lenses considered no attempt is made to regulate, by external means, the currents induced in the shields. Under these circumstances singly-connected superconducting bodies can be considered, to a first approximation, to consist of a passive diamagnetic material. (See, for example, Lynton (1962).)

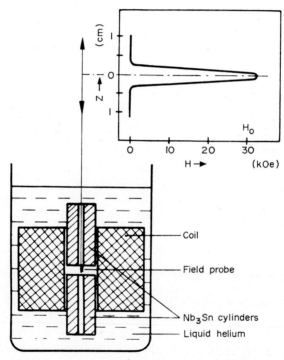

Fig. 16. Sketch of a typical "shielded flux" lens. (Reproduced with permission from Dietrich *et al.* (1967).)

Dietrich *et al.* (1967) were the first to build a lens of this type. It consisted of a superconducting solenoid with two sintered Nb_3Sn hollow cylinders placed on its axis, symmetrically about the centre, as shown schematically in Fig. 16. Although specific figures were not mentioned in this paper it appears that halfwidths of about 2 mm were obtained with a peak flux density of 30 kG. This lens would be suitable for operation with a beam voltage of 250 kV and would have a figure of merit of 1·66.

In the conventional lens the flux density in the gap between the pole pieces will increase if the pole pieces are brought closer together. Exactly the opposite occurs in lenses using diamagnetic shielding. Thus, as we attempt to reduce the flux density distribution halfwidth by decreasing the gap between the shielding cylinders, the value of the peak flux density on the axis falls rapidly if the current through the solenoid is kept constant.

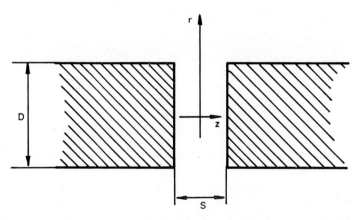

FIG. 17. Model for the calculation of the characteristics of a "shielded flux" lens.

To achieve high peak flux densities and narrow distribution widths the shielding cylinders must be placed close together and subjected to a very intense external magnetic field. The limit is reached when the flux density at the surface of the cylinders is so great that flux penetrates into the bulk of the cylinders as far as the inner wall and breaks through into the bore. The cylinders are then no longer acting as flux shields.

It is not easy to predict the configuration which will make the best electron lens. Hardy (1968) found that by making several sweeping assumptions about the nature of the superconducting material and the form of the flux distribution in the gap, it was possible to obtain a relationship between $(B_o)_{max}$ and d. The argument is as follows.

The magnetostatic potential distribution in the disc-shaped volume between the plane ends of two identical solid cylinders of perfectly diamagnetic material is a solution of the Laplace equation in cylindrical co-ordinates satisfying the boundary conditions $B_z = 0$ at $z = \pm\frac{1}{2}s$ (Fig. 17). This solution takes the form

$$\psi = \sum_{n=0}^{\infty} a_n \sin kz . I_o(kr)$$

where $k = (2n+1)\dfrac{\pi}{s}$, a_n are constants, and $I_o(kr)$ is the zeroth order

Bessel function of imaginary argument. Assuming that the first term of the series is dominant then

$$B_z(r, z) = B_o \cos\frac{\pi z}{s} I_o\left(\frac{\pi r}{s}\right),$$

and the distribution halfwidth is thus

$$d = s/3.$$

If the cylinders are $2a$ in diameter and the flux density at their outer surfaces is B_e, then

$$B_o \approx \frac{B_e}{I_o\left(\dfrac{\pi a}{s}\right)}.$$

These results will also apply to the case of the two hollow cylinders, if the bore is small.

To obtain an estimate of the magnitude of B_e that the shielding cylinder can withstand we use the flux penetration equation due to Kim et al. (1963). The flux density in the bore of a hollow infinitely long cylinder B_i is related to the external flux density B_e in the following way:

$$(B_i + \beta)^2 = (B_e + \beta)^2 - 0\cdot 8\pi\alpha(a - R),$$

where α, β are constants of the superconductor, a is the outer radius of the cylinder and R is the bore radius. It follows that the maximum external flux density that can be applied to the cylinders without flux breakthrough is

$$(B_e)_{\max} = (\beta^2 + 0\cdot 8\pi\alpha t)^{\frac{1}{2}} - \beta$$

where $t = a - R$, the wall thickness. Hence the maximum value of B_o for a particular lens design is

$$(B_o)_{\max} = \frac{(\beta^2 + 0\cdot 8\pi\alpha t)^{\frac{1}{2}} - \beta}{I_o\left(\dfrac{\pi a}{s}\right)}.$$

This gives a direct relationship between $(B_o)_{\max}$ and d. Figure 18 shows the results for shielding cylinders with a bore diameter of 2 mm. The values of α and β were taken to be $6 \cdot 10^6$ kG A cm^{-2} and 5 kG respectively following the work of Kim *et al.* (1963) on some typical Nb_3Sn samples.

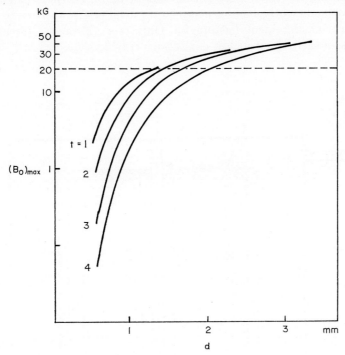

FIG. 18. Characteristic B_0-d curve for a model "shielded flux" lens. (Reproduced with permission from Hardy (1968).)

In spite of the crude approximations made, this approach produces results which compare well with measurements of Dietrich *et al.* (1969, 1970) who have reported that with cylinders of dimensions $a = 4$ mm, $R = 1$ mm, $s = 3$ mm, flux densities of 40 kG were obtained with halfwidths of 2·1 mm. A schematic diagram of the actual lens is shown in Fig. 19. Such a lens would be suitable for use at beam voltages of 285 kV and would have a figure of merit of 2·2.

The same authors have also carried out tests on a model lens in an electrolytic tank to determine the effect of construction errors. They simulated the effect of flux penetration by modifying the shape of the superconducting cylinders (Fig. 20). The conclusions were that the lateral relative displacement of the cylinders should not exceed 1 micrometer and that the angle between the coil axis and the axis of the cylinders should not exceed $5 \cdot 10^{-5}$ radians if the theoretical resolution was to be achieved.

While it may well be possible to obtain this accuracy when aligning the lens mechanically there is some doubt as to whether the sintered Nd_3Sn is sufficiently homogeneous in its magnetic properties to make this form of alignment meaningful. Only crude electron optical tests have been carried out at low excitations (12·7 kG).

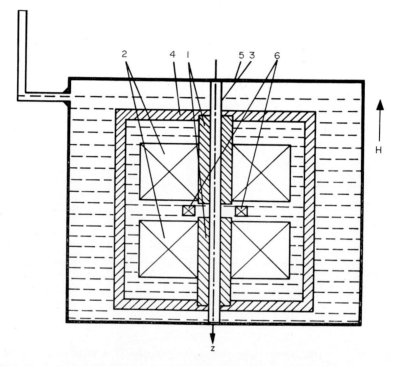

Fig. 19. A "shielded flux" lens with additional external shielding. (1. shielding cylinders; 2. superconducting coils; 3. beam tube; 4. outer shielding; 5. helium container; 6. stigmator and deflection system.) (Reproduced with permission from Dietrich *et al.* (1969).)

Recently Dietrich and Koller (1971) have developed a computer program which used a relaxation technique to predict the flux density distribution in an axially symmetric lens. The program takes account of flux penetration by allowing the current density distribution through the volume of the material of the shielding cylinders to follow the Kim-Hempstead relationship

$$|j \times H| = \text{constant.}$$

Early results showed good agreement between calculation and experimental measurements.

When using trapped field lenses, great care must be taken to avoid flux jumps in the superconductor when increasing the current through the coil, as a considerable quantity of magnetic energy would have to be dissipated should a flux jump occur. This means that the lens has to be run up to full strength over a period of minutes, and fast changes of excitation are not possible.

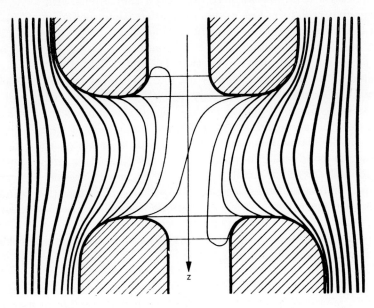

FIG. 20. An electrolytic tank determination of the magnetic flux distribution in a misaligned "shielded flux" lens. (Reproduced with permission from Dietrich *et al.* (1969).)

V. CONCLUSIONS

A. *Future Prospects in Electron Microscopy*

Before any lens design can be seriously considered for use in an electron microscope three important questions must be answered satisfactorily. These are:

1. Does the lens, in theory, have better optical characteristics than a conventional lens would have in the same circumstances?

2. Is the promised improvement in the theoretical resolving power useful?

3. Can this theoretical resolving power be achieved regularly in practice?

On the evidence that is currently available the first question is easily answered. With the superconducting materials at present in use superconducting lenses are generally not competitive with conventional lenses when beam voltages are of the order of 100 kV or less and k^2 values lie below 3. For 100 kV lenses having multiple foci ($k^2 > 3$), which we have not discussed in this review, the prospects are marginally better. Siegel et al. (1966) have calculated that a lens with $k^2 = 25\cdot8$, having five real foci, has a spherical aberration coefficient 12% less than that of the optimum conventional lens.

At higher beam voltages the superconducting lenses begin to offer real advantages. We have seen that Dietrich et al. (1969) have constructed a "shielded flux" lens with a 2·2 figure of merit suitable for use with a beam voltage of only 280 kV. As the operating voltage increases the figure of merit increases slowly, reaching a level of 3·5 at 4 MV for the shrouded solenoid lens of Genotel et al. (1967a,b). It seems unlikely that much improvement will be made on these figures unless superconducting materials with markedly better critical current characteristics become available.

Superconducting lenses designed for special applications (for example, lenses with large bores and long working distances) are in a separate class. It is unlikely that a superconducting lens will have better optical properties than the "optimum" conventional lens but it is probable that it will be easier to build.

We now turn to the question of whether these improvements in lens performance were valuable in terms of better resolution. If the resolution of a microscope is limited by the spherical aberration of its objective lens C_s, then the limit of resolution is

$$\delta = k_1 C_s^{\frac{1}{4}} \lambda^{\frac{3}{4}}$$

where λ is the electron wavelength and k_1 is a constant of the order of unity. A lens with a figure of merit of 4 will then only have a resolution which is 40% better than a conventional lens.

If, on the other hand, an electron microscope is used to observe thick specimens in which a large number of electrons undergo inelastic collisions, the resolution can be limited by the chromatic aberration of the objective lens. In that case

$$\delta = k_2 C_c^{\frac{1}{2}} \left(\frac{\Delta V}{V}\right)^{\frac{1}{2}} \lambda^{\frac{1}{2}}$$

where k_2 is a constant and ΔV is a measure of the width of the energy distribution of the electrons after passing through the specimen. Here it is seen that a figure of merit of 4 will reduce the value of δ by a factor of two.

Up to the present there has been some progress towards demonstrating that the promised improvements in resolving power can be achieved in practice. Bonhomme and Laberrigue (1969) showed that a superconducting lens can perform as well as a conventional lens. Genotel *et al.* (1971) have built a 400 kV microscope which incorporates five superconducting lenses. These results show that it is possible to integrate a highly complex piece of cryogenic engineering into the column of the electron microscope without causing serious deterioration of its electrical and mechanical stability. However, in both cases the lenses used have been of such a design that they are subject to the same iron saturation limitation as conventional lenses and so striking improvements in resolution cannot be expected at present.

The electron lens designer is still confronted with two major difficulties if he requires higher resolution than can be obtained with iron lenses. The first difficulty is that there is little information available about the microstructure of the basic materials used in superconducting lens construction. The homogeneity of the superconductors and exotic pole piece materials is almost certain to have an influence on the axial symmetry of the magnetic flux and consequently on the quality of the lens itself. Secondly, these "ironless" designs will not lend themselves to incorporation in a microscope in quite the same way as their iron counterparts and the task of ensuring good mechanical stability may be more difficult.

These problems are not easily overcome. The present design of the electron microscope has already taken many years to evolve and so it would seem that much painstaking work still has to be done before the advantages of a superconducting lens are fully realized.

Acknowledgements

I wish to thank Associated Electrical Industries for providing financial support for the collection of much of the material included in this review. I am most grateful to Dr. V. E. Cosslett, Dr. P. W. Hawkes and the staff of the Electron Microscopy Section of the Cavendish Laboratory for their generosity in allowing me to make use of their research facilities. I am also indebted to Professor B. M. Siegel and my colleagues in the Applied Physics Department of Cornell University for their advice and assistance with the many practical problems encountered in the construction of superconducting lenses.

REFERENCES

Abrikosov, A. A. (1957). *Sov. Phys.—JETP*, **5**, 1174.
Amboss, K. and Jennings, J. C. E. (1970). *J. Appl. Phys.* **41**, 1608.
Berjot, G., Bonhomme, P., Payen, F., Beorchia, A., Mouchet, J. and Laberrigue, A. (1970). *Proc. VIIth Int. Conf. E.M.* (*Grenoble*), **2**, 103.
Boersch, H., Bostanjoglo, O. and Grohmann, K. (1966). *Z. Ange. Phys.* **20**, 193.
Boersch, H., Bostanjoglo, O., Lischke, B. (1966/67). *Optik* **24**, 460.
Bonhomme, P. and Laberrigue, A. (1969). *J. Microsc.* (*Paris*) **8**, 795.
Bonjour, P. and Septier, A. (1967a). *C.R. Acad. Sci.* (*Paris*) **264**, 747.
Bonjour, P. and Septier, A. (1967b). *C.R. Acad. Sci.* (*Paris*) **265**, 1392.
Bonjour, P. and Septier, A. (1968). *Proc. IVth Eur. Conf. E.M.* (*Rome*), **1**, 189.
Bonjour, P. (1969). *C.R. Acad. Sci.* (*Paris*), **268**, 23.
Bonjour, P. (1970). *Proc. VIIth Int. Conf. E.M.* (*Grenoble*), **2**, 105.
Chester, P. F. (1967). *Rep. Prog. Phys.* **30**, 561.
Dietrich, I., Weyl, R. and Zerbst, H. (1967). *Cryogenics*, **7**, 179.
Dietrich, I., Pfisterer, H. and Weyl, R. (1969). *Z. Ange. Phys.* **28**, 35.
Dietrich, I., Weyl, R. and Zerbst, H. (1970). *Proc. VIIth Int. Conf. E.M.* (*Grenoble*), **2**, 101.
Dietrich, I. and Koller, A. (1971). Private communication. To be published.
Der-Schwartz, G. V. and Makarova, I. S. (1968). *Radio Eng. Electron. Phy.* **13**, 1100.
Fernández-Morán, H. (1965). *Proc. Nat. Acad. Sci. U.S.A.* **53**, 445.
Fernández-Morán, H. (1966a). *Proc. Nat. Acad. Sci. U.S.A.* **56**, 801.
Fernández-Morán, H. (1966b). *Proc. VIth Int. Conf. E.M.* (*Kyoto*), **1**, 147.
Genotel, D., Laberrigue, A., Levinson, P. and Severin, C. (1967a). *C.R. Acad. Sci.* (*Paris*), **265**, 226.
Genotel, D., Severin, C. and Laberrigue, A. (1967b), *J. Microsc.* (*Paris*), **6**, 933.
Genotel, D., Balossier, G., Severin, C., Girard, M., Homo, J-C. and Laberrigue, A. (1971). *C.R. Acad. Sci.* (*Paris*), **272B**, 1461.
Glaser, W. (1952). "Grundlagen der Elektronenoptik," Springer, Vienna.
Hardy, D. F. (1968). AEI Internal Report.
Kawakatsu, H., Plomp, F. H. and Siegel, B. M. (1968). *Proc. IVth Eur. Conf. E.M.* (*Rome*), **1**, 193.
Kim, Y. B., Hempstead, C. F. and Strnad, A. R. (1963). *Phys. Rev.* **129**, 528.
Kitamura, N., Schulhof, M. P. and Siegel, B. M. (1966). *Appl. Phys. Lett.* **2**, 277.
Kunzler, J. E. (1961). *Rev. Mod. Phys.* **33**, 501.
Laberrigue, A. and Levinson, P. (1964). *C.R. Acad. Sci.* (*Paris*), **259**, 530.
Laberrigue, A. and Severin, C. (1967). *J. Microsc.* (*Paris*), **6**, 123.
Laberrigue, A., Levinson, P., Berjot, C. and Bonhomme, P. (1967). *Ann. de l'Université et de l'ARERS* (*Reims*), **5**, 50.
Le Poole, J. B. (1964). *Proc. IIIrd Eur. Conf. E.M.* (*Prague*), **1** (Appendix), p. 6.
Levinson, P., Laberrigue, A. and Testard, O. (1965). *Cryogenics*, **5**, 344.
Lewin, J. D., Smith, P. F., Spurway, A. H., Walters, C. R. and Wilson, M. N. (1969). Rutherford Laboratory Rep. RPP/A73.
Lowell, J. (1965). *Cryogenics* **5**, 185.
Lynton, E. A. (1962). "Superconductivity," Methuen, London.
Merli, P. G. (1970). *Proc. VIIth Int. Conf. E.M.* (*Grenoble*), **2**, 99.
Merli, P. G. and Valdrè, U. (1968). *Proc. IVth Eur. Conf. E.M.* (*Rome*), **1**, 197.

Montgomery, D. B. (1969). "Solenoid Magnet Design," Wiley-Interscience, New York.

Ozasa, S., Katagiri, S., Kimura, H. and Tadano, B. (1966). *Proc. VIth Int. Conf. E.M.* (*Kyoto*), **1**, 149.

Ozasa, S., Kitamura, N., Katagiri, S. and Kimura, H. (1968). *Proc. IVth Eur. Conf. E.M.* (*Rome*), **1**, 185.

Prior, A. C. (1967). *Cryogenics*, **7**, 131.

Schulhof, M. P. (1967). Thesis, Cornell University, Ithaca.

Siegel, B. M., Kitamura, N., Kropfli, R. A. and Schulhof, M. P. (1966). *Proc. VIth Int. Conf. E.M.* (*Kyoto*), **1**, 151.

Träuble, H. and Essmann, U. (1968). *Phys. Status Solidi*, **25**, 373.

Trinquier, J. and Balladore, J.-L. (1968). *Proc. IVth Eur. Conf. E.M.* (*Rome*), **1**, 191.

Trinquier, J. and Balladore, J.-L. (1970). *Proc. VIIth Int. Conf. E.M.* (*Grenoble*), **2**, 97.

Trinquier, J., Balladore, J.-L. and Murillo, R. (1969). *C.R. Acad. Sci.* (*Paris*), **268**, 1707.

Lorentz Microscopy or Electron Phase Microscopy of Magnetic Objects

R. H. WADE

*Département de Recherche Fondamentale, Laboratoire de Physique du Solide,
Centre d'Etudes Nucléaires de Grenoble, Grenoble, France*

I. GENERAL INTRODUCTION

A. *Aims of This Chapter*

IN classical mechanics the interaction of a charged particle with a static electromagnetic field is given by the Lorentz force expression. The same interaction is described in wave mechanics by a change in the phase of the wave function associated with the particle. In the domain of wave optics similar phase variations are induced in a transmitted wave by a medium of spatially fluctuating refractive index. A variety of techniques enable an image contrast to be obtained in light optical microscopy of phase objects (Françon, 1950). Of these it is the defocusing method which is most readily transposable to the transmission electron microscope. This method, although often used to detect the presence of phase variations, is rarely applied to quantitative measurements in light optical microscopy since other techniques can yield a contrast proportional to the phase variation within the object.

Magnetic structures in thin films were first observed in the transmission electron microscope by this method (Fuller and Hale, 1960a, b; Boersch and Raith, 1959; Boersch et al., 1960, 1961, 1962). It remains the principal technique in use in all branches of electron phase contrast microscopy (Scherzer, 1949; Thon, 1971).

As for its use in imaging magnetic structures it was immediately evident that the technique was extremely sensitive in yielding good contrast even from very small angular deviations undergone by the electron beam within the magnetic sample. The ripple structure characteristic of polycrystalline ferromagnetic films was discovered by this technique although the variations of deflections involved are of the order of 10^{-6} rad, well below the angular resolution usually attainable in the electron Fraunhofer diffraction image. By way of comparison we remark that the Bragg angles for crystalline diffraction from metals are of the order 10^{-2} rad and the total Lorentz deflection undergone by a 100 kV electron beam in passing through a 500 Å thick iron film is of the order 10^{-4} rad.

In addition several interesting magnetic configurations such as domain wall structures and flux lines in type II superconductors have dimensions well above the resolution limit of the electron microscope. Domain wall widths are typically of the order $10^{2}-10^{4}$ Å whilst even a modest modern electron microscope is capable of resolutions around 20–30 Å be it in the hands of a yet more modest operator. This allowed high hopes for achieving direct experimental measurements of structures until then restricted to the theoretical domain.

This optimism stimulated a large number of experimental investigations especially of domain walls. In the interpretation of these experiments two distinct approaches were made. Either one had faith in the simplicity of a geometrical optical interpretation (Fuchs, 1962; Suzuki et al., 1968; Wade, 1962, 1966) or one opted for the rigour of a full wave optical calculation (Hothersall, 1969; Cohen, 1967; Wohlleben, 1967). And never the twain met.

Since then a certain amount of effort has been made to establish a formal link between these two extremes and to define criteria allowing one to decide just when a geometrical approach is valid and when it is necessary to use wave optics to interpret the image contrast (Wohlleben, 1966, 1967; Cohen, 1967; Cohen and Harte, 1969; Guigay and Wade, 1968).

Whatever the theoretical interpretation involved the justification of Lorentz microscopy is in attempts to make quantitative measurements of phase variations within the object from the corresponding image contrast. A magnetic object represents perhaps the simplest type of phase object which we find in electron microscopy. The interaction between an electron and a magnetic field is a simple elastic process and the electron deflections are so small that the electron microscope acts as a perfect image transfer system. If then it turns out to be impossible to make quantitative measurements of these objects it is unlikely that we will be more successful in other domains of electron phase microscopy.

It is for these reasons that we feel justified to present fully in the present article the theory of image contrast in the defocused mode. We describe the interaction of a magnetic field and an electron, ignoring spin dependent effects, and subsequently develop the contrast theories of the defocused mode in such a way that the relation between geometrical and wave optics becomes apparent. It is important to remark that our discussion of the validity conditions of geometrical optics applies in the *coherent* case. The effects of partial coherence and incoherence on image contrast are not treated explicitly in this chapter. We will endeavour throughout to emphasize the connections between Lorentz microscopy and phase contrast microscopy in general.

In no way do we attempt to give a detailed description of experimental techniques and results nor to discuss certain interesting recent developments such as the problem of measurement of weak objects, the use of holographic methods, the prospect of high voltage microscopy, two dimensional wall structures, the practise of optical diffraction. Many of these topics are treated in review articles (Grundy and Tebble, 1968; Wade and Guigay, 1969; Wohlleben, 1971; Wade, 1971) or are the subject of recent papers (Olivei, 1969, 1971; Harrison and Leaver, 1972; Kappert et al., 1972).

B. *Notions of Resolution*

The simplest notion of the resolution capabilities of an aberration free optical system, such as a telescope and optical or electron

microscopes, is concerned with the use of a system of finite aperture Γ
to observe two independent self-luminous point sources separated by
the distance ρ. Diffraction of light within the optical system limits
the minimum resolvable separation to a value $\imath$ given by the radius
of the Airy disc associated with the image of each point source. In the
limit of small apertures and for an object space of refractive index
$n = 1$ we have $\imath \simeq 0\cdot6\lambda/\Gamma$; λ is the wavelength of the illumination. This
expresses the condition that the first intensity minimum in the image
of one point falls on the central maximum of the image of the other
point (Born and Wolf, 1964). The two points are resolved if $\imath/M \leqslant \rho$;
M is the magnification of the system.

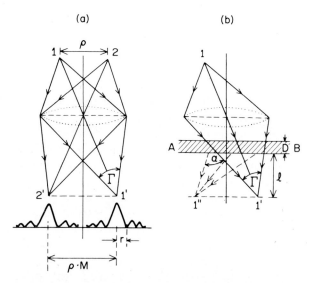

Fig. 1. (a) Two incoherent point sources 1 and 2 separated by a distance ρ are imaged
by a lens into two Airy discs of radius r separated by a distance ρM. If $\rho M > r$ the
images are resolved. (b) A uniform magnetic field in the region AB below the lens
deviates the electron beam through the angle α. As the field varies from $H = 0$ to
$H = H$ the image of source 1 scans across from 1′ to 1″. These two images are resolved
if $\Delta\Phi > hc/e$.

Consider now an imaginary electron microscope in which we block-off
one source, number 2 in Fig. 1(a), whilst in the region below the lens,
AB in Fig. 1(b), we place a coil system allowing a uniform magnetic
field H to be applied perpendicular to the optical axis in a region of
limited thickness D.

When $H = 0$ the image of the source 1 falls on 1′. With the field
applied, the image scans across to 1″ under the influence of the Lorentz

force exerted on the electron beam by the field. The distance $1'1'' = \alpha\ell$ where the angular deflection of the beam in the field region is given by $\alpha = (e/hc) \cdot \lambda DH$. In this expression, $-e$ is the electron charge, h is Planck's constant and c is the vacuum velocity of light. The approach outlined in the previous paragraph predicts the spot separation to be detectable if $1'1'' > \imath$. From this inequality we obtain the resolution conditions $\Delta\Phi > hc/e$ where $\Delta\Phi$ is the flux quantity $D \cdot \delta \cdot H$ and $\delta = \Gamma\ell$ is the diameter of the field region illuminated by the beam. We find then the rather remarkable result that the condition necessary for resolution of a magnetic flux is that the quantity $\Delta\Phi$ be large compared to the flux unit $hc/e = 4 \times 10^{-7}$ gauss cm². The two quantities λ and ρ familiarly involved in the notion of point resolution play no direct part if we are concerned with the detection of a magnetic flux.

This somewhat academic example shows that the notion of resolution of magnetic structures may turn out to be rather different to the concepts of resolution with which we are more accustomed. We will see later that the inequality found above is especially applicable to the case of Fraunhofer diffraction.

Another consequence of the above discussion is to emphasize the need for extremely low variations of magnetic fields within an electron microscope being used for high resolution observations. The stray flux variations must be such that the resulting image shift $1'1''$ be less than the resolution limit r. This implies that the flux variations in the objective lens region must satisfy the inequality $\Delta\Phi < hc/e$.

C. *Notions of Image Formation*

Everyone who has some knowledge of geometrical optics is familiar with the ray tracing process by which a lens can be considered to form an image. In Fig. 2 the points O_1 and O_2 of an object placed a distance u in front of a lens are imaged into the points O_1' and O_2' a distance v behind the lens. The magnification of the image is given by $M = v/u$. In the focal plane a distance f behind the lens all the rays diffused through an angle θ are focused into a point $P(\theta)$ a distance $s = f\theta$ from the optical axis OO'.

A wave optical treatment of this same process is given by the Abbe theory of image formation. The effect of the object on an incident plane wave is described by the object transmission function $h(x)$. The image of this function $h(x)$ can be considered to be formed by a two stage process. The first stage is a spectral decomposition of the object function in the focal plane of the lens. This is described

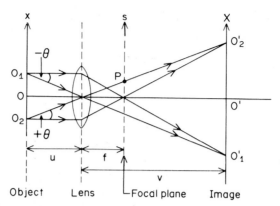

FIG. 2. Ray diagram for the imaging of two object points O_1 and O_2 into O'_1 and O'_2. Rays diffused through the angle θ in the object are focused at P in the focal plane a distance f behind the lens. The distance of P from the axis OO' is $s = f\theta$.

mathematically by the Fourier transform $\tilde{h}(s_1)$ of the object function where $s_1 = s/\lambda f$:

$$\tilde{h}(s_1) = \int_{-\infty}^{+\infty} h(x) \exp(i2\pi s_1 x) \, . \, \mathrm{d}x$$

The intensity $\tilde{h}\tilde{h}^*$ is the familiar diffraction image of the object. The image function $h(X)$ is given by another Fourier transform:

$$\tilde{h}(-X) = \int_{-\infty}^{+\infty} \tilde{h}(s_1) \, . \, \exp(-i2\pi s_1 x) \, . \, \mathrm{d}s_1 = h(x).$$

These expressions are correct only to within constant multiplying and constant phase factors. The expression for $h(-X)$ shows the image to be inverted and magnified by M since $X = M \, . \, x$. This result can be established by three successive applications of the Fresnel-Kirchoff diffraction integral, equation (24), to calculate the wave function in the lens plane, in the diffraction plane and finally in the image plane. It must be remembered that the lens multiplies the incoming wave by a phase factor of the form $\exp(-i2\pi\eta^2/2\lambda f)$, where η is a variable in the plane of the lens. This describes the transformation by the lens of an incident plane wave into an outgoing convergent spherical wave.

The aberrations of the lens can be accounted for by multiplying the diffraction amplitude $\tilde{h}(s_1)$ by a phase term of the form $\exp(-i2\pi W(s_1)/\lambda)$. The function $W(s_1)$, called the wave aberration, takes account of the distortion from the ideal spherical form of the convergent wave coming from the lens. In an electron lens of cylindrical symmetry the principal defect which cannot be corrected is that due to spherical aberration characterized by the constant C_s. In addition an off-focus image has a defocusing aberration. In the presence of these two aberrations the total wave aberration has the form:

$$W(s_1) = (C_s \lambda^4 s_1^4/4) + (z\lambda^2 s_1^2/2).$$

The modified diffraction amplitude becomes:

$$\tilde{h}_1(s_1) = \tilde{h}(s_1) . \exp(-i2\pi W(s_1)/\lambda).$$

The modified image function $h(X)$ is now somewhat complicated as it is given by the convolution of $h(X)$ with the Fourier transform of $\exp(-i2\pi W(s_1)/\lambda)$.

If the object diffuses the incident beam through very small angles, $\theta = \lambda s_1$, the modified image function is considerably simplified. As we will see later for $\theta < 10^{-4}$ rad, the spherical aberration term, function of θ^4, is much smaller than the defocusing term, itself a function of θ^2. In this case the modified image function is given to within constant amplitude and phase factors by:

$$h_1(X) = \int_{-\infty}^{+\infty} h(u)\exp(i2\pi(x-u)^2/2\lambda z) \, \mathrm{d}u.$$

The right-hand side of this equation is the Fresnel-Kirchoff integral relating the wave amplitude in a plane a distance z from the object to that in the object. In the image plane this expression is modified simply by the magnification factor M. For this reason we will always ignore the optical system and merely calculate defocused images in the object space. This situation is much simpler than the image transfer in the case of atomic resolution when the spherical aberration term is important (Lenz, 1971; Hanszen, 1971).

In the Abbe theory outlined above it is important that the object and image points be close to the optical axis and that the lens aperture is sufficient to accept all the rays diffused by the object.

II. The Interaction of an Electron with a Magnetic Field

A. *The Classical Lorentz Force*

A stationary electromagnetic field is represented by two vector quantities the electrostatic field $\mathbf{U}$ and the magnetic field $\mathbf{B}$ defined respectively by a scalar and a vector potential, V and $\mathbf{A}$, according to the relations:

$$\mathbf{U} = -\nabla V; \; \mathbf{B} = \nabla \times \mathbf{A}.$$

The movement of an electron of charge $-e$ and velocity v in the electromagnetic field is obtained from the Lagrangian equations:

$$\mathrm{d}\mathbf{P}/\mathrm{d}t = \mathrm{d}L/\mathrm{d}\mathbf{r}, \tag{1}$$

9

where the Lagrangian function L in the non-relativistic realm of Newtonian mechanics is $L = mv^2/2 + eV - (\mathbf{v} \cdot \mathbf{A})e/c$, and the generalized momentum is $\mathbf{P} = \delta L/\delta \mathbf{r} = m\mathbf{v} - (e/c)\mathbf{A}$. Substitution of these expressions for $\mathbf{P}$ and L in equation (1) gives the classical Lorentz force equation (de Broglie, 1950; Landau and Lifchitz, 1965).

$$\text{Force} = \mathrm{d}(m\mathbf{v})/\mathrm{d}t = -e(\mathbf{U} + (1/c)\mathbf{v} \times \mathbf{B}). \tag{2}$$

The energy of the electron in this electromagnetic field is given by $E = \mathbf{P} \cdot \mathbf{r} - L = (mv^2/2) - eV$. The form of this equation shows that only the electric field can do work on the electron. A static magnetic field cannot change the magnitude of the velocity of the electron but only its direction.

It is interesting to remark that the invariance of equation (2) under time reversal requires the transformations:

$$t \to -t; \quad \mathbf{U} \to \mathbf{U}; \quad \mathbf{B} \to -\mathbf{B}.$$

These transformations leave the scalar electrostatic potential unchanged whilst the vector potential changes sign, signifying that a given trajectory is reversible only if the field direction is also reversed. This property can be used to distinguish the magnetic or electrostatic origin of contrast in electron images. Inverting an electron microscope specimen is equivalent to the transformation $t \to -t$; if the image contrast is reversed it has a magnetic origin (Wohlleben, 1971).

B. *The Semi-classical Approximation to the Schrödinger Equation*

The behaviour of an electron wave in the presence of a magnetic field $\mathbf{B}(\mathbf{r})$ and an electrostatic field $\mathbf{U}(\mathbf{r})$ is described by the time independent Schrödinger equation in the form:

$$\left\{ \frac{1}{2m} \left(\frac{\hbar}{i} \mathbf{V} + \frac{e}{c} \mathbf{A} \right)^2 - (E + W) \right\} \psi = 0. \tag{3}$$

The vector potential $\mathbf{A}$ is defined by $\mathbf{B} = \mathbf{V} \times \mathbf{A}$; the electrostatic scalar potential V is defined by $\mathbf{U} = -\mathrm{grad}\ V$ whilst the potential energy function $W = eV$: the electron mass and charge are respectively m and $-e$; $\hbar = h/2\pi$ where h is Planck's constant; c is the velocity of light; E is the total electron energy; ψ is the electron wave function.

In the usual W.K.B. approximation applied to one dimensional problems it is supposed that the equation (3) has solutions of the form $\psi = \exp(iS/\hbar)$, where S can be expanded in the power series (Landau and Lifchitz, 1966):

$$S = S_0 + (\hbar/i)S_1 + (\hbar/i)^2 S_2 + \text{etc.}$$

Note that as $\hbar \to 0$ the wave function takes the form $\Psi = a \cdot \exp(iS_0/\hbar)$, where the total phase $S/\hbar$ is very large and the amplitude $a = \exp(S_1)$. This leads us to seek a solution of first order in $\hbar$ having the form $\Psi = a \cdot \exp(iS_0/\hbar)$. Substitution of this form for Ψ in equation (3) yields the following two equations for the real and imaginary parts separately equated to zero:

$$\left(\nabla S_0 + \frac{e}{c} . \mathbf{A}\right)^2 = \{2m(E + W) + \hbar^2 \nabla^2 a/a\} \tag{4}$$

$$\frac{1}{2m}\left\{a\nabla^2 S_0 + 2\nabla a . \left(\nabla S_0 + \frac{e}{c}\mathbf{A}\right) + a . \frac{e}{c} . \nabla . \mathbf{A}\right\} = 0 \tag{5}$$

The real part, equation (4), can also be written in the form:

$$\left(\nabla S_0 + \frac{e}{c} . \mathbf{A}\right)^2 = p^2\left(1 + \lambda^2 \frac{\nabla^2 a}{a}\right) \tag{4'}$$

where $\mathbf{p} = m\mathbf{v}$ is the classical electron momentum and λ the de Broglie wavelength. In the second term on the right the quantity $(\lambda^2 \nabla^2 a/a)$ represents, to within a numerical factor, the mean variation of the amplitude a within a region of dimension λ about a point (x, y, z). If $(\lambda^2 \nabla^2 a/a) \ll 1$ then this term can be neglected. The inequality is satisfied if the mean variations of a within distances comparable to the wavelength λ are small compared to the amplitude a itself. The inequality cannot be satisfied near the edge of a geometric shadow nor in the focal region of a lens where the amplitude is a rapidly varying function of position.

In the regions where the inequality $(\lambda^2 \nabla^2 a/a) \ll 1$ holds equation (4') becomes:

$$\nabla S_0 = \mathbf{p} - \frac{e}{c} . \mathbf{A} \tag{6}$$

This equation is identical to the solution of the classical Hamilton-Jacobi equation for the action S_0 of a particle of charge $-e$ in an electromagnetic field.

Equation (5) can be rewritten more concisely as:

$$\mathbf{\nabla} . \left(a^2\left(\nabla S_0 + \frac{e}{c} . \mathbf{A}\right)/m\right) = 0 \tag{7}$$

Since $a^2 = \Psi\Psi^*$ is the probability density for the presence of a particle and $\mathbf{p}/m = \mathbf{v}$ is the classical velocity of the same particle the equation (7) can be considered to have a direct physical significance as the continuity equation for the particle current density.

The solution to the Hamilton-Jacobi equation (6), yields the classical electron trajectories. The current flow is locally delimited by the tube of adjacent trajectories which cut the surface elements $d\Sigma_0$, $d\Sigma_1$, shown in the Fig. 3. The equation (7) describing the conservation of current can be integrated within a volume limited by a surface σ comprising the trajectory tube and the facets $d\Sigma_0$ and $d\Sigma_1$. The integral takes the form $\int a^2(\mathbf{n}.\mathbf{v})\,d\sigma = 0$ where $\mathbf{n}$ is a unit vector normal to the surface σ. On the side surfaces of the tube $\mathbf{n}.\mathbf{v} = 0$ whilst on $d\Sigma_0$ and $d\Sigma_1$, supposed normal to the current flow, we have $\mathbf{n}.\mathbf{v} = v$. This leads us to the expression:

$$a_1 = a_0\left(\frac{v_0}{v_1}.\frac{d\Sigma_0}{d\Sigma_1}\right)^{\frac{1}{2}} \tag{8}$$

in which a_0, v_0 are the amplitude and velocity on $d\Sigma_0$ and a_1, v_1 the same on $d\Sigma_1$ (Durand, 1970).

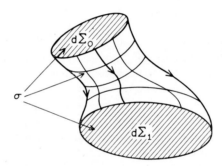

FIG. 3. The classical particle trajectories form a current tube flowing perpendicularly across the surfaces $d\Sigma_0$ and $d\Sigma_1$. The total current is conserved within the surface σ.

Starting from a reference surface of known a_0, chosen if possible such that a_0 is constant, we can use (8) to obtain a_1 for all other points. The probability density for the presence of a particle $|a_1|^2$ is inversely dependent on v_1 and $d\Sigma_1$. In a region where a particle is brought to rest $|a_1|^2 \to \infty$. Similarly if $d\Sigma_1 \to 0$, as on an envelope of a family of classical trajectories (caustic surfaces and focal points) $|a_1|^2$ also tends towards infinite values. It is evident that in all such regions the semi-classical approximation is not applicable since the amplitudes calculated from the Schrödinger equation (3) without any approximations will always have a finite value.

In the case of a pure electrostatic potential, $\mathbf{A} = 0$, $V = V(\mathbf{r})$, we obtain for equation (6) the solution $S_0 = \int (2mE.\{1 + W/E\})^{\frac{1}{2}}.\,dl$ where the integral is taken along the classical electron trajectory. The solution so obtained forms the basis of the "phase grating" theory of electron diffraction (Cowley and Moodie, 1957) and gives the object phase function used in the theory of the contrast transfer characteristics of the electron microscope (Lenz, 1971; Hanszen, 1971).

When $V = 0$ and $\mathbf{A} \neq 0$ equation (6) yields $S_0 = \int \left(\mathbf{p} - \frac{e}{c} . \mathbf{A} \right) . d\mathbf{l}$ where the integral is again taken along the classical electron trajectory. This expression forms the basis of the theory of electron image contrast formation for magnetic objects. Note that the expression holds for any charged particle upon replacement of $-e$ by the appropriate charge.

Whether the object be electrostatic or magnetic the respective image contrast theories are different aspects of a general theory of phase contrast. Indeed many imaging techniques in electron microscopy are but transpositions of well established light optical techniques such as strioscopy, Zernicke phase contrast, Foncault contrast, zone plates and defocusing contrast.

C. *The Magnetic Phase Object*

We now consider the interaction of an electron beam with a ferromagnetic film of thickness D. The magnetic field is defined by $\mathbf{B} = 0$ above and below the film whilst $\mathbf{B} = 4\pi\mathbf{M}_s$ within the film of saturation magnetization $\mathbf{M}_s$.

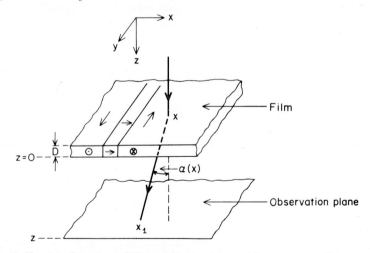

FIG. 4. Showing the set-up of the coordinate system with respect to a film containing a one dimensional magnetic structure such as a domain wall. An electron impinging on the film at x is deviated through the angle $\alpha(x)$ and intersects the image plane at x_1.

Stray fields H arising from $\mathbf{V}.\mathbf{M}_s \neq 0$ within the film are not them-selves confined to the film. For the present we ignore such fields which are usually, but not always, unimportant in calculating image contrast.*

For simplicity we limit our discussion to one dimensional structures of infinite extent in the y direction, see Fig. 4. Magnetic domain walls and flux lines in type II superconductors are essentially of this type. In calculating the image contrast it will only be necessary to consider the variation of the y component of the magnetization vector as a function of the x coordinate. We can suppose that $B_x = B_z = 0$, and $B_y = B_y(x)$. The magnetic vector potential can be defined in the following way:

above and below the film: $\quad \mathbf{A} = 0$

within the film: $\qquad\qquad A_x = A_y = 0,\ A_z = \int B_y(x).\mathrm{d}x \quad \Big\}\quad (9)$

The vector potential so defined is not unique. Other possible defini-tions $\mathbf{A}'$, are related to $\mathbf{A}$ by a gauge change of the form $\mathbf{A}' = \mathbf{A}+\nabla f$ where f is an arbitrary scalar function of the coordinates. Any physically measurable quantity is invariant under such a gauge change; for example we find that $\Psi' = \Psi \exp(i2\pi f.e/hc)$, $\mathbf{B}' = \mathbf{B}$, $\mathbf{v}' = \mathbf{v}$. This led to the vector potential being erroneously considered as devoid of any direct physical significance and as being merely a mathematically convenient means of defining the magnetic field (Aharanov and Bohm, 1959).

As an illustration the reader can readily verify that a field $B_y = B$ is equally well defined by the vector potential $A_x = A_y = 0$, $A_z = B.y$ as by $A'_x = 0$, $A'_y = -B.z/2$, $A'_z = B.y/2$. In this case the two vector potentials are related by $\mathbf{A}' = \mathbf{A}+\nabla(B.y.z)$.

We take the z direction to coincide with the initial direction of the electron trajectories; the set-up of the coordinate system with respect to the object is shown in Fig. 4. Using the vector potential defined in equation (9) we integrate equation (6) to find S_0:

above the film $S_0 = p.z$

within the film $S_0 = z.(p+(e/c)\int_0^x B_y(x)\,\mathrm{d}x)$

below the film $S_0 = p.(z^2+(x-x_1)^2)^{\frac{1}{2}}+(e/c).D.\int_0^x B_y(x)\,\mathrm{d}x$

$\qquad\qquad\qquad\qquad\qquad\qquad\qquad\qquad\qquad\qquad\qquad (10)$

The direction of the beam is given by $\nabla S_0/p$. The difference in directions above and below the film gives the angular deflection

---

* In the determination of the exact two dimensional form of the Fraunhofer diffraction image it is essential to take account of these stray fields, otherwise, as shown by Wade (1968), we are led to false conclusions concerning the possibility of distinguishing struc-tures such as Bloch and Néel type domain walls.

$\alpha(x) = DeB_y(x)/mvc$. This corresponds to the deflection calculated directly using the classical Lorentz force equation (2).

We now need to calculate the amplitude $a(x_1, z)$ which is given by equation (8) (with $v_0 = v_1$) in the one dimensional form $a(x_1, z) = a_0(dx/dx_1)^{\frac{1}{2}}$. The ratio dx/dx_1 is obtained using the classical trajectories below the film defined by the solutions for S_0 found in equation (10). By reference to Fig. 5 we see that:

$$dx_1 = dx + z.(\text{slope } CD - \text{slope } AB)$$
$$= dx.\lambda z.d^2S_0/dx^2 \tag{11}$$
$$a(x_1, z) = a_0.(\lambda z.S_0'')^{-\frac{1}{2}}.$$

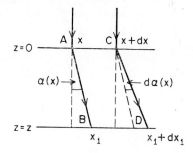

FIG. 5. The difference in deflection $d\alpha(x)$ between adjacent electron trajectories separated by dx at the specimen gives rise to the amplitude term of equation (11) in a plane a distance z below the film.

At the exit surface of the film, $z = 0$, the amplitude can be taken to be constant and equal to the incoming plane wave amplitude $a_0(x, 0)$. This follows from consideration of the electron deflections within the film backed up by the experimental observation that the in-focus image shows no contrast. The complete wave function at the exit surface, given by

$$\psi(x, 0) = a_0(x, 0).\exp(i2\pi.(e/hc).D.\int_0^x B_y(x)\,dx) \tag{12}$$

is such that the intensity is indeed constant in this plane. To obtain an image contrast it is necessary to observe an off-focus plane a distance z above or below the object where the complete semi-classical expression for the wave function is given by:

$$\psi(x_1, z) = a(x_1, z).\exp(iS_0(x_1, z)./\hbar).$$
$$= \psi_0.(\lambda z S_0'')^{-\frac{1}{2}}.\exp(i2\pi\left(\frac{(x-x_1)^2}{2\lambda z} + \frac{e.D}{hc}.\int_0^x B_y(x).dx\right) \tag{13}$$

where ψ_0 is the incident plane wave $a_0\exp(i2\pi z/\lambda)$.

Note that in the presence of the vector potential the direction of the classical trajectories is no longer orthogonal to the wave fronts since $\mathbf{p} = \nabla S + (e/c)\mathbf{A}$. This in no way effects the expressions obtained above which do not attempt to follow the rays in detail through the magnetic film. The wave amplitude (11) is found by a ray tracing procedure only in the regions above and below the film where $\mathbf{A} = 0$; here $\mathbf{p} = \nabla S_0$ so that the geometrical rays are perpendicular to the wave fronts.

The usual wave mechanical boundary conditions at the entry and exit surfaces of the film ensure that the total electron current is conserved. Since our treatment makes direct use of the continuity equation (7) to calculate the local amplitudes of the wave function along the classical trajectories the conservation of the total current is automatically ensured.

The magnetic phase term $(e/hc).\int \mathbf{A}\, dz$, which appears in terms of the local magnetic field in equations (10), (12) and (13), is independent of the electron wavelength and thereby of the accelerating potential of the incident electron beam. The electrostatic phase shift has been shown in Section II(B) to depend on $(E)^{-\frac{1}{2}}$.

D. *The Aharanov and Bohm Effect*

The phase terms in the wave functions deduced in the previous section represent the solutions to the expression $S_0 = \int (\mathbf{p} - (e/c).\mathbf{A}).d\mathbf{r}$ for the passage of an electron wave through a magnetic film. We consider now the somewhat different circumstance of an interference experiment shown schematically in Fig. 6. Two coherent electron beams coming from the same point source situated at P_0 recombine at P after having followed the two different trajectories 1 and 2. Their mutual interference at P is determined by the phase difference $\Delta S_0/\hbar$ between the two rays. The total phase along each ray being given by $S_0/\hbar$ we find,

$$\Delta S_0/\hbar = (2\pi\Delta\ell/\lambda) - (2\pi e/hc).\left(\int_1 \mathbf{A}.d\mathbf{r} - \int_2 \mathbf{A}.d\mathbf{r}\right).$$

The last embracketed term on the righthand side is the circulation $\oint d\mathbf{r}.\mathbf{A}$ which by Stokes' theorem can be rewritten $\int d\mathbf{S}.\mathbf{B}$ where $\mathbf{B}$ is the magnetic field and $d\mathbf{S}$ is a surface element directed perpendicular to the plane of the Fig. 6. The phase difference is now,

$$\Delta S_0/\hbar = 2\pi(\Delta\ell/\lambda - (e/hc).\Phi). \tag{14}$$

The first term on the righthand side is the geometrical path length difference between the two rays whilst the second term is proportional to the total magnetic flux Φ enclosed between the two trajectories. The mathematical form of the magnetic phase difference in equation (14) does not require the electron trajectories to pass through the field region itself. The field **B** may be entirely confined to the interior of a solenoid C placed between the two rays so that the electron trajectories are not directly influenced by any magnetic field from the solenoid. Aharanov and Bohm (1959,1961) showed that a modification of the magnetic field in the solenoid will change $\Delta S_0/\hbar$ through the flux variation $\Delta\Phi$, producing a shift of the interference fringes, observed in the plane AA', by the distance $\Delta\Phi . \delta/(hc/e)$ where the fringe periodicity is δ. The essential features of this magnetic phase shift had in fact previously been derived by Franz (1940) and by Ehrenberg and Siday (1949).

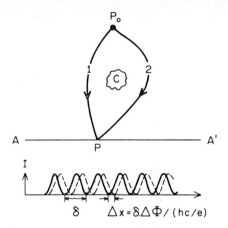

FIG. 6. An interference experiment in which electrons emitted by a point source P_0 follow the trajectories 1 and 2 to interfere at P in the plane AA'. A flux change $\Delta\Phi$ within a region C between the beams shifts the interference fringes of period δ by a distance $\Delta x = \delta . \Delta\Phi/(hc/e)$.

The experimental verification of this remarkable effect by Chambers (1960) and by Bayh (1962) proves beyond any doubt that the vector potential **A** is as physically "real" as the field **B** which it defines.

As for the magnetic structures with which we are mainly concerned in this article, the experimental situation is generally such that the electron beam *does* intersect the field region. We have already seen that in such a case the classical Lorentz force and the wave mechanical treatment predict identical deflections of the electron beam. Even so there are many examples where a classical explanation fails to account

even qualitatively for the experimental results. We give a brief
description of three examples.

1. *Interference fringes in domain wall images*

Figure 7 shows a situation in some ways rather similar to that just
treated. The distinction is that the electrons emitted by the source P_0
are actually deviated in opposite senses as they pass through the
magnetic field of the domains on either side of a wall O in a thin ferromagnetic film AB. The converged beams overlap in the region $P_1'P_2'$
below the film. Clearly the interference fringes formed in this region
must be treated as a wave phenomenon. One is tempted to compare the
situation with that of the Fresnel biprism, Fig. 7(b), in which the
interference can be supposed to be due to the path difference between
the waves coming from the two virtual sources P_1 and P_2 to combine
at the point P' in the observation plane. The fringe separation δ is given
by $\delta = \lambda(z+z_0)/2z_0\alpha_0$, where α_0 is the electron beam deflection. The
measured values of δ in fact agree well with this expression.

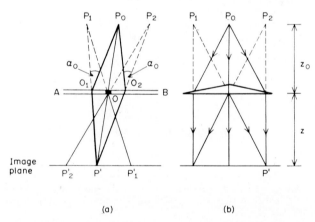

(a)   (b)

FIG. 7.(a) Ray diagram for interference in a magnetic domain wall image. (b) The
Fresnel biprism of classical light optics. In (a) the phase difference between rays P_0O_1P'
and P_0O_2P' is due solely to the enclosed flux term of equation (14).

Boersch *et al.* (1962) showed the defect of this explanation to lie in
the fact that the position of the virtual sources is independent of the
wall position O; it depends only on the position of the real source P_0,
the deflection α_0 and the value of z_0. The fringes should then always be
aligned parallel to the projection onto the image plane of the perpendicular
bisector of the line joining P_1P_2. Experiment shows the fringes to follow
the local wall direction always with a constructive interference fringe

at the centre of the wall image. This is illustrated in Fig. 8 which is a defocused image of a thin permalloy film.

In a correct wave optical interpretation it is the phase difference between the paths $P_0 O_1 P'$ and $P_0 O_2 P'$ which must determine the interference at P'. It is possible to show that in the approximation of small deflection angles there is no difference in the geometrical path lengths of the two rays. The phase difference must then come from the enclosed flux term of equation (14). The points O_1 and O_2 equidistant from O, have both a phase lag of $2\pi(e/hc)\int_0^{\Delta x} B_y(x)\,\mathrm{d}x$ with respect to O; $\Delta x = OO_1 = OO_2$. The two rays passing through these points therefore always arrive in phase at P', the centre of the wall image. This maximum and the other interference maxima are then fixed in position relative to the wall image and by projection back to the object plane they are also fixed with respect to the wall itself. This explanation then correctly accounts for the experimental observations since, in addition the fringe separation is found to be exactly that of the biprism interpretation.

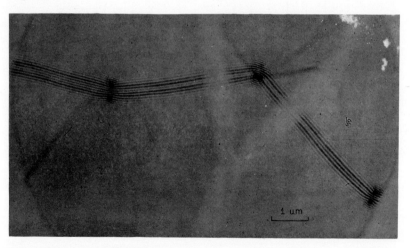

Fig. 8. Interference fringes in the image of a magnetic domain wall in a permalloy film. Note that the fringes follow the wall as it bends and that the central fringe is always dark although of varying contrast. The photograph is in negative contrast.

In reality there is a three beam interference in the converging wall image, the two rays passing through the domains interfere with a ray passing through the wall region. Although the central fringe is always a maximum its intensity relative to the other maxima depends on the difference in phase between the ray from the wall, $P_0 O P'$ in the figure, and the two side rays. This phase difference, varying with the defocusing distance, depends on the exact wall model.

2. *Fraunhofer diffraction images from periodic magnetic structures*

Consider the one dimensional periodic variation of magnetic field shown in Fig. 9(a) which corresponds approximately to the structure found in a uniaxial material such as cobalt. Classically the transmitted beam is deflected through the angle $+\alpha_0$ and $-\alpha_0$; Fig. 9(b). This gives two distinct diffraction images centred on the reciprocal lattice points $s = \pm\alpha_0/\lambda$ with a mismatch between the diffraction maxima of each system of $\Delta s = (2\alpha_0/\lambda - n/a)$, where n is the integral number of diffraction maxima between the two image centres; see Fig. 9(c).

In the wave picture the field distribution of Fig. 9(a) gives the phase

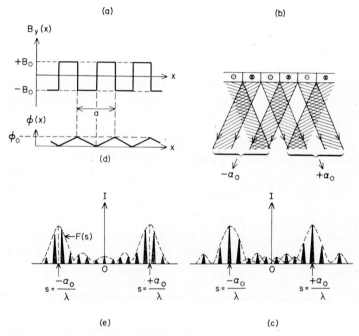

FIG. 9.(a) The magnetization distribution in a one dimensional periodic structure of period a. (b) The classical electron deflections due to this structure give rise to two amplitude modulated beam systems propagating along $+\alpha_0$ and $-\alpha_0$. (c) The geometrical diffraction image of (b) is a mismatched superposition of the images from the two systems centred at $+\alpha_0/\lambda$ and $-\alpha_0/\lambda$. (d) The phase structure corresponding to the magnetization distribution (a). (e) The correct wave optical diffraction image consists of a single system of discrete maxima of separation $s = 1/a$ centred on the origin $s = 0$ with relative intensities given by the envelope $F(s)$, which itself has principal maxima at $s = \pm\alpha_0/\lambda$.

structure shown in Fig. 9(d). The diffraction image is a single series of discrete maxima centred on the origin within the envelope $F(s)$ whose maxima are situated at $s = \pm\alpha_0/\lambda$. This explanation is in good agreement with experimental images, an example of which is shown in Fig. 10 (Wade, 1967; Goringe and Jakubovics, 1967).

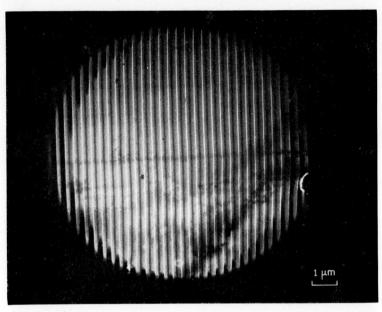

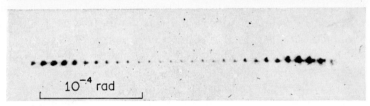

Fig. 10.(a) Image of a cobalt foil whose magnetic structure is approximately that of Fig. 9(a). (b) The Fraunhofer diffraction image shows discrete maxima corresponding to the schema 9(e).

3. Fraunhofer diffraction from a discontinuous film

Consider now the case of a discontinuous film uniformly magnetized in the y direction Fig. 11(a). The film can be supposed to be formed of a regular island structure of period a with a gap of width $(b-a)$ between the crystallites. That this is a very much simplified picture of a real island film does not effect the essential result.

Classically the situation is simply that part of the incident beam passes through the crystallites and is deflected through the angle $\alpha_0 = (e/hc).D.B.\lambda$; the rest passes through the gaps and is undeflected. The Fraunhofer diffraction image will consist of two maxima separated by the angle α_0.

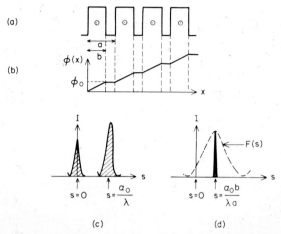

FIG. 11.(a) Columnar crystallites in a discontinuous uniformly magnetized magnetic film. (b) The corresponding phase structure. (c) The "geometrical" Fraunhofer image of (a). (d) The wave optical Fraunhofer image of the phase structure (b).

Wave optically the structure constitutes the phase grating shown in Fig. 11(b). This can be regarded as a periodic modulation of the phase about a mean slope of $\alpha_0 b/\lambda a$. The full calculation (Wade, 1968) shows there to be a single principle diffraction maximum at the angle $a_0 b/a$. The other diffraction maxima coming from the periodicity of the structure are almost entirely suppressed since $(b-a) < a$; the form factor $F(s) \simeq 0$ at the positions $s = (\alpha_0 b/\lambda a) \pm n/a$. This agrees with the experimental result that the deflection is proportional to the density of such an island film (Ferrier and Wade, 1964), which can often be considered as being made up of adjacent columnar crystallites (Wade and Silcox, 1967).

III. CALCULATION OF THE IMAGE INTENSITY

A. *The Huygens-Fresnel Principle*

Consider a constant phase surface σ a distance r_0 from a point source at P_0. The spatial part of the wave function $\psi(\mathbf{r}_0)$ at each point on the surface has the form $\psi(\mathbf{r}_0) = A(\mathbf{r}_0)\exp i\phi(\mathbf{r}_0)$.

The disturbance at a point P, Fig. 12, can be calculated according to the Huygens' principle by considering each element $d\sigma$ of σ to act as a secondary source of coherent spherical wavelets with a maximum intensity normal to the initial wave surface.

$$d\psi(P) = A \cdot \frac{\exp(ikr_0)}{r_0} \cdot \frac{\exp(iks)}{s} K(\chi)\, d\sigma \tag{15}$$

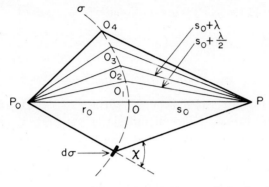

FIG. 12. The light intensity at P due to the point source P_0 can be obtained by summing the contributions of the spherical wavelets from elements $d\sigma$ of the equi-phase surface σ. The Fresnel zone construction considers separately the surface elements OO_1, O_1O_2, ... O_nO_{n+1} where $O_nP = OP + n\lambda/2$.

In (15) the terms $1/r_0$, $1/s$ ensure the satisfaction of the basic photometry law that the intensity varies as the inverse square of the distance from a point source.

The coefficient K depends on the wavelength and the angle χ. In fact the Huygens-Fresnel formula is valid only for small χ.

The total wave at P is obtained by integrating the equation (15) over the spherical surface σ. The integral is carried out by the use of the Fresnel zone construction. We mark off points on σ, O, O_1, $O_2 \ldots O_n$ in Fig. 12, such that the path differences $(OP - O_1P) \ldots (O_nP - O_{n+1}P)$ are all equal to $\lambda/2$.

The radius of the nth Fresnel zone is given by $R_n = \sqrt{n\lambda(1/r_0 + 1/s_0)^{-1}}$ which reduces to $R_n = \sqrt{n\lambda s_0}$ for $r_0 \gg s_0$. If both r_0 and s_0 are large compared with λ the inclination factor K can be supposed to have a constant value K_n across each zone. The contribution of the nth zone is:

$$\psi_n(P) = 2i\lambda(-1)^{n+1} \cdot K_n \cdot A \cdot \frac{\exp(ik(r_0 + s_0))}{(r_0 + s_0)}$$

The total effect obtained by summing over all zones is found to be:

$$\psi(P) = i.\lambda.K_1.A.\frac{\exp(ik(r_0+s_0))}{(r_0+s_0)} = \frac{1}{2}\psi_1(P) \tag{16}$$

This remarkable result shows the total disturbance to be just one half that of the first zone alone. It is valid when the phase varies as a quadratic function of the coordinates.

Since the function $\psi(P)$ is given directly by $\psi(P) = A\dfrac{\exp(ik(r_0+s_0))}{(r_0+s_0)}$

we find that $K_1 = \exp(-i\pi/2)/\lambda$.

B. *Kirchoff Diffraction Integral*

Equation (15) integrated over the surface of an arbitrary aperture constitutes the Fresnel-Kirchoff diffraction integral. Kirchoff showed this integral to be an approximate solution of a homogeneous wave equation the spatial part of which satisfies the time independent Helmholtz wave equation:

$$(\nabla^2+k^2)\psi = 0 \tag{17}$$

The integral theorem of Helmholtz and Kirchoff allows the wave function ψ to be obtained for any point P in the field in terms of the values of ψ and $\partial\psi/\partial n$ on S an arbitrary closed surface surrounding the point: $\partial/\partial n$ denotes differentiation along the inward normal to the surface.

$$\psi(P) = \frac{1}{4\pi}\int_S\left\{\psi.\frac{\partial}{\partial n}\left(\frac{\exp(iks)}{s}\right) - \frac{\exp(ikS)}{s}.\frac{\partial\psi}{\partial n}\right\}dS. \tag{18}$$

In equation (18) s is the distance from P to a point (x, y, z) on the surface. For a detailed demonstration of this formula consult Born and Wolf (1964).

C. *The Diffraction Theory*

In Fig. 13 we consider an arrangement corresponding to a certain diffraction experiment in which a monochromatic wave emitted by a point source P_0 passes through the opening A in a plane screen DD'. The opening is supposed large compared to the wavelength of the illumination but small compared to the distances r_0 and s_0.

The total integral (18) over a closed surface surrounding P, the observation point, is made up of the sum of the integrals over the opening A, over the shadow side of the screen B and of the part C of a large sphere of radius R_0 centred at P. The Kirchoff boundary conditions to be applied to equation (18) are:

$$\left. \begin{array}{ll} \text{on } A \colon \psi = \psi_0(r) = A \cdot \dfrac{\exp(ikr)}{r}; & \dfrac{\partial \psi}{\partial n} = A \cdot \dfrac{\exp(ikr)}{r}\left\{ik - \dfrac{1}{r}\right\} \cdot \cos(n,r). \\[3mm] \text{on } B \colon \psi = 0 & \dfrac{\partial \psi}{\partial n} = 0 \end{array} \right\} \quad (19)$$

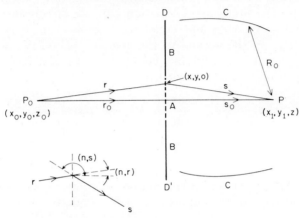

FIG. 13. The diffraction arrangement used in the derivation of the Fresnel-Kirchoff formula (20).

The contribution from the spherical surface C is supposed to be zero. Substitution of (19) into (18) yields the familiar form of the Fresnel-Kirchoff diffraction formula:

$$\psi(P) = -\frac{iA}{2\lambda} \cdot \int_A \mathrm{d}S \cdot \frac{\exp(ik(r+s))}{r \cdot s}\left\{\cos(n,\,r) - \cos(n,\,s)\right\} \quad (20)$$

Note that this formula is symmetric with respect to the source and observation point. A point source at P_0 produces the same effect at P as an equivalent source at P would produce at P_0. This is the Helmholtz reciprocity theorem.

D. Fraunhofer and Fresnel Diffraction

Usually we are not concerned with diffraction by a simple aperture but by an object which may impose variations of both amplitude and phase on the transmitted wave. In general any such object can be described by a transmission function $h(x, y) = \psi(x, y)/\psi_0(x, y)$ where the disturbance in the reference plane (x, y, O) is ψ_0 in the absence of the object and ψ in the presence of the object. If arg $h = 0$ we call the object an amplitude object whilst if $|h| = 1$ for all points we have a phase object. Usually it is convenient to take the reference plane to be the exit surface of the object.

In addition we can describe an object of limited dimensions in the (x, y, O) plane as the product of an aperture function $B(x, y)$ and an illimited object function $f(x, y)$. In this case $h = B.f$.

For aperture diameters much smaller than r and s the inclination factor $(\cos(n, r) - \cos(n, s))$ of equation (20) can be considered as constant over the aperture and equal to $2 \cos \delta$ where δ is the angle between PP_0 and the normal to the aperture plane. We also replace the slowly varying multiplying factor $1/r.s$ by the constant value $1/r_0.s_0$. Equation (20) now becomes:

$$\psi(x, y, z) = -\frac{A.i.\cos \delta}{\lambda.r_0.s_0} \int_A h(x, y)\exp(ik(r+s)) \, dS. \qquad (21)$$

Reference to the Fig. 13 shows that:

$$(r+s) = \{(x_0-x)^2+(y_0-y)^2+z_0^2\}^{\frac{1}{2}}+\{(x-x_1)^2+(y-y_1)^2+z^2\}^{\frac{1}{2}}.$$

If the maximum lateral dimension of the aperture is $(x^2+y^2)^{\frac{1}{2}}_{max} = b$ then consideration of the expression for $(r+s)$ above shows that if,

$$b \ll \left\{\lambda\left(\frac{1}{z_0}+\frac{1}{z}\right)^{-1}\right\}^{\frac{1}{2}} \qquad (22)$$

the formula (21) can be written in the much simplified form:

$$\psi(x_1', y_1', z) = C_1\int_S dS.h(x, y).\exp\left\{ik\left\langle x\left(\frac{x_1}{z}+\frac{x_0}{z_0}\right)+y\left(\frac{y_1}{z}+\frac{y_0}{z_0}\right)\right\rangle\right\}. \qquad (23)$$

This is the case known as Fraunhofer diffraction.

If the inequality (22) is reversed the quadratic terms in $(r+s)$ cannot be ignored and we have the case of Fresnel diffraction described by the formula:

$$\psi(x_1, y_1, z) = C_2\int_S dS.h(x, y).\exp\left\{\frac{ik}{2}\left(\frac{1}{z_0}+\frac{1}{z}\right).\left((x-x_1)^2+(y-y_1)^2\right)\right\}. \qquad (24)$$

C_1 and C_2 in formulae (23) and (24) are constants.

The right-hand side of the inequality (22) is nothing more than the radius of the first Fresnel zone discussed in Section III(A). We thus find a very simple condition for determining the nature of the diffraction in a given problem. If the first Fresnel zone has a diameter greater than that of the object aperture we have Fraunhofer diffraction in which the entire object contributes to the image without any geometrical phase difference. In the case of Fresnel diffraction the object size is greater than that of a Fresnel zone and only a part of the object contributes to the intensity at a given image point.

Note that the equations (23) and (24) allow us to calculate the intensity distribution in any plane provided that the function $h(x, y)$ be known in an arbitrary reference plane. For convenience we usually consider this reference plane to be the exit plane of the object. The means of calculating h in this plane depends on the problem in hand. In the present case it is obtained from the wave function immediately below the object, calculated in Section II(B) by a semi-classical approximation to the Schrödinger equation.

We now simplify somewhat by considering only our one dimensional magnetic objects which from equation (12) can be described by:

$$h(x, y, O) = \exp\{i2\pi . D . (e/hc) . \int_0^x B_y(x) . \mathrm{d}x = \exp(i2\pi\gamma(x)).$$

If in addition we suppose $z_0 \gg z$ the diffraction integrals (23) and (24) can now be written in the form:

$$\psi(x_1, z) = \text{constant} \int_{-\infty}^{+\infty} \mathrm{d}x . \exp(i2\pi . \varphi(x_1, x)) \tag{25}$$

where in the case of Fresnel diffraction by a magnetic object the phase φ is given by:

$$\varphi(x_1, x) = \frac{(x_1 - x)^2}{2\lambda z} + \gamma(x) \tag{26}$$

whilst for Fraunhofer diffraction:

$$\varphi(x_1, x) = \frac{x_1 x}{\lambda f} + \gamma(x) \tag{27}$$

f being the focal length of the imaging lens.

E. The Stationary Phase Approximation to the Diffraction Integral

The stationary phase approximation to the integral (25) consists in remarking that in an integral of this type the principle contribution to the integral comes from the region or regions in the neighbourhood of the stationary phase points x_i for which $\partial\varphi/\partial x_i = 0$. The Taylor expansion of φ around x_i up to the second order is given by:

$$\varphi(x_1, x) = \varphi(x_1, x_i) + \Delta x . \varphi'(x_1, x_i) + \frac{\Delta x^2}{2} . \varphi''(x_1, x_i) + \ldots \tag{28}$$

where $\Delta x = (x - x_i)$.

Since the second term on the right-hand side of equation (28) is zero, the stationary phase approximation to (25) consists of substituting

therein, $\varphi(x_1, x) = \varphi(x_1, x_i) + \dfrac{\Delta x^2}{2} \cdot \varphi''(x_1, x_i)$. This yields:

$$\psi_{\text{S.P.}}(x_1) = \frac{2}{(\lambda z)^{\frac{1}{2}}} \cdot \sum_{x_i} \exp(i2\pi\varphi(x_1, x_i)) \cdot \int_0^\infty dx \exp(i\pi\Delta x^2 . \varphi''(x_1, x_i))$$

The integral in the above expression is put in the form of a standard Fresnel integral $\displaystyle\int \exp(i\pi u^2/2) . du$ by substituting $u = \Delta x . (2\varphi'')^{\frac{1}{2}}$. This gives:

$$\psi_{\text{S.P.}}(x_1) = \frac{\exp(\pm i\pi/4)}{(\lambda z)^{\frac{1}{2}}} \cdot \sum_{x_i} \frac{\exp(i2\pi\varphi(x_1, x_i)}{(\varphi''(x_1, x_i))^{\frac{1}{2}}} \tag{29}$$

where the positive and negative signs hold respectively for $\varphi'' > 0$ and $\varphi'' < 0$. In the case of Fresnel diffraction the wave amplitude is obtained by substituting the expression (26) for φ into equation (29).

$$\psi_{\text{S.P.}}(x_1) = \exp(\pm i\pi/4) \sum_{x_i} \frac{\exp(i2\pi\varphi(x_1, x_i))}{(1 + z\alpha'(x_i))^{\frac{1}{2}}} \tag{30}$$

where x_i is defined by the condition $\varphi'(x_1, x_i) = 0$ to be

$$x_1 = x_i + z . \alpha(x_i). \tag{31}$$

The local deflection of the electron beam is defined by $\alpha(x) = (e/hc)\lambda . D . B_y(x)$. The treatment outlined above is that of Guigay and Wade (1968).

F. *The Classical Intensity*

The geometrical optics treatment follows directly from the relation (31) which defines the classical electron trajectories. An electron passing the point x_i in the specimen is deflected through the angle $\alpha(x_i)$ and intersects the point P in the observation plane with the coordinate (x_1, z) which satisfies the relation (31).

As shown in the Fig. 14 a beam element dx_i at the object plane produces in the observation plane an element of width $dx_1 = dx_i(1 + z . \alpha'(x_i))$. The conservation of current leads to the following expression for the intensity at x_1.

$$\mathscr{I}(x_1) = \frac{I(x_1)}{I_0} = \frac{dx_i}{dx_1} = \mid 1 + z\alpha'(x_i) \mid^{-1} \tag{32}$$

where I_0 is the incident beam intensity.

In general several geometrical trajectories (AP, BP, x_iP) may intersect at the point P. In this case the geometrical optics intensity is found by summing the contributions from each trajectory:

$$\mathscr{I}(x_1) = \sum_{x_i} |\, 1 + z\alpha'(x_i) \,|^{-1}. \tag{33}$$

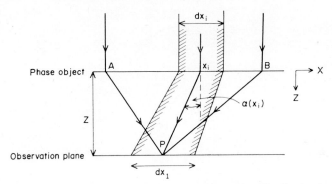

FIG. 14. Illustrating the derivation of the classical intensity distribution in a plane a distance z below a transparent object in which the phase, and consequently the transmitted beam deflection $\alpha(x)$, varies as a function of the position x.

G. Comparison of Different Results

We are now in a position to compare the different results which we have established for the image amplitude or intensity.

First, the diffraction integral in the form of equation (25) is clearly the most exact solution which we have developed. In it we sum over the entire object the intrinsic phase at each point plus the geometric phase due to the path length of the ray from the object to the image point. We see that the semi-classical and stationary phase approximations, equations (13) and (30), give identical expressions for the image wave function. Both are pseudo-classical approximations in that they consider only the contributions of the classical trajectories to the total wave function at each image point. They are more complete than the classical approximation as they give both the amplitude and the phase of the wave function along the trajectory. Two or more intersecting trajectories can thereby interfere through their different phase terms. Where only one ray passes through a given image point the pseudo-classical and the classical treatments predict identical intensities. Both predict infinite intensities whenever $(1 \pm z\alpha'(x)) = 0$, and manifestly cannot be valid in the region of caustic surfaces or focal points where this equality is satisfied.

Any discussion of the pseudo-classical approximations automatically includes classical mechanics, and by analogy geometrical optics, as a special case. Our discussion in Section IV of the validity of a classical interpretation of image contrast will consist of an examination of the validity conditions of the pseudo-classical approximations.

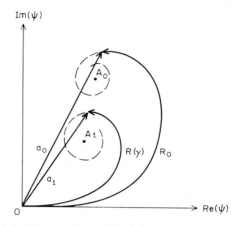

Fig. 15. Amplitude phase construction for the Fresnel integral. The amplitude contributed by the first Fresnel zone is proportional to the radius of the zone. R_0 and $R(\gamma)$ are the zone radii in the absence and presence of the phase object. The complete Fresnel integral gives amplitudes proportional to the lengths OA_0 and OA_1 whilst the values obtained using the first Fresnel zone only are a_0 and a_1 where $a_0 = OA_0/2$ and $a_1 = OA_1/2$. The figure is not drawn to scale.

It is somewhat surprising that the amplitude of the pseudo-classical wave functions, given by $(\lambda z \varphi'')^{-\frac{1}{2}}$ can be written in the form $R(\gamma)/R_0$. According to the stationary phase approximation the width of the Fresnel zone contribution to the intensity at a given image point is R_0 in the absence of the object and $R(\gamma)$ in the presence of the object. In fact a little foresight would have enabled us to predict this result from equation (16), which shows the total wave amplitude to be half that due to the first zone whenever the phase is limited to terms up to the second order. The stationary phase approximation limits the Taylor expansion of φ to just such second order terms. A direct integration of equation (25) or an amplitude-phase construction similar to that of the Cornu spiral (Fig. 15) shows the amplitude contributed to the image by the first zone to be proportional to the radius of the zone.

H. Reduced Parameters in the Image Intensity Equations

The local electron beam deflection in the case of a one dimensional magnetic object is given by:

$$\alpha(x) = \gamma'(x) = (e/hc) . \lambda . D . B_y(x),$$

where $B_y(x)$ is the y component of the magnetic field in the specimen. In the case of a ferromagnetic domain wall aligned along the y axis we can put $B_y(x) = B_0.f(x/w_1)$ where w_1 is the domain wall half width $(2w_1 = w)$, and $B_y(x) = B_0$ for $x \gg w_1$.

The wave and geometrical intensity expressions contain the parameters: λ the electron wavelength; z the off-focus distance (or f the focal length of the imaging lens); D the film thickness; $B_0 = 4\pi M_s$ the film saturation magnetization; w the domain wall width and $f(x/w_1)$ the function describing the normalized wall magnetization distribution.

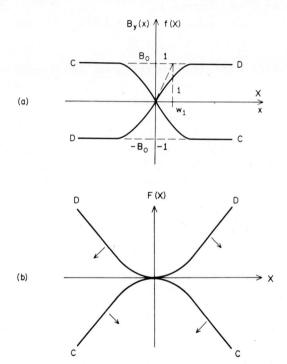

FIG. 16.(a) Magnetization distributions across a diverging wall (D) and a converging wall (C) plotted in terms of $B_y(x)/x$ and $f(x)/x$. (b) The corresponding phase profiles. The arrows show the direction of propagation of the wave fronts.

As in many optical diffraction problems we find that a number of reduced parameters suffice to completely describe the diffraction integral (25) and its various approximate forms. We use the reduced object and image coordinates $X = x/w_1$ and $X_1 = x_1/w_1$ and write the deflection angle as $\alpha(X) = \alpha_0 f(X)$ where $f(X)$, shown in Fig. 16(a), has the properties $f(X) \to 1$ for $|X| > 1$ and $f(O) = 0$. The diffraction integrals become:

Fresnel: $\psi(X_1) = \beta \int_{-\infty}^{+\infty} dX \exp\left(i2\pi\left\{\frac{\beta^2}{2}(X-X_1)^2 + \beta_0^2 F(X)\right\}\right)$ (34)

Fraunhofer: $\psi(X_1) = \beta \int_{-\infty}^{+\infty} dX \exp(-i2\overline{\wedge}\{\beta^2 X . X_1 + \beta_0^2 . F(X)\})$ (35)

The geometrical intensity expression can be written:

$$\mathscr{I}(X) = I(X_1)/I_0 = \beta^2/(\beta^2 \pm \beta_0^2 f'(X).).$$ (36)

These expressions contain only the two reduced parameters $\beta^2 = w_1^2/\lambda z$ and $\beta_0^2 = w_1 . \alpha_0/\lambda$ which together with the wall phase function $F(X) = \int_0^X f(X) . dX$ completely describe the problem. The reduced parameters are therefore extremely useful in all problems of magnetic imaging and in the discussion of the validity of the pseudo-classical approximation. The parameter β_0^2 turns out to be a measure of the number of fluxon units associated with a variation of the magnetization within a magnetic object. The fluxon is $hc/e = 4 . 10^{-7}$ gauss cm². Our parameter β_0^2 is equal to $\Delta\Phi/(2hc/e)$. The inhomogeneity $\Delta\Phi = \Delta x . \Delta(D . B)$ is a flux variation of an arbitrary magnetic field. In the case of a linear domain wall of width w separating two anti-parallel domains of internal field B_0 in a film of thickness D the inhomogeneity is $\Delta\Phi = w . D . B_0$.

IV. VALIDITY CRITERIA FOR THE PSEUDO-CLASSICAL APPROXIMATIONS

A. *Generalities on the Correspondence Limits of Wave Optics and Wave Mechanics*

It is well known that quantum mechanics contains classical mechanics in the limit $h \to 0$ and that in a similar way wave optics reduces to geometrical optics as $\lambda \to 0$. These correspondence limits and the relation between wave optics and wave mechanics can be established by a discussion of the Hamilton Analogy.

In scalar wave optics the wave disturbance satisfying the time independent Helmholtz equation $(\nabla^2 + k^2)\psi = 0$ is given by an expression of the form $\psi = a \exp(i\varphi)$, where a the amplitude and φ the phase are real quantities and $k = 2/\pi\lambda$ is the local wave vector. Substitution of this form for ψ into the Helmholtz equation gives:

$$(\nabla\varphi)^2 = (2\pi n/\lambda_0)^2$$ (37)

where n is the local refractive index, $n = \lambda_0/\lambda$; λ_0 is the vacuum wave length. Equation (37) is the equation of geometrical optics since $\nabla\varphi$ defines the rays which propagate perpendicular to the constant phase surfaces. The equation is valid if n varies slowly on the scale of the wavelength. Equation (37) can also be expressed in terms of Fermat's Principle according to which the geometrical ray is that of the ensemble of possible rays joining two points for which the optical path is minimum. The optical path is the total phase difference $\Delta\varphi$ between the beginning and end of a ray, $\Delta\varphi = (2\pi/\lambda_0).\int n.dl$.

There is a striking similarity between the equation of geometrical optics (37) and the Hamilton-Jacobi equation of classical mechanics in which the action S_0 is given, for stationary electrostatic fields, by:

$$(\nabla S_0)^2 = (\mathbf{p})^2 = 2m(E+W) \tag{38}$$

where we use the same symbolism as in Section II(B). This analogy led Hamilton to remark that the motion of material particles in potential fields is equivalent to the passage of light rays through a medium of variable refractive index.

Comparison of equations (37) and (38) leads to the identity:

$$\varphi = S_0/h \tag{39}$$

where h, Plancks constant, has the dimensions of action. If we suppose that this equality carries over into the wave domain we obtain from equations (38) and (39)

$$\lambda = h/p = h/\{2m(E+W)\}^{\frac{1}{2}}.$$

Substituting this form of λ into the Helmholtz equation yields the stationary, non-relativistic, no spin Schrödinger equation for a particle.

The wave function for the particle can then be expressed in the form $\psi = \exp iS_0/h$. Equation (38) shows the trajectories of the classical particle, given by $\mathbf{v} = \nabla S_0/m$, to be perpendicular to the surfaces of constant phase (or constant S_0) of the wave function.

In the presence of the magnetic vector potential $\mathbf{A}$ the velocity vector is not colinear with the momentum. For an electron of charge $-e$ we have the relation $\mathbf{v} = (\nabla S_0+(e/c).\mathbf{A})/m$. The trajectories are no longer perpendicular to the wave fronts. This situation is similar to the passage of rays through an anisotropic medium in geometrical optics.

The analogy between equations (37) and (38) also allows us to define an electron optical refractive index

$$n = (1+W/E)^{\frac{1}{2}}-\left(\frac{\lambda_0 e}{hc}\right).\mathbf{A}.\mathbf{u}$$

where **u** is a unit vector in the direction of motion and λ_0 is the electron wavelength for $W = 0$, $\mathbf{A} = 0$.

We have established that in the classical limit, $h \to 0$, the Schrödinger equation has solutions of the form $\psi = \exp(iS_0/\hbar)$. The semi-classical or W.K.B. approximation to the Schrödinger equation is more complete in that it considers the first two terms in the expansion of a certain function S as a power series in $(\hbar/i)$:

$$S = S_0 + (\hbar/i)S_1 + (\hbar/i)^2 S_2 + \text{etc.} \ldots$$

Classical mechanics considers only the first term in this expansion. In both the semi-classical and classical approximations the phase term $(S_0/\hbar)$ is a large quantity (this is necessarily so since $\hbar \to 0$) whilst in addition the semi-classical amplitude $a = \ln S_1$ varies only slowly over distances compared to the particle wavelength. The condition $\lambda^2 \nabla^2 a / a \ll 1$ cannot be satisfied in regions where the amplitude varies rapidly as is the case at focal points, near caustic surfaces, or near the edge of a geometrical shadow.

Discussions of these general considerations are to be found in the books by Landau and Lifchitz (1965, 1966), by de Broglie (1950, 1968) and by Messiah (1961) and no doubt in numerous other texts.

In the context of the present article we seek a criterion for determining when the pseudo-classical treatments give a good approximation to the image intensity distributions predicted by wave optics. In this perspective the general considerations outlined above are useful as a guide but cannot offer a direct criterion except in the extreme $h \to 0$.

B. *The Fluxon Criterion*

It is possible to apply the Heisenberg inequality $\Delta x \Delta p_x \geqslant h$ relating the uncertainties in the position of a particle and its lateral momentum to show that the detection of a magnetic flux variation by means of a charged particle is possible classically if

$$\Delta\Phi > hc/|q|$$

where q is the charge of the particle (Wohlleben, 1966).

A simple derivation of this inequality was established in Section I(B) for the case of Fraunhofer electron diffraction.

In the Fraunhofer diffraction condition the impact position x_1 in the observation plane of an electron deflected through an angle α within the object is given by the relation:

$$x_1 = f \cdot \alpha(x) = f \cdot p_x/p_0,$$

where f is the focal length of the imaging lens, and p_0 is the incoming electron momentum which we suppose unchanged by the object for small deflections. A measurement of the impact position x_1 is then equivalent to a measurement of the small lateral momentum p_x which the electron acquires by interaction with the object, see the schema of Fig. 17(a).

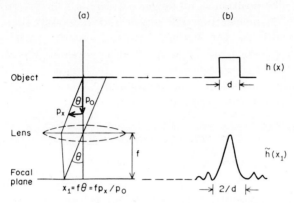

FIG. 17.(a) The impact position x_1 of an electron in the focal plane of a lens is proportional to the lateral momentum of the electron p_x. (b) An aperture of width d has a Fraunhofer image (in the focal plane of a lens) of width proportional to $2/d$.

It is well established that an object function $h(x)$ and its Fraunhofer image function $\tilde{h}(x_1)$ are related by a Fourier transformation,

$$\tilde{h}(x_1) = \int h(x) . \exp(i2\pi x x_1) . dx.$$

This relation implies that the widths of the functions $h(x)$ and $\tilde{h}(x_1)$ cannot be made simultaneously arbitrarily small. The variables x and x_1 have uncertainties whose product is constrained to satisfy a Heisenberg-like relation.

As a simple illustration consider the aperture function of Fig. 17(b) which has a width d, defined by

$$h(x) = 1 \qquad | x | < d/2$$
$$h(x) = 0 \qquad | x | > d/2$$

The Fourier transform of $h(x)$ is given to within a constant factor by

$$\tilde{h}(x_1) = \sin(\pi x d)/\pi x d$$

The aperture corresponds to a measurement of the lateral position of a passing electron with an inherent error $\varDelta x = d$. The momentum distribution $\tilde{h}(x_1)$ occasioned by the position measurement has a spread

$\Delta x_1 = 2/d$, corresponding to $\Delta p_x = 2h/d$. The product $\Delta x . \Delta p_x = 2h$ satisfies the Heisenberg inequality.

The uncertainty relation itself is evidently independent of the mode of observation. However if we consider the case of Fresnel diffraction we find that the relation between position in the object plane and in the observation plane a distance z below the object is given by $x_1 = x + z . \alpha(x)$. The position x_1 no longer corresponds directly to the lateral momentum of the electron. The object and image functions are related mathematically by the Fresnel integral, equation (34), which has different properties to those of the Fourier integral. We can no longer directly apply the uncertainty relation to position measurements of x and x_1. In consequence the relation $\Delta \Phi > hc/e$ cannot serve as a direct criterion in this observation mode.

C. *The Generalized Criterion*

1. *Applications to isolated objects*

We have already remarked that the semi-classical treatment of image contrast presented in Section II(B and C) and the stationary phase approximation to the Kirchoff diffraction integral, Section III(E), predict identical wave functions in the image plane. When only a single classical trajectory contributes to the intensity at a given image point both treatments yield a geometrical optical intensity distribution. We have also established in Section III(G) the reasons for which we need discuss only the validity of the pseudo-classical approximations since if these hold then the classical approximation necessarily holds for uniquely related object and image points.

We give first a qualitative introductory discussion of the Fresnel case for which we have already remarked that the pseudo-classical image amplitude has the form $a(X_1, z)/a_0 = R(\gamma)/R_0$. The incident beam amplitude is a_0. In the presence of a phase object the total phase at a given image point X_1 given by expression (34),

$$\varphi(X_i, X_1) = 2\pi \left\{ \frac{\beta^2}{2}(X_i - X_1)^2 + \beta_0^2 F(X_i) \right\}$$

consists of the β^2 observation condition dependent term and the β_0^2 object dependent term. We recall that X_i is the stationary phase point in the object plane from which comes the main contribution to the total wave at X_1. For a displacement ΔX around the point X_i one or other of the two terms may dominate in its contribution to the total phase variation $\Delta \varphi$. When $\Delta X = R(\gamma)$ the total phase variation is $\Delta \varphi(R) = \pi$.

Consider an arbitrary phase object of limited width d. This object is weak if the intrinsic phase variation across the object $\Delta\gamma$ is small. We write this condition as $\Delta\gamma \ll 2\pi$. The total contribution of the object to the phase variation $\Delta\gamma(R)$ is then necessarily small and consequently $R(\gamma) \approx R_0$, where R_0 the radius of the Fresnel zone in the absence of the object depends uniquely on the β^2 term. The image contrast, defined by $C(X_1) = [I_0 - I(X_1)]/I_0$, becomes for the classical approximation,

$$C(X_1) = (R_0 - R(\gamma))^2/R_0^2.$$

If then $R(\gamma) \approx R_0$ the image contrast is small and in addition is due almost entirely to the imaging condition in the sense that we cannot distinguish the details of one weak phase object from another.

In the case of a strong object, $\Delta\gamma > 2\pi$, it follows that $R(\gamma) < d$ and that $R(\gamma)$ can be sufficiently different from R_0 to give a strong image contrast. It seems intuitively probable that in these circumstances we can distinguish image details finer than the object dimensions. The inequality $R(\gamma) < d$ can be rewritten in the form:

$$\beta^2 + \beta_0^2 F''(X) > 1,$$

which like the total Fresnel phase contains an imaging term β^2 and an object dependent term β_0^2.

Before discussing this inequality in detail we attempt to establish a criterion based on a more quantitative argument. This discussion concerns the validity of the stationary phase approximation.

The total phase φ of the Fresnel diffraction integral expressed in terms of the reduced parameters and normalized co-ordinates is given by (34) as:

$$\varphi(X,\ X_1)) = 2\pi\left\{\frac{\beta^2}{2} \cdot (X - X_1)^2 + \beta_0^2 F(X)\right\}$$

The stationary phase approximation gives for the radius of the first Fresnel zone $R(\gamma) = (\varphi''(X_i))^{-\frac{1}{2}}$. It is this region around the stationary phase point X_i which gives the main contribution to the wave amplitude at the point X_1 in the observation plane. The difference in phase $\Delta\varphi_{\text{S.P.}}$ between the points $(X_i + R,\ X_1)$ and $(X_i,\ X_1)$ is evidently π by definition. The complete phase expression gives the phase difference:

$$\Delta\varphi = \varphi(X_i + R,\ X_1) - \varphi(X_i,\ X_1). \tag{40}$$

If the stationary phase method is a good approximation over the first Fresnel zone:

$$\Delta\varphi \rightarrow \Delta\varphi_{\text{S.P.}} = \pi.$$

Putting $\Delta\varphi = \pi$ and substituting the complete phase expressions found from (34) into (4_0) we obtain:

$$\beta^2 R^2 \pm 2\beta_0^2 \{F(X+R) - F(X) - RF'(X)\} = 1.$$

The upper sign holds for the diverging case the lower for the converging case. We have written R for $R(\gamma)$ and X for X_i. Using the Taylor expansion of $F(X+R)$ and remembering that $F'(X) = f(X)$ we can rewrite this expression in the form:

$$R^2\{\beta^2 \pm \beta_0^2 f'(X)\} \pm \tfrac{1}{3}\beta_0^2 R^3 f''(X) + \text{etc.} = 1$$

The first term on the left-hand side is equal to unity. The equality above will then hold if:

$$|R'| < 1 \tag{41}$$

where $R' = dR/dX = \tfrac{1}{3}R^3 . \beta_0^2 . f''(X)$. The inequality (41) can also be written in the form:

$$\tfrac{1}{3}\beta_0^2 f''(X) < (\beta^2 \pm \beta_0^2 f'(X))^{\frac{3}{2}} \tag{42}$$

This is exactly the form found by Guigay and Wade (1968) by a somewhat different argument. They showed that averaging over a domain wall the condition can be simplified to:

$$\beta^2 \pm \beta_0^2 > 1. \tag{43}$$

(Remember that the mean values across the wall $f'(x) = \alpha_0/w_1$ and $f'' = \alpha_0/w_1^2$ become $f'(X) = f''(X) = 1$ in terms of the normalized co-ordinates). Note that the inequality (43) contains the imaging term β^2

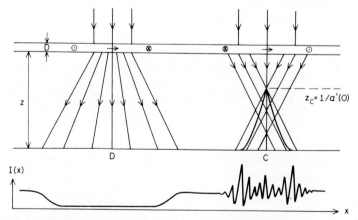

Fig. 18. Ray diagrams for defocused images of magnetic domain walls. Interference fringes occur in the converging image C within the caustic envelope (heavy curve). The caustic cusp is at $z_c = 1/\alpha'(O)$. Geometrical optics is more readily applicable to the diverging image D.

and the object term β_0^2 and is valid for both the Fresnel and Fraunhofer diffraction conditions. Fraunhofer diffraction is just the limiting case of Fresnel diffraction as $\beta^2 \to 0$. Usually we obtain the Fraunhofer condition by letting z approach infinity; this amounts to letting $\beta^2 = (w_1^2/\lambda z)$ approach zero. In this case the inequality (43) reduces to $|\beta_0^2| > 1$ which is exactly the fluxon criterion $\Delta \Phi > hc/e$.

In the Fresnel case the positive sign in (43) holds for a diverging image and the negative sign for the converging image; see Fig. 18 for a schema showing the ray diagrams of such images. We conclude that the diverging case more readily satisfies the inequality and that the geometrical approach will be more readily applicable in this case. This seems intuitively obvious since only one classical ray contributes to the

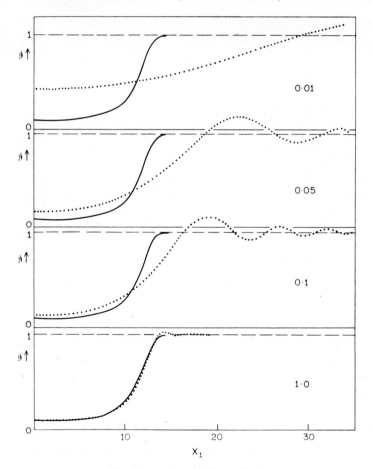

Fig. 19(a)—*See caption overleaf.*

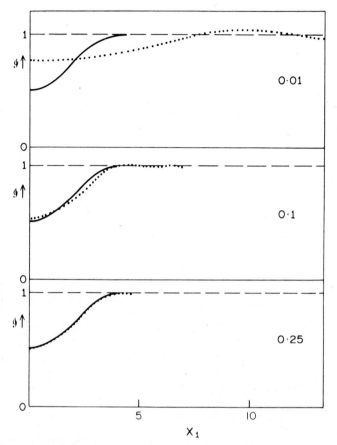

FIG. 19.(a) Intensity distributions in diverging wall images with a central intensity $\mathscr{J}(0) = 0\cdot09$ for various values of the parameter β_0^2 marked on the curves. The parameter $\beta^2 = \beta_0^2/10$. (b) Similar curves for $\mathscr{J}(0) = 0\cdot5$ corresponding to $\beta^2 = \beta_0^2$. The geometrical intensities are shown as the full lines whilst the dotted lines show the wave optical intensities.

intensity at each point in the image plane. The inequality is less easily satisfied in the case of the converging wall. In particular when $\beta^2 = \beta_0^2$ (or when $\beta^2 = \beta_0^2 f'(X)$ in (42)) the condition is impossible to satisfy. The image points for which this situation arises lie on or near the caustic surface where geometrical optics predicts an infinite intensity. We have already established that the semi-classical treatment is never valid in such regions.

As for the correspondence limits discussed in Section IV(A), we note that as λ or h approach zero the inequality (43) is always satisfied.

We can therefore be confident that an inequality of the type (43) is at least a qualitatively acceptable criterion.

The form (41) of the inequality implies that the variations of image intensity:

$$\mathrm{d}I(X)/\mathrm{d}X \propto \mathrm{d}R/\mathrm{d}X$$

are themselves small. This is again in agreement with the general remarks on the variation of the image amplitude.

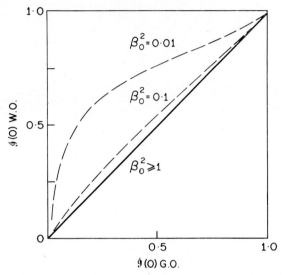

FIG. 20. A plot of $\mathscr{I}(0)$ according to wave optics (W.O.) against the geometrical $\mathscr{I}(0)$. G.O. for various values of β_0^2 for diverging wall images. For $\beta_0^2 \geqslant 1$ the two treatments are in agreement over the entire contrast range whilst for $\beta_0^2 < 1$ agreement is limited to lower contrast regions. This figure reproduced by courtesy of J. P. Guigay.

Figure 19 shows diverging wall image profiles, for a wall model $f(X) = \tanh(X)$ calculated according to wave and geometrical optics for two values of image contrast with β_0^2 as the variable parameter. As predicted by the inequalities (41) to (43) we find that geometrical optics is most readily applicable to objects of large β_0^2 and to images of low contrast. Note in particular that the smaller the value of β_0^2 the lower the contrast in the image for which a geometrical treatment is valid. This is made clear by Fig. 20 in which the image intensity at the centre of a diverging wall according to wave optics is plotted against the intensity given by geometrical optics, for various values of the parameter β_0^2. The full line is obtained when wave and geometrical optics agree. For a wall model of the type $B_y(X) = B_0 \tanh(X)$ this

10

agreement is obtained over the complete contrast range if $\beta_0^2 \geqslant 1$. Marked differences occur for $\beta_0^2 \ll 1$ as witnessed by the dashed curves which indicate that the geometrical treatment can now only regain validity in the low contrast limit.

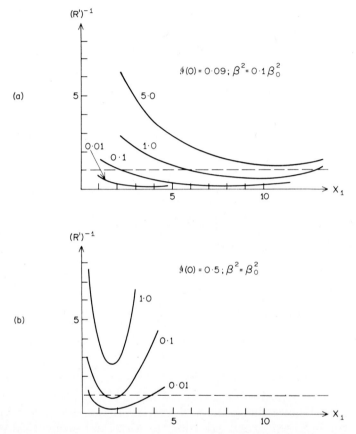

FIG. 21. Plots of $(R')^{-1}$ against X_1 corresponding to the image profiles of Fig. 19. The values of β_0^2 are marked on the curves. Note that in the lower contrast case (b) the validity condition for geometrical optics $(R')^{-1} > 1$ is more readily satisfied than for the higher contrast case (a).

Furthermore an examination of the image intensity profiles of Fig. 19 shows that the geometrical approximation is often valid even when the simplified inequality (43) is not satisfied. In Fig. 21 we plot the values of $(R')^{-1}$ corresponding to the image profiles of Fig. 19. Comparison of the curves of Figs. 19 and 21 shows the condition $(R')^{-1} > 1$ to give a better indication of the local validity of the geometrical approximation. However it is clearly not an absolutely exact criterion and there are several obvious reasons for this:

1. The inequality (41) is established by using a Taylor expansion of $F(X+R)$ limited to the third order term. If this term becomes small, as is the case at the centre of a domain wall where $R' = 0$, it is necessary to consider other terms in the expansion.

2. The wave optical Fresnel zone around each object point can be quite strongly asymmetric. This is not taken account of in our treatment where we compare the phases at positions X and $(X+R)$ but not at X and $(X-R)$.

3. We have supposed that the wave optical and geometrical image intensities will be identical if the phase terms in the Fresnel integral and in the stationary phase approximation are in good agreement over a full zone. This condition may be too strict.

In spite of these defects the criteria which we have developed have at least the merits of simplicity, of giving a good physical description of the problem, of being in complete agreement with the general corres-pondence limit conditions, of applying to both Fresnel and Fraunhofer diffraction and hence to the entire defocusing image domain, of giving a good overall indication of whether geometrical optics is valid. The principal defect in the criteria is that they are systematically somewhat pessimistic. In view of their merits however it hardly seems fruitful to attempt to obtain more exact criteria which will necessarily be more complicated.

2. *Applications to periodic objects*

In the case of a one dimensional periodic object defined by $h(x) = h(x+a)$ we can rearrange the Fresnel integral to give the wave function $\psi(x_1, z)$ in a plane a distance z below the object in the form:

$$\psi(x_1, z) = \exp(i\pi/4) . \sum_n A_n \exp\left(i2\pi x_1 \frac{n}{a}\right) . \exp\left(-i2\pi\lambda z \frac{n^2}{2a^2}\right) \qquad (44)$$

where

$$A_n = \frac{1}{a} \int_{-a/2}^{+a/2} dx . h(x) . \exp(-i2\pi xn/a)$$

The expression (44) has the remarkable property that for the defocusing planes $z_m = ma^2/\lambda$ where m is an integer,

$$\psi(x_1, z_m) = \psi(x+ma/2,0) = h(x+ma/2),$$

to within a constant phase factor. Hence for a pure phase object, $h(x) = \exp i\varphi(x)$, no contrast is visible in these planes whilst maximum contrast is found in the intermediate planes $z = (2m+1)a^2/2\lambda$.

The radius of the first Fresnel zone around the point X_i depends in the stationary phase approximation only upon the local value of $\varphi''(X_i)$ whilst the oscillatory nature of $\varphi(X)$ is not considered. It is clear that the stationary phase approximation can only be valid if the Fresnel zone radius is much smaller than the object periodicity. In terms of the reduced parameters this conditions yields:

$$| \, \beta^2 + \beta_0^2 f'(X) \, | > 1,$$

in which $f'(X)$ is a periodic function oscillating about a mean value of zero so that the inequality can only be satisfied completely if $\beta^2 > 1$. This limits the defocusing distance to the range $0 < z < a^2/\lambda$ where $z = a^2/\lambda$ is the first defocusing plane, above or below the object, in which the image intensity reproduces that in the object.

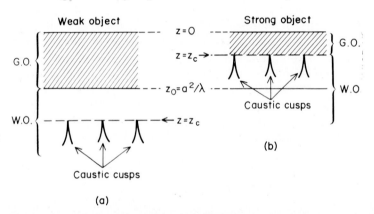

FIG. 22. The position z_c of the caustic cusps associated with periodic phase objects shown relative to the first defocused zero contrast plane $z_0 = a^2/\lambda$. (a) Corresponds to a weak and (b) to a strong phase object. Geometrical optics may be valid in the shaded zones.

This is a supplementary condition to the inequalities (41) to (43) and applies to all periodic phase objects whether they be strong or weak. If we consider the example of a sinusoidal phase object numerical calculation confirms that for a weak object the application of geometrical optics to calculate the image intensity is limited by the condition $\beta^2 < 1$, whilst for a strong object it is limited by the conditions (41) to (43).

These distinct limits have the geometrical interpretations shown in

Fig. 22 which compares the two defocusing quantities $z_0 = a^2/\lambda$ and $z_c = 1/\alpha'_{max}$ which is the distance below the object of the caustic cusp. If $z_c > z_0$ we have the situation of Fig. 22(a) where geometrical optics may be applied in the region $z < z_0$. Image intensity profiles are shown in Fig. 23(a) for this case. When $z_c < z_0$ the use of geometrical optics is limited to the region $z < z_c$ as is shown in Fig. 22(b). Corresponding image intensity profiles are shown in Fig. 23(b).

These considerations apply also to the case of magnetization ripple which contains a range of periodicities. Whether or not it be a weak or strong object it is the smallest periodicity present which will limit

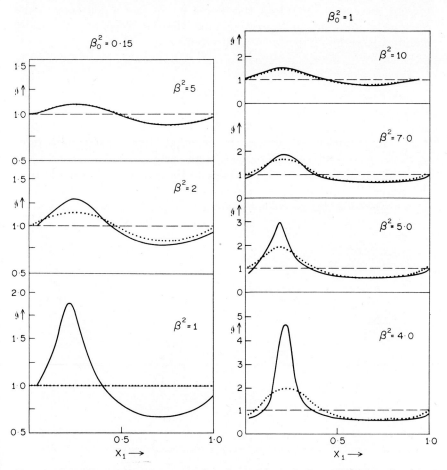

FIG. 23. Intensity profiles for a periodic phase object of sinusoidal form. The dotted curves are the wave optical profiles, the full curves correspond to geometrical optics. (a) $\beta_0^2 = 0.15$; the condition $z_c > z_0$ is fulfilled in this case. (b) $\beta_0^2 = 1$; this corresponds to $z_c < z_0$.

the application of geometrical optics to the entire image intensity distribution. In the case of ripple where the dispersion of periodicities seems to be in the range 10^{-5}–10^{-4} cm a geometrical treatment will be limited to the defocusing region $z < 0.25$ cm at 100 keV. Beyond this region it is essential to apply a wave optical treatment.

D. *Physical Manifestations of the Fluxon*

All discussions of the validity of geometrical optics make consider-able use of the fluxon unit hc/e, which also appears in the reduced parameters used in the diffraction integral. It is the purpose of the present section to show that the fluxon is not just a mathematically convenient unit of measurement but that it becomes physically manifest in certain experimental situations.

1. *Fresnel images from domain walls*

This example was first discussed by Wohlleben (1967). We have already shown that the fringe separation in convergent wall images is given by $\delta = [(z_0+z)/z_0] \cdot (hc/2eD \cdot B_0)$. These fringes are visible only if the illumination is sufficiently coherent. The geometrical term $(z_0+z)/z_0$ is simply the magnification by projection from the object to the image plane. If we project back to the object plane we find that the fringe separation at the object is given by $\delta_0 = hc/2eDB_0$. This gives as the total flux between two fringes: $\delta_0 \cdot D \cdot 2B_0 = hc/e$. As a matter

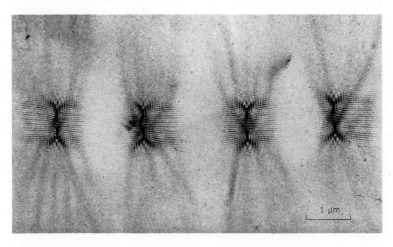

FIG. 24. A Fresnel image of a converging wall region in a permalloy film. The inter-ference fringes represent the finest detail of magnetic origin visible in the image. The photograph is in negative contrast.

of convenience we have already taken the fluxon unit as hc/e but it could equally well be considered as any multiple or submultiple of the same unit. Note that the fringes are the finest details of magnetic origin visible in the image. This is evident in the complex fringe system of Fig. 24, which is a Fresnel image of a cross-tie wall in a thin permalloy film. The variations of phase across the wall can only affect the position or relative intensities of the fringes, so that the fine scale phase structure of the wall can at best only be determined from the images by comparison of microphotometer profiles with intensity profiles calculated from the complete Fresnel diffraction integral.

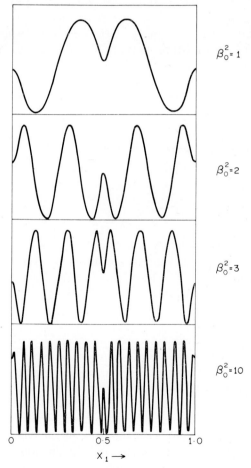

FIG. 25. Fresnel image profiles calculated for a triangular phase grating for various values of β_0^2. There are N complete fringes per period where $N = 2\beta_0^2$.

2. Fresnel images of periodic structures

Consider a magnetic phase object of period a. A defocused image of this object will show both the fundamental periodicity a and interference fringes of period $\delta = \lambda/2\alpha_0$ similar to those behind a domain wall. We suppose in the present case that $z_0 \gg z$ and that the Lorentz deflection in the magnetic object is α_0. The number of interference fringes per period in the image is given by $N = a/\delta = 2\alpha_0 a/\lambda = 2\beta_0^2$.

The fringes are again the finest detail visible in the image. Simply counting the fringes gives a measure of the strength of the object in fluxon units. This is clearly shown in the image profiles of Fig. 25 calculated for a phase grating of triangular form. The regular spacing of the fringes shows that the phase varies linearly in the object.

If $\delta > a$ the fringe counting method of determining the flux breaks down and it is necessary to use a full wave optical calculation, equation (44), to determine the phase distribution in the object. This is also true for the case $\delta < a$ if we wish to measure the flux on a scale finer than the fluxon unit.

3. Fraunhofer images of periodic structures

The same one dimensional field distribution, constituting the phase object shown in Fig. 9(d), can be described mathematically by the convolution

$$h(x) = g(x) \otimes \sum_n \delta(x - na)$$

where $g(x)$ is the unit cell function describing one period of the object, whilst the repetition of this motif is ensured by the convolution with the delta function array. The Fraunhofer diffraction amplitude of $h(x)$ is given by its Fourier transform $\tilde{h}(s)$

$$\tilde{h}(s) = \tilde{g}(s) . \sum_n \delta(s - n/a)$$

where $\tilde{g}(s)$ is the Fourier transform of $g(x)$. The diffraction image intensity distribution $I(s) = \tilde{h}\tilde{h}^*$, shown schematically in Fig. 26(a), consists of the discrete delta function maxima of angular separation λ/a within the envelope $F(s) = gg^*$ which has principal maxima at the angles $\pm\alpha_0$, where $\alpha_0 = (e/hc).\lambda.D.B_0$ is the classical Lorentz deflection angle Note that the delta function series does not necessarily have a maximum coincident with the peak of the envelope.

If we wish to measure the geometrical deflection angle α_0, we are obliged to count the number n of delta function maxima separating the two strongest peaks from the zero order maximum. As a measure of α_0 this procedure clearly has an inherent error of $\pm\lambda/a$. This measurement yields:

$$(e/hc)\lambda.D.B_0 = \frac{\lambda}{a}(n\pm1)$$

This gives for the total flux over one period in the object:

$$\Delta\Phi = D.B_0.a = \frac{hc}{e}(n\pm1).$$

The precision of the measurement is to within one fluxon unit.

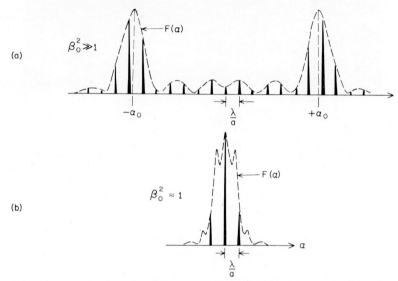

FIG. 26. Representation of Fraunhofer images of (a) a strong and (b) a weak periodic magnetic structure. A measure of the deflection α_0 by counting the number of maxima between the principal peaks is possible only if $\beta_0^2 \gg 1$.

In the case of a weak object the diffraction image has the form of Fig. 26(b). Application of the same method yields

$$\Delta\Phi = \frac{hc}{e} \pm \frac{hc}{e};$$

such a measurement is clearly meaningless. A measurement of the classical Lorentz deflection angle can therefore only be possible for a strong object for which $\Delta\Phi \gg hc/e$. This is the case of the diffraction image shown in Fig. 10. It is also possible for the image shown in Fig. 27(a). It becomes impossible for an image such as that of Fig. 27(b) where $\Delta\Phi \leqslant hc/e$. The images of Fig. 27 are taken from different stripe domain structures in a nickel-iron film.

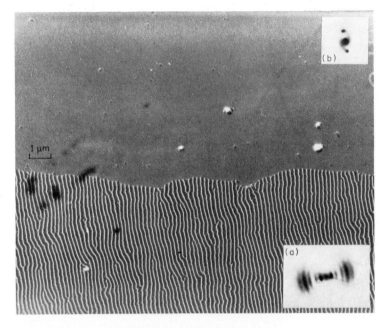

F<small>IG</small>. 27. An off-focus (Fresnel) image of stripe domain structures in a vacuum condensed permalloy film. The Fraunhofer image of inset (a) corresponds to a strong object $\beta_0^2 > 1$ that of (b) corresponds to a weak object $\beta_0^2 < 1$. The images were obtained at 100 keV.

V. I<small>MAGE</small> T<small>RANSFER</small> T<small>HEORY</small>

A. *Basic Theory*

The theory of image transfer can be extremely useful in giving information on electron microscope performance. The theoretical and experimental aspects of this subject are presented in two excellent recent review articles by Lenz (1971) and by Thon (1971). Subject to certain restrictions the theory is based on the following schema, which the reader will recognize as being essentially that of the Abbe theory of image formation modified to take account of defects in the electron optical imaging system. The terminology is essentially that used in information theory.

1. The diffusion of an incident electron beam by an object gives rise to an input signal proportional to the object transmission function $h(\mathbf{r}_0)$.

2. The input signal passes into the objective lens of the electron microscope. In the focal plane of this lens we find a spectral decomposition $\tilde{h}(\mathbf{s}_1)$ of the input signal. This so-called input spectrum is the Fourier transform of the input signal.

3. The input spectrum is multiplied by a transfer function $T(s_1)$ which takes account of the aberrations of the optical system, in particular of the spherical aberration, of the defocusing aberration and of the aperture of the system. The product of the input spectrum and the transfer function gives the output spectrum $\tilde{h}_1(s_1)$.

4. The output signal $h_1(r_1)$, which is the wave amplitude in the image plane, is given by the Fourier transform of the output spectrum.

5. The image contrast is given by $C(r_1) = \{M^2 \mid h_1(r_1) \mid^2 - 1\}$, where M is the magnification of the electron optical system. This is what is recorded on a photographic plate, which we suppose to be a linear recording device.

6. We place the photographic plate on an optical bench and form its Fraunhofer diffraction pattern. This gives us the contrast transfer function $K(s_1)$ defined by:

$$K(s_1) = 2\tilde{h}(s_1) \cdot B(s_1) \cdot \sin\left(\frac{2\pi}{\lambda} \cdot W(s_1)\right). \tag{45}$$

The variable s_1 is the spatial frequency proportional to $1/r_0$; $\tilde{h}(s_1)$ is the Fourier transform of the object function $h(r_0)$; $B(s_1)$ is an aperture function; $W(s_1)$ is the wave aberration essentially due to defocusing and spherical aberration. It is defined by:

$$W(s_1) = \frac{C_s}{4}(\lambda s_1)^4 + \frac{z}{2}(\lambda s_1)^2. \tag{46}$$

The main assumptions involved in the derivation of equation (45) are (i) isoplanacy and (ii) the object is weak. In addition the object is chosen to contain a wide range of spatial frequencies such that, ideally, it can be considered to be a white object, $\mid \tilde{h}(s_1) \mid = 1$. If this is so, $K(s_1)$ can be used to obtain information on the resolution of electron micrographs and on the spherical aberration of the objective lens of the electron microscope.

We show a schematic plot of $\sin(2\pi W(s_1)/\lambda)$ in Fig. 28. It is important to notice that as a function of the defocusing certain frequencies are eliminated and others are accentuated independently of the spatial frequency distribution present in the object.

The in-focus image ($z = 0$) is perturbed by the spherical aberration term. A defocusing of $z_s = C_s\theta^2/2$ (where $\theta = \lambda/a$) allows the object function to be recuperated in the case of a periodic object. In the case of an atomic repeat lattice of period 4 Å imaged at 100 keV ($\lambda = 3.7 \times 10^{-10}$ cm), with an objective lens of $C_s \simeq 0.1$ cm, we find $z_s = 500$ Å. In this range of defocusing and frequency ($0 < z < 10^{-5}$ cm,

$\theta \approx 10^{-2}$ rad) the defocusing term $z\theta^2/2$ and the spherical aberration term $C_s\theta^4/4$ are of the same order of magnitude. In the case of magnetic objects we are concerned with angular deflections $\theta = \lambda s_1$ in the range $\theta \leqslant 10^{-4}$ rad and with defocusing distances $z > 0{\cdot}1$ cm; under these conditions $C_s\theta^4 \approx 10^{-14}$ cm (we take the highly unfavourable value of $C_s = 100$ cm) whilst $z\theta^2 > 10^{-9}$ cm. In this situation we can safely ignore the effect of spherical aberration on the defocused image.

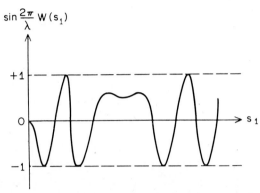

Fig. 28. Representation of the wave aberration term $\sin 2\pi W(s_1)/\lambda$, which has zeros for values of s_1 for which $W(s_1) = n\lambda/2$. The contrast transfer function of equation (45) will then show zeros which are independent of the object.

B. *Application to Small Deflections*

We can develop the following image transfer theory for magnetic objects and for objects of small spatial frequency (Guigay *et al.*, 1971). We describe the object by its one dimensional complex transmission function $h(x)$ whilst the partially coherent electron illumination is characterized by its angular intensity distribution $S(\chi)$. The mutual intensity function ρ of the electron beam at the object plane is given by:

$$\rho(x, x') = \tilde{S}((x-x')/\lambda).h(x).h^*(x')$$

where $\tilde{S}$ is the Fourier transform of S. The intensity distribution $I(x)$, registered on the electron micrograph, has a Fourier transform given by

$$\tilde{I}(s) = \tilde{S}(zs).\exp(-i\pi\lambda zs^2)\int dx.\exp(i2\pi xs).h(x).h^*(x-\lambda zs). \qquad (47)$$

The effect of the electron source on the optical diffraction amplitude, represented by $\tilde{I}$, is contained in the factor $\tilde{S}$. In the perfectly coherent case $\tilde{S} = 1$. In the case of partial coherence, which is the usual practical situation, frequencies $s > 1/\chi_0 z$ are increasingly attenuated in the image due to the form of $\tilde{S}$, which is usually taken to be Gaussian in form.

This is the reverse situation to that found in the usual direct Fraunhofer electron diffraction images where it is the small spatial frequencies $s < \chi_0/\lambda$ which are difficult to resolve due to the effect of the finite source size.

In the case of a phase object defined by $h(x) = \exp(i\varphi(x))$ we have $h(x)h^*(x-\lambda zs) = \exp(i\Delta\varphi)$ where $\Delta\varphi = \varphi(x)-\varphi(x-\lambda zs)$. If $\Delta\varphi \ll \pi/2$ for all values of x we can write $\exp(i\Delta\varphi) = 1+i\Delta\varphi$. Equation (47) then yields:

$$\text{Intensity} = |\,\tilde{I}(s)\,|^2 = |\,\tilde{S}(zs).[\delta(s)+2\tilde{\varphi}(s).\sin(\pi\lambda zs^2)]\,|^2. \qquad (48)$$

This is a familiar form of the diffraction image equivalent to that of equation (45). The present derivation assumes only $\Delta\varphi \ll \pi/2$, which is a much less restrictive condition than the usual $\varphi \ll \pi/2$. Equation (48) is not then restricted in application to a weak phase object as usually defined. It may be applied, within a certain z dependent frequency interval, to phase objects not satisfying the condition $\varphi \ll \pi/2$.

C. Magnetization Ripple

The magnetic object most susceptible to be investigated by this means is the magnetization ripple found in thin polycrystalline films. The magnetization direction varies locally about the mean direction in the manner shown in Fig. 29. The fluctuation is due essentially to the variation of the anisotropy direction from one region to another, probably on the scale of the crystallites. The fluctuation is aperiodic and essentially one dimensional. An experimental knowledge of the spatial frequency distribution and amplitude of the ripple is of some interest in verifying theoretical estimates of a structure which is of considerable importance in describing the macroscopic magnetic properties of films.

A number of investigations of this ripple structure, the most recent being that of Suzuki (1971), are based on visual estimates of the strongest periodicities present in defocused images of ripple. However it is well established in theory, equations (45), (48), and by experiment (Thon, 1971; Reimer et al., 1969) that defocused images of a completely white object have a z dependent spatial frequency spectrum determined by $\sin(2\pi W(s)/\lambda)$. We must then be careful as to whether in a given image we are measuring $\tilde{\varphi}(s)$ on rather $\sin(2\pi W(s)/\lambda)$. In reality of course we measure both at once.

Using equation (48) we can propose the following schema for a complete experimental investigation of ripple. For a number of different defocusing distances, calibrated in a separate experiment, we find $|\tilde{I}(s)|^2$ by measurement on the light optical diffraction image of the electron micrographs. We calculate for each the $\sin(\pi z\lambda s^2)$ curve and seek the distribution $\tilde{\varphi}(s)$ which by multiplication with $\sin(\pi z\lambda s^2)$ can yield the experimental curve in each case. From equation (48) ignoring the central maximum and since all the terms are real we find

$$|\tilde{I}(s)| = 2\tilde{S}(zs).\tilde{\varphi}(s).\sin(\pi\lambda z s^2).$$

If we know $\tilde{S}$ and $\sin(\pi\lambda z s^2)$ a measurement of $\tilde{I}(s)$ allows us to find $\tilde{\varphi}(s)$ and by Fourier transformation $\varphi(x)$.

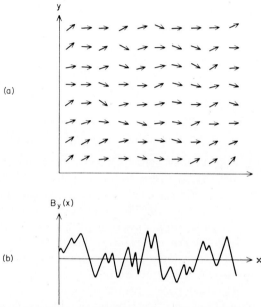

(a)

(b)

FIG. 29.(a) Schema of ripple structure in a magnetic film. The arrows represent the local magnetization direction. (b) Schematic plot of $B_y(x)$ against x.

Figure 30 shows a defocused image of a ripple structure in a thin permalloy film together with its light and electron optical Fraunhofer diffraction images. It is not possible to obtain a useful direct electron diffraction image from such a structure. The intensity distribution in the optical diffraction image can yield the object phase function. Some preliminary measurements of this type have already been published by Ajeian et al. (1970). A serious obstacle to quantitative measurements by this technique is that the photographic emulsion is not a simple amplitude object for a transmitted light beam. Differential hardening of the emulsion around the silver deposits during development of the recorded image produce "a relief image" (Smith, 1968;

Lamberts, 1970). The combined relief and silver images form a mixed amplitude and phase object for a transmitted light beam. This considerably complicates the interpretation of the resulting diffraction pattern.

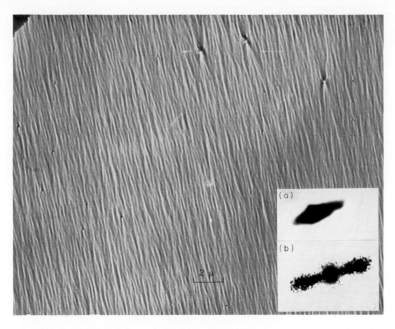

FIG. 30. A defocused image of a ripple structure in a permalloy film with insets (a) the electron Fraunhofer image (b) the light optical Fraunhofer image of the electron micrograph; the images (a) and (b) are to scale.

VI. REMARKS ON DOMAIN WALL MEASUREMENTS

We cannot justifiably claim to have determined the structure of a phase object unless our experimental technique allows us to distinguish the image of this object from that of a slightly different object. In the case of domain wall measurements it is useful to use as a standard reference the zero width wall, $w = 0$. The magnetization distributions across walls $w = 0$ and $w \neq 0$ are shown in Fig. 31(a), whilst the corresponding phase structures are shown in (b). The total phase difference with respect to the reference structure is given by $\beta_0^2 k$ where the constant k, defined in the figure, is used by Guigay (1970) in characterizing a wall.

If a certain property of an image is identical to that given by a zero width wall it is impossible to make a measurement using that particular property. This holds regardless of whether the interpretation of the image contrast is that of wave or geometrical optics.

Consider a measurement using the central intensity, $\mathscr{I}(0) = I(0)/I_\infty$ of a diverging wall image. The background intensity on either side of

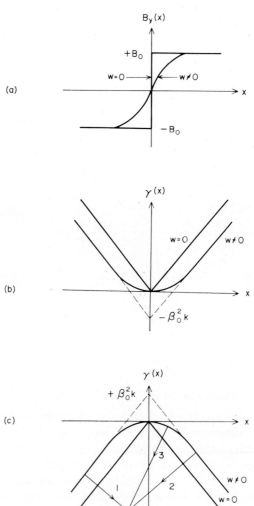

FIG. 31.(a) Magnetization distribution across zero width ($w = 0$) and finite width domain walls, $w \neq 0$. (b) Phase structure of these walls in the divergent case. (c) Phase structure in the convergent case. Three beams interfere at P below the object. The difference between the interference systems of a zero and a finite width domain wall depends on the phase contribution of the "wall" ray 3 relative to the "biprism" rays 1 and 2.

the wall is I_∞. Figure 20 indicates that a geometrical treatment gives the correct intensity for a strong object $\beta_0^2 \gg 1$ whilst for weak objects $\beta_0^2 \ll 1$ it is not valid. In this range we are obliged to use wave optics to interpret the image contrast. Figure 32 shows $\mathscr{I}(0)$ calculated according to wave optics plotted against the parameter $\alpha(z/\lambda)^{\frac{1}{2}}$ for domain walls of various strength β_0^2. The full line is for the zero width wall. The wave optical curves for $\beta_0^2 \leqslant 0.5$ are indistinguishable from the curve for $w = 0$. The physical reason for this is simply the smallness of the quantity $\beta_0^2 k$ which gives a measure of the phase difference between the structures. We can conclude that in this range of β_0^2 we cannot make a wall width measurement by this means. This same conclusion was drawn by Bostanjoglo and Vieweger (1969) in an investigation of chromium tribromide, which turns out to be a weak phase object with $\beta_0^2 \approx 0.01$.

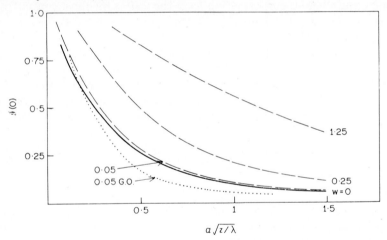

FIG. 32. Plot of the wave optical values of $\mathscr{I}(0)$ against the parameter $\alpha(z/\lambda)^{\frac{1}{2}}$ for a divergent wall. The continuous line is for $w = 0$, the dashed lines are for the marked values of β_0^2. The dotted line corresponds to the geometrical $\mathscr{I}(0)$ for $\beta_0^2 = 0.05$. Note that the curves for $\beta_0^2 \ll 1$ are indistinguishable from that for $w = 0$. This figure reproduced by courtesy of J. P. Guigay.

A somewhat similar effect arises in converging wall images showing interference fringes as in Figs. 10 and 24. The fringes arise from three beam interference as shown in Fig. 31(c), two "biprism" beams coming from the domains on either side, of the wall and one beam coming from the wall itself. The interference state of the three beams depends on their relative phases and thereby directly on $\beta_0^2 k$. Here again we will have difficulty distinguishing a weak object. Furthermore since k depends on the wall model the phase difference between the rays, and consequently the fringe intensity distribution, will depend on both the wall width w and the wall model. Hothersall (1969) found an ambiguity of precisely this type in an investigation using converging wall images for which he could fit a given experimental intensity profile with theoretical profiles due to different wall models by suitable adjustment of the wall widths.

The conclusion is that experimental measurements of weak objects are very difficult and that the use of a wave optical interpretation does not reduce this problem, which is fundamentally a question of detection: we need to count a lot of electrons (Wohlleben, 1971). There is need for very careful consideration of the best experimental conditions for resolving wall structures since even the interpretation of the image of a strong object is not necessarily unambiguous. There would seem to be an interest in working near the caustic cusp in a converging wall image, since here the information from the wall is the most concentrated in the same way that light passing through a lens is most densely concentrated near the focal point.

We should remark that in most cases of interest magnetic domain walls are not strong objects. A wall of width 10^{-5} cm in a permalloy film of thickness 10^{-5} cm with $4\pi M_s \approx 10^4$ gauss represents a value $\beta_0^2 \approx 1$. A wall of width 10^{-6} cm in a 10^{-5} cm thick cobalt foil, $4\pi M_s \approx 1 \cdot 8 \times 10^4$ gauss, represents a value $\beta_0^2 \approx 0 \cdot 25$. In practice we find that almost all the objects which we encounter in Lorentz microscopy fall in the range $\beta_0^2 \leqslant 1$.

VII. Conclusions

Phase microscopy is concerned with the visualization and measurement of the phase information contained in the illumination transmitted by an object. An imaging theory must first describe the interaction of the illumination with the object and secondly the transformation of the information into an image contrast.

We have shown that the interaction of an electron beam with a magnetic object can be treated by the W.K.B. approximation. We have subsequently treated essentially only the defocused image technique, the wave theory of which has long been established; the conditions of application of the pseudo-classical approximations are now fairly clear. Despite this satisfactory formal situation it is improbable that great faith can be placed in the many experimental measurements which have been made on magnetic domain walls. It is well known that there are many experimental difficulties involved in such investigations. There is also the more basic difficulty that the objects in question interact relatively weakly with the electron illumination. The future of quantitative magnetic phase microscopy must surely lie in the development of greatly refined phase detection methods.

ACKNOWLEDGEMENTS

It is a pleasure to acknowledge many working discussions over the past years with my friend and colleague J. P. Guigay. The W.K.B. approximation of Section II was first used in the present context by him. He is also responsible for the explicit use of the reduced optical parameters in Lorentz microscopy. The idea of using the zero width wall as a reference structure is due to D. Wohlleben.

REFERENCES

Aharanov, Y. and Bohm, D. (1959). *Phys. Rev.* **115**, 485.
Aharanov, Y. and Bohm, D. (1961). *Phys. Rev.* **123**, 1511.
Ajeian, R., Kappert, H. and Reimer, L. (1970). *Z. angew. Phys.* **31**, 80.
Bayh, W. (1962). *Z. Phys.* **169**, 492.
Boersch, H. and Raith, H. (1959). *Naturwiss.* **20**, 574.
Boersch, H., Raith, H. and Wohlleben, D. (1960). *Z. Phys.* **159**, 388.
Boersch, H., Hamisch, H., Wohlleben, D. and Grohmann, K. (1960). *Z. Phys.* **159**, 397.
Boersch, H., Raith, H. and Weber, H. (1961). *Z. Phys.* **161**, 1.
Boersch, H., Hamisch, H., Grohmann, K. and Wohlleben, D. (1962). *Z. Phys.* **167**, 72.
Born, M. and Wolf, E. (1964). "Principles of Optics," 2nd Ed., Pergamon Press, Oxford.
Bostanjoglo, O. and Vieweger, W. (1969). *Phys. Stat. Sol.* **32**, 311.
Broglie, L. de (1950). "Optique Electronique et Corpusculaire", Hermann, Paris.
Broglie, L. de (1968). "Théorie de la Quantification dans la Nouvelle Mécanique", Hermann, Paris.
Chambers, R. G. (1960). *Phys. Rev. Lett.* **5**, 3.
Cohen, M. S. (1967). *J. Appl. Phys.* **38**, 4966.
Cohen, M. S. and Harte, K. J. (1969). *J. Appl. Phys.* **40**, 3597.
Cowley, J. M. and Moodie, A. F. (1957). *Acta Cryst.* **10**, 609.
Durand, E. (1970). "Mécanique Quantique", Vol. 1, pp. 176–177, Masson, Paris.
Ehrenberg, W. and Siday, R. E. (1949). *Proc. Phys. Soc.* **62**, 8.
Ferrier, R. P. and Wade, R. H. (1964). "Proc. Int. Conf. on Magnetism, Nottingham", p. 873, Institute of Physics, London.
Françon, M. (1950). "Le contraste de Phase en Optique et en Microscopie", Masson, Paris.
Franz, W. (1940). *Physik. Berichte.* **21**, 686.
Fuchs, E. (1962). *Z. angew. Phys.* **14**, 203.
Fuller, H. W. and Hale, M. E. (1960a). *J. Appl. Phys.* **31**, 238.
Fuller, H. W. and Hale, M. E. (1960b). *J. Appl. Phys.* **31**, 1699.
Goringe, M. J. and Jakubovics, J. P. (1967). *Phil. Mag.* **15**, 393.
Grundy, P. J. and Tebble, R. S. (1968). *Advan. Phys.* **17**, 153.

Guigay, J. P. (1970). "VII International Congress on Electron Microscopy, Grenoble", Vol. II. (P. Favard, ed.), p. 605.

Guigay, J. P. and Wade, R. H. (1968). *Phys. Stat. Sol.* **29**, 799.

Guigay, J. P., Wade, R. H. and Delpla, C. (1971). "Proc. 25th Anniv. Meeting E.M.A.G.", p. 238, Institute of Physics, London.

Harrison, C. G. and Leaver, K. D. (1972). *Phys. Stat. Sol.(a)*, **12**, 413.

Hanszen, K. J. (1971). *In* "Advances in Optical and Electron Microscopy" (R. Barer and V. E. Cosslett, eds.), Vol. 4, pp. 1–84, Academic Press, London and New York.

Hothersall, D. (1969). *Phil. Mag.* **20**, 89.

Kappert, H., Fellenberg, F. and Rausch, W. (1972). *Intern. J. Magnetism* **3**, 93.

Lenz, F. (1971). *In* "Electron Microscopy in Materials Science" (U. Valdrè, ed.), pp. 540–569, Academic Press, New York and London.

Lamberts, R. L. (1970). *J. Opt. Soc. Am.* **60**, 1389.

Landau, L. D. and Lifchitz, E. M. (1965). "The Classical Theory of Fields", Pergamon Press, Oxford.

Landau, L. D. and Lifchitz, E. M. (1966). "Mécanique Quantique", Editions Mir, Moscow.

Messiah, A. (1961). "Quantum Mechanics", Vol. 1, North-Holland, Amsterdam.

Olivei, A. (1969). *Optik*, **30**, 27.

Olivei, A. (1971). *Optik*, **33**, 93.

Reimer, L., Heine, H. G. and Ajeian, R. (1969). *Z. Naturforsch*, **24**, 1846.

Scherzer, O. (1949). *J. Appl. Phys.* **20**, 20.

Smith, H. M. (1968). *J. Opt. Soc. Am.* **58**, 533.

Suzuki, T. (1971). *Phys. Stat. Sol.* **37**, 101.

Suzuki, T., Wilts, C. H. and Patton, C. E. (1968). *J. Appl. Phys.* **39**, 1983.

Thon, F. (1971). *In* "Electron Microscopy in Materials Science" (U. Valdrè, ed.), pp. 570–625, Academic Press, New York and London.

Wade, R. H. (1962). *Proc. Phys. Soc.* **79**, 1237.

Wade, R. H. (1966). *J. Appl. Phys.* **37**, 366.

Wade, R. H. (1967). *Phys. Stat. Sol.* **19**, 847.

Wade, R. H. (1968). *J. de Phys.* **29**, C2–95.

Wade, R. H. (1971). *In* "Electron Microscopy in Materials Science" (U. Valdrè, ed.), pp. 680–711, Academic Press, New York and London.

Wade, R. H. and Guigay, J. P. (1969). *In* "Ecole d'Eté de Perros-Guirec".†

Wade, R. H. and Silcox, J. (1967). *Phys. Stat. Sol.* **19**, 57 and 63.

Wohlleben, D. (1966). *Phys. Lett.* **22**, 564.

Wohlleben, D. (1967). *J. Appl. Phys.* **38**, 3341.

Wohlleben, D. (1971). *In* "Electron Microscopy in Materials Science" (U. Valdrè, ed.), pp. 712–757, Academic Press, New York and London.

† Published in 1972 as "Méthodes et Techniques Nouvelles d'Observation en Metallurgie Physique" (B. Jouffrey, ed.), pp. 369–384, Soc. Française de Microscopie Electronique, Paris.

The Electron Microscopical Observation of Aqueous Biological Specimens

R. T. JOY

Zoology Department, The University, Nottingham, England

I. Introduction

THE first published electron micrographs of biological material depicted unfixed specimens which had been exposed directly to the column vacuum (Marton, 1934). Their appearance seemed to indicate that the preparations had suffered from dehydration and incineration in the electron beam. In order to avoid these difficulties "environmental chambers", designed to maintain specimens in a hydrated condition, were discussed and constructed (Marton, 1935; Krause, 1937; Abrams and McBain, 1944). Ultimately, however, alternative preparative techniques were developed which involved either the fixation and ultrathin sectioning of cells or the shadowing of intrinsically thin specimens.

The original objective, the observation of organic preparations in a more natural environment, has never been completely abandoned, however. A number of publications have attempted to define those conditions which are optimal for the examination of organic material in environmental chambers. In some studies conventional electron microscopes were employed (Sugata *et al.*, 1956; Ito and Hiziya, 1958; Stoyanova and Mikhailovskii, 1959; Stoyanova and Nekrasova, 1960; Stoyanova *et al.*, 1960a,b; Stoyanova, 1961; Heide, 1960, 1962; Moretz *et al.*, 1970), whilst in others use was made of high voltage instruments (Dupouy *et al.*, 1960, 1962; Dupouy and Perrier, 1962; Matricardi *et al.*, 1972 a,b; Ward and Mitchell, 1972).

Inferior contrast in the final image has always proved to be a major practical limitation in the use of environmental chambers. The extent to which specimens suffer radiation damage during observation is another matter of serious concern. In order to minimize ultrastructural alterations there are several phenomena which must be avoided or controlled in environmental chamber experiments. The most important of these are:

(1) the dependence of image contrast on the addition of heavy metal atom "stains" to the specimen;

(2) the heating and ionizing effects of irradiation by the incident beam of electrons;

(3) excessive dehydration.

The methods by which hydrated specimens are examined are technically complex because simultaneous control is required over a variety of interdependent physical parameters. The purpose of this review is to examine all those factors which may affect the design and operation of environmental chambers.

II. RESOLUTION AND CONTRAST

Electron optical lens aberrations and instabilities limit the resolution attainable within a particular microscope. The type of instrumental imperfection which is critical depends on the thickness of the specimen. In those organic preparations which are 10 nm or less in thickness, mains fluctuations or spherical aberration restricts the resolution to approximately 0·2 nm. (Parsons, 1970). In conventionally stained sections 60 nm thick a resolution of 1·5 nm has been achieved at 500 kV (Hama and Porter, 1969).

Chromatic aberration becomes a limiting factor whenever relatively thick specimens are examined. Individual electrons lose differing amounts of energy during interaction with the specimen. Consequently, there is a wide variation in de Broglie wavelength within the transmitted beam. Owing to the chromatic error of the objective lens, the resolution predicted for a collodion specimen 1 μm thick is no better than 5 nm at 200 kV and 2 nm at 500 kV (Cosslett, 1970). Quantitative measurements of energy losses during the transmission of electrons through collodion of this thickness (Considine, 1969) have been used to calculate a practical resolution of 11 nm at 200 kV and 2·7 nm at 500 kV. If 2·5 μm thick carbon specimens are examined at 500 kV under normal operating conditions ($C_c = 4$ mm; $\alpha_0 = 5 \times 10^{-3}$), a theoretical resolution of 10 nm should be attainable (Cosslett, 1971).

Little intrinsic contrast is exhibited by organic materials because of the low atomic weight constituents of their molecules. Except at very low accelerating voltages, thin sections of unstained biological material are relatively electron transparent. In certain biological specimens, the nuclear regions have sufficient inherent density to be visible at conventional voltages without being stained, but these are exceptional cases. In the majority of specimens examined at 50 to 100 kV, contrast is usually enhanced by the addition of heavy metal atoms. Preparative techniques, such as shadow casting or staining, produce granules of metal whose dimensions are of the order of 1·0 nm or more. Consequently, it is highly unlikely that the resolution of material prepared by these methods can exceed this lower limiting value.

When electron micrographs of organic material are examined in environmental chambers, however, it is frequently apparent that both the resolution and the contrast actually attained are poorer than those which have been anticipated. Contrast becomes extremely important in the examination of unstained organic specimens because the supporting film is produced from material of about the same density. This lack of contrast between specimen and supporting film in environmental chamber experiments becomes even more critical at high voltages.

Phase contrast and dark-field electron microscopy are two of the most suitable methods available for the improvement of resolution and contrast.

The phase contrast contribution to the image may outweigh that of amplitude contrast when the specimen is not in perfect focus (Cowley and Grinton, 1970). Optical diffraction data obtained from underfocused electron micrographs of catalase crystals has been used to reconstruct the two-dimensional image which would have been observed if an aberration-free phase plate had been used (Erickson and Klug, 1970). The catalase molecules examined, however, were dry and had been negatively stained. Whether comparable results can be attained in unstained and wet crystals has yet to be demonstrated.

In some circumstances, phase contrast effects are disadvantageous since they complicate the interpretation of transmission electron micrographs. For example, the observed image densities of artificial lipid bilayers cannot always be correlated with their known ultra-structure (Schidlovsky, 1965).

In dark-field electron microscopy, the undeviated beam is prevented from reaching the plane at which the image is recorded. This result may be accomplished by tilting the beam (Ottensmeyer, 1969), by using a condenser aperture which is annular in shape (Dupouy *et al.*, 1966; Dubochet *et al.*, 1971) as shown in Fig. 1(a) or by using a beam stop in the vicinity of the back focal plane of the objective lens (Dupouy *et al.*, 1966; Kleinschmidt, 1970a) as indicated in Fig. 1(b). The last of these methods is referred to as "contrast stop" or "strioscopy".

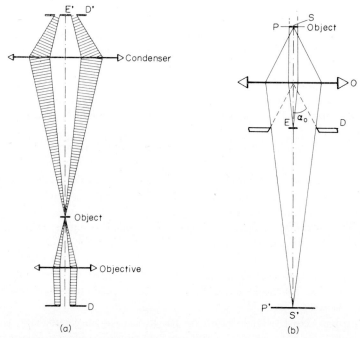

(a)   (b)

FIG. 1. Dark-field illumination produced by (a) an annular condenser aperture and (b) an objective lens back focal plane beam stop. (After Dupouy *et al.*, 1969.)

Thick sections of unstained keratin have been examined at high accelerating voltages by means of contrast stop techniques. These preparations have revealed finer ultrastructural detail than thin sections of stained keratin viewed at 100 kV by transmission electron micro-scopy. Much thinner specimens, such as bacterial flagellae (Dupouy *et al.*, 1969) and cell walls (Dupouy, 1971), have been observed at 1 MV and 3 MV respectively. The high contrast which they exhibit when compared to the background of supporting film is shown in

Fig. 2. Micrographs of negatively stained cell wall preparations from *Achromobacter* 130 have been published previously (Lapchine and Enjalbert, 1971). The micrographs shown in Fig. 2, however, are of completely unstained and unshadowed material.

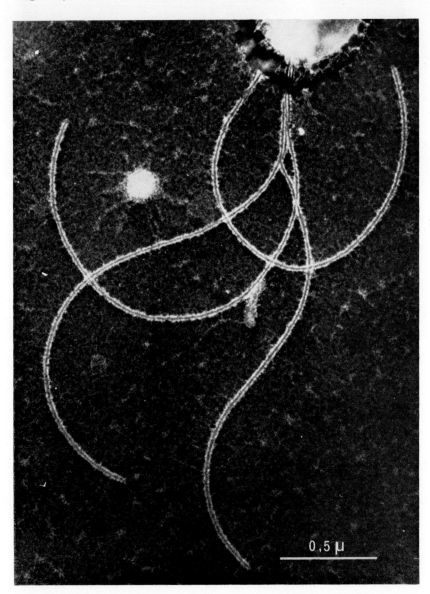

FIG. 2(a)—*See caption overleaf.*

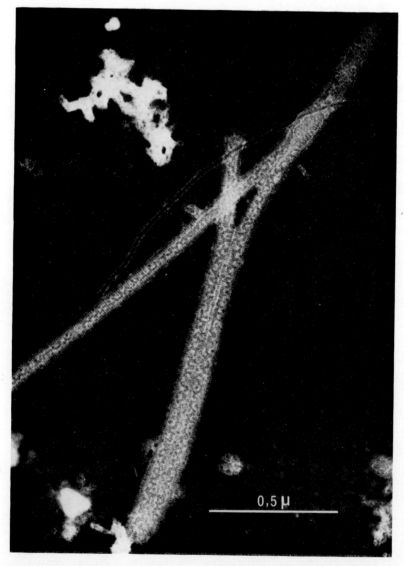

FIG. 2. Contrast stop micrographs of (a) *Achromobacter* flagellae at 1 MV. (After (Dupouy *et al.*, 1969) and (b) *Achromobacter* 130 preparation at 3 MV (Dupouy, 1971).)

The resolution at present attainable in dark-field electron microscopy seems to be limited to about 1 nm by the structure of the thin carbon specimen support films. For example, although unstained complexes between DNA and cytochrome have been resolved (Kleinschmidt,

1970b), these are significantly thicker than 2 nm. It has subsequently been demonstrated that DNA helices which are free from protein can be detected by dark-field microscopy whether they are positively stained (Dubochet et al., 1971) or not (Ottensmeyer, 1969).

There is one definite potential disadvantage associated with the adoption of dark-field techniques. Depending upon the nature of the specimen, the amount of radiation damage could be increased because the electrons contributing to the image represent only a small proportion of those present in the portion of the beam interacting with the specimen.

Dark-field methods might find useful applications in the examination of fixed aqueous preparations in environmental chambers. Whenever heavy metal atoms are not required to enhance contrast, other fixatives may be used more advantageously. It might be possible, for example, to obtain better resolution in aldehyde fixed materials. Whether such specimens will continue to retain functional enzyme molecules after electron irradiation remains to be investigated.

III. Interactions between Specimens and Incident Electrons

There are several ways in which the properties of organic specimens are affected by exposure to an incident beam of electrons. The structural and electron optical characteristics of the sample may be altered during irradiation by contamination, sublimation, electrostatic charging, heating, ionization and nuclear displacement phenomena.

A. Contamination and Sublimation

The precise conditions of irradiation and the properties of the specimen determine whether the thickness of an electron microscope preparation is increased or decreased. During prolonged periods of irradiation, image quality, contrast and resolution gradually deteriorate in certain specimens (Watson, 1947; Hillier, 1948; König, 1948; Ennos, 1953, 1954). This process, which is known as "contamination", was observed *in situ* and attributed to the deposition of amorphous organic molecules present within the vacuum system.

There are various methods by which contamination may either be reduced or avoided. Below 10^{-2} amp cm^{-2} the rate of contamination is proportional to the current density (Heide, 1965a). Consequently, it is desirable to work at the lowest acceptable magnification in order to limit the current incident upon the specimen. The standard procedure by which contamination may be avoided involves the use of cold traps; these prevent volatile hydrocarbons from reaching the specimen (Heide, 1965b).

In a completely closed or "static" environmental chamber, contamination is unlikely to affect the specimen itself. Indeed, one of the earliest uses of a microchamber was to show that contamination of MgO was prevented by maintenance in air in a closed cell instead of exposure to the column vacuum (Dupouy et al., 1962). Contamination could, however, reduce transmission through the windows used in certain types of environmental chamber.

The thickness of specimens before and after examination has been measured by means of quantitative interference microscopy. This technique revealed that the mass thickness of certain embedding media actually decreased during exposure to the electron beam. This second phenomenon is often referred to as "sublimation".

Whilst all embedding media lose some of their mass during irradiation, the degree of loss varies. Sections of n-butyl polymethacrylate lose approximately half their thickness (Reimer, 1959; Cosslett, 1960; Lippert, 1961, 1962), whilst those of Vestopal W (Reimer, 1959; Cosslett, 1961), Araldite, Epon and Maraglas (Bahr and Zeitler, 1965; Wachtel et al., 1966) lose less. Of the water miscible epoxy resins, glycol methacrylate is slightly unstable; only 2-hydroxypropyl methacrylate is reported to be relatively stable in an electron beam (Leduc and Bernhard, 1962).

Sublimation could involve a number of different phenomena. Interaction between electrons in the beam and the irradiated material could result in the oxidation of molecules at the surface of the specimen. Both CO and CO_2 have been detected in the irradiation products of methacrylate (Reimer, 1965). It has also been demonstrated that carbonaceous particles and sections are diminished in environmental chambers containing oxygen (Escaig and Sella, 1966). Other reactions, such as a loss of entire fragments of polymerized material, may also contribute to sublimation.

Whilst contamination may be effectively prevented by using cold traps, sublimation can only be avoided by reducing the effects of ionizing radiation. It would appear, therefore, that the latter constitutes a more serious potential problem.

B. *Charge and Temperature Variations*

Electrostatic charge effects have been observed during specimen irradiation (Krause, 1937). It has been discovered, however, that maintenance of the specimen in air or argon at a pressure of 0·3 mmHg or more allows the complete neutralization of induced electrostatic charges on the surface of the specimen by the production of ionized gas molecules (Stoyanova and Morozova, 1963). Induced charges will also be rapidly transferred from a specimen which is in contact with a continuous layer of water, because of the increased conductivity of such a preparation.

Temperature increases in an organic specimen during electron irradiation could result in an irreversible molecular denaturation. It has been claimed that temperatures in excess of 100°C may be attained by specimens during irradiation (von Borries and Glaser, 1944; Hall, 1966). The sublimation points of various compounds have been used for the quantitative determination of specimen temperature. It has been suggested, however, that certain factors preclude this particular phase change from being used for the accurate measurement of temperature (Reimer and Christenhusz, 1962). There is some evidence that certain proteins, viruses and bacteria are not denatured specifically by high temperatures, provided that water is absent (Eidus and Ganassi, 1960). When protein molecules are hydrated, however, there is usually a serious risk of denaturation above 60°C. The thermal energy transferred to unfixed proteins during heat denaturation disrupts their secondary and tertiary molecular structure. It has been calculated that a 0·1 μm thick layer of organic material will reach a temperature of 24°C, if various assumptions about the geometrical and physical parameters of the system are made (Stenn and Bahr, 1970). By substituting the appropriate value for the thermal conductivity of the sample it may be calculated that a layer of water 1·0 μm thick will reach a temperature of 15°C under the same conditions. It is assumed in this calculation that good thermal contact and conductivity are maintained between specimen, grid and grid holder. In practice heat transfer may not be optimal; the value calculated should be considered to represent the minimum predictable temperature in the absence of accessory heat sinks. An even greater source of possible error lies in the specification that the distance between the illuminated region of the specimen and the metal grid bars is exactly 20 μm. If this dimension were increased by a factor of twenty, an event which could occur in HVEM environmental chamber work, the protein denaturation temperature region would be reached. Balanced against these pessimistic considerations there is the evidence that liquid phase water has been observed in a number of different environmental chambers. It is unlikely, therefore, that very high temperatures are attained during actual operating conditions.

Paraffin of 71°C melting point might prove to be a useful indicator in the range of specimen temperatures of interest to persons studying organic materials. It has been claimed that this type of paraffin can be melted in the electron microscope without undergoing serious radiation damage (Yamaguchi, 1956).

If thermal damage did prove to be a limiting factor in a particular environmental chamber experiment, it might be circumvented by the use of fixed material. Cross-linkages formed between molecules during fixation should stabilize ultrastructural features. Osmium tetroxide, for example, is able to prevent the normal heat coagulation response of albumen (Millonig and Marinozzi, 1968). Of the various aldehydes, some are noted for their ability to produce cross-linkages between molecules (Sabatini *et al.*, 1963; Riemersma, 1970), whilst others are able to preserve the activity of some enzymes (Sabatini *et al.*, 1964).

In dealing with unfixed aqueous material, the logical method of avoiding thermal damage is to cool the specimen directly. Not all of the energy transferred to a specimen from incident electrons is converted into heat, however. In thin specimens, ionizing damage is more critical. The thickness at which heating and charge effects become serious depends upon the accelerating voltage. In the most favourable circumstances, when HVEM techniques are used, the limiting thickness is approximately 3 μm.

In any experiments in which it is desired to use environmental chambers to examine dry specimens, the nature and thickness of the material will once again determine whether heating or radiation damage is the more serious problem. Even in thin specimens, if the material is insensitive to radiation damage, heating could become a critical factor. If environmental chamber experiments are carried out on such specimens, however, there are several methods by which heating can be minimized. These consist primarily of techniques involving a reduction of beam intensity.

Since organic materials in an unfixed condition are usually sensitive to ionization damage, it is probably advisable to concentrate all available techniques on the reduction of the effects of radiation. It should be possible to minimize thermal damage by using specimen cooling attachments.

C. *Effects of Ionizing Radiation*

An incident beam of electrons may affect atoms in the specimen either directly or indirectly. Direct interactions include scattering, excitation, ionization and atomic displacement. Indirect interactions consist of the production of free radicals in the surrounding medium or the secondary emission of other types of ionizing radiation.

1. *Ionization*

Inelastic collisions may result in an energy transfer of such magnitude that specimen ionization takes place. The spectral analysis of electrons transmitted through thin organic films has revealed a range of losses, distributed on either side of a maximum at about 25 or 30 eV (Ruthemann, 1942; Möllenstedt, 1949; Watanabe, 1956; Cosslett, 1970). Values for the integrated energy loss (Rauth and Simpson, 1964) vary from 37 to 95 eV per electron in a carbon specimen. These values of energy transfer are sufficient to produce secondary reactions in organic molecules. The form and degree of damage produced depends on the nature of the organic molecule which is irradiated. Radiation damage is frequently measured by the radiolysis yield G, which is defined as the number of molecules fragmented by the absorption of 100 eV of energy. At 100 kV this amount of energy is absorbed in about 150 nm of water or hydrated tissue. The lowest values of G, ranging from 0·2 to 1·0, are exhibited by organic molecules containing aromatic groups. The relative insensitivity of these compounds to ionizing radiation may be related to the ability of the carbon atoms in benzene residues to share electrons. Unsaturated hydrocarbons exhibit the highest values of G, ranging from 10 to 10^4, whilst intermediate values are characteristic of saturated hydrocarbons and other organic molecules which do not contain aromatic groups (Reimer, 1965).

The ratio of inelastic to elastic scattering is an important parameter. The ratio between integral scattering cross-sections (Lenz, 1954, 1970) is given by

$$\frac{\sigma_{inelastic}}{\sigma_{elastic}} \approx \frac{20}{Z} \tag{1}$$

Consequently, the lightest elements are subjected to the highest proportion of inelastic collisions. Since the absolute values of the scattering cross-sections are affected independently by other factors, such as the accelerating voltage, no more than a qualitative emphasis should be placed on the ratio expressed by equation (1).

Both theory and experiment have shown that the percentage of electrons undergoing inelastic scattering is reduced if the voltage is increased to values in the vicinity of 500 kV or 1 MV (Molière, 1947; Agar *et al.*, 1949). Studies of damage in polyethylene crystals indicate that the cross-section for inelastic scattering decreases gradually between 75 and 500 kV (Kobayashi and Sakaoku, 1965). The interaction

of electrons with atoms decreases as the voltage is increased from
100 kV to 1 MV since the linear energy transfer is reduced by a
factor of 2·9 over this voltage range (Glaeser, 1970). Above 1 MV,
however, there is an increase in both linear energy transfer and in
displacement cross-section (Thach and Thach, 1970; Makin, 1970).
These factors probably contribute to the predicted increase in ionization beyond 1·7 MV (Sternheimer, 1961). Most contemporary
HVEM work will not be affected, however; it is only the relatively
small number of instruments operating at 3 MV which will be involved
(Dupouy and Perrier, 1969; Sakitani et al., 1971).

2. *Atomic displacement*

The molecular structure of organic specimens is unlikely to be
altered by the elastic scattering of 60 kV incident electrons (Haine,
1957). At much higher voltages, however, elastic scattering is accompanied by the displacement of atoms. Early studies of atomic displacement were carried out on metals which, because of their high conductivity,
are not subject to ionization damage. By contrast, both atomic displacement and ionization are important in organic compounds, which
are relatively non-conducting substances. Atomic displacement is
characterized by a minimum threshold voltage. Electrons accelerated
by greater potentials transfer sufficient energy to the nucleus to enable
the bonds holding atoms in place to be broken. The threshold voltage
is proportional to the atomic weight of the target atom (Makin, 1968;
Cosslett, 1970) but is slightly modified by variations in inter-atomic
forces. The presence of inter-atomic bonds in lattices, for example,
results in a threshold voltage of over 40 kV for crystalline graphite or
diamond (Scherzer, 1970). In contrast, amorphous carbon atoms have
a threshold voltage of 27 kV (Cosslett, 1970). The displacement cross-
section increases between threshold and approximately 54 kV. Above
that potential, the cross-section decreases slowly. In thick specimens
subjected to incident electrons of 60 kV or more, however, the energy
of the displaced atoms is sufficient to initiate a cascade type process in
which additional atoms may be affected. At 100 kV, it has been calculated that 0·03% of the carbon atoms present would be displaced per
second whilst the corresponding figure at 1 MV would be 0·04%
(Cosslett, 1970). Other estimates of the rate of elastic displacement of
carbon atoms have varied from 0·1% for dark-field conditions to
0·01% for transmission microscopy (Scherzer, 1970).

Hydrogen atoms should be more susceptible to displacement because
of their small mass. Irradiation at conventional voltages has, in fact,
resulted in the removal of slightly greater amounts of hydrogen,

varying from 0·5 to 1·2% s⁻¹ (Thach and Thach, 1971). At high voltages, however, the reduction in scattering cross-section for elastic collisions may compensate for the relatively low mass of the hydrogen atom. The calculated values of displaced hydrogen atoms do not differ greatly from those of carbon; a figure of 0·06% has been predicted for transmission microscopy (Scherzer, 1970).

D. *Methods of Reducing Radiation Damage*

Attempts have been made to alleviate radiation damage by using increased accelerating voltages, image intensification, a reduction in the total irradiation time or a lowering of specimen temperature.

It has been reported that an increase in voltage from 80 to 500 kV is accompanied by a significant reduction of damage in crystals of ℓ-valine (Glaeser *et al.*, 1970; Glaeser, 1971). The electron diffraction pattern of polyethylene is maintained for a longer period if the voltage is increased from 50 to 500 kV (Kobayashi and Sakaoku, 1965; Kobayashi and Ohara, 1966). However, it has also been demonstrated that the fading of such a diffraction pattern does not bear a direct relationship to radiation damage in all materials (Reimer, 1965).

One of the advantages of high voltage electron microscopy lies in the reduction of both specimen heating and ionization. Contamination should also be reduced because column pressures are maintained at lower absolute values. A slight potential disadvantage of HVEM techniques, however, lies in the production of X-rays from the objective lens aperture or the specimen holder. It has been suggested, however, that the amount of ionizing radiation from these sources may be minimized by using low atomic weight metals such as aluminium or beryllium (Ohr and Noggle, 1970).

Whilst techniques to reduce the intensity of the electron beam are relatively simple, it subsequently becomes necessary to employ some method of image enhancement. The usual procedure by which a low intensity image is amplified, without increasing radiation damage, involves the use of an image intensifier (Haine and Einstein, 1962; Anderson, 1968). Early models of image intensifiers proved to be more useful in the recording of high contrast electron diffraction patterns than in the amplification of ordinary transmission images (Morrow and Horner, 1966; Kobayashi and Ohara, 1966). Subsequent technical developments have improved the signal-to-noise ratio which previously limited the resolution and image quality. For example, computer enhancement processing of the image from a three-stage intensifier, coupled to a Vidicon by means of a fibre optic plate, has produced an improved image of negatively stained catalase (Nathan, 1970). The higher resolution attainable in this particular specimen, however, may partially depend on the regular repetition of structure in a crystalline material.

A second method by which the signal-to-noise ratio may be improved involves the use of a high efficiency Orthicon tube. This is attached to a fluorescent screen by means of a fibre optic plate (Mayeda *et al.*, 1970a,b; Imura *et al.*, 1971a). Although no intermediate amplification system is required, the resolution is limited by the diameter of the fibre optic elements and the granularity of the fluorescent material. Significant improvements have been made recently in the physical properties of the fluorescent screens used (Imura *et al.*, 1971b).

The present state of technological development is such that image intensification can be expected to decrease by two or three orders of magnitude the radiation dose required to obtain an image from a specimen (Reynolds, 1968). In one instance an improvement of up to five orders of magnitude has been attained, if one takes into account the capability of recording an image in only one thirtieth of a second (Imura *et al.*, 1971a).

Attempts to reduce exposure time by the production of more sensitive photographic emulsions have met with only moderate success (Valentine, 1965) but have not yet been abandoned (Hashimoto *et al.*, 1970).

There are also well-known methods of examining the specimen which avoid subjecting it to a longer period of irradiation than is required for the actual recording of the image. This result may be accomplished by focusing on one region and then moving the specimen laterally so that a previously unirradiated area is photographed.

The results of experiments in which specimens were maintained at low temperatures during EM examination have been extremely variable. Whilst the theoretical mean energy required to disrupt a bond is higher at reduced temperatures (Venables and Bassett, 1967), some hydrocarbon molecules appear to derive no benefit from cooling (Kobayashi and Sakaoku, 1965). Although *E. coli* exhibits an apparent five-fold reduction in radiation sensitivity over the range 0 to −196°C, this has been shown to be dependent upon the presence of oxygen (Stapleton and Edington, 1956). It is possible that latent phenomena, which occur at low temperatures, produce actual structural damage only when the specimen is allowed to thaw. Delayed changes of this nature are exhibited by both paraffin and tetracene crystals when irradiated at −269°C (Siegel, 1970b). Dry spores of *Bacillus megaterium*, however, appear to be protected at low temperatures under anaerobic conditions (Powers *et al.*, 1959). The degree of damage which is produced after the spores are rewarmed and cultured is proportional to the absolute temperature, between -145 and $+36°C$, at which irradiation is carried out.

IV. RADIATION DAMAGE IN UNPROTECTED ORGANIC SPECIMENS

In order to place radiation results on a quantitative basis, the dose received by the specimen must be ascertained. The relevant literature, however, contains two major collections of data expressed in different units. Radiation biologists use "rads" as their standard unit of measurement of dosage. Electron microscopists, however, record beam currents in amp cm^{-2} and, multiplying by the time of irradiation, arrive at a dosage expressed in coulomb cm^{-2}.

It may not be immediately obvious that most radiobiological data can be directly compared with results attained by electron microscopy. Whichever type of ionizing particle or radiation is employed, however, the incident radiation normally serves merely as a source of energy which is gradually converted into the production of large numbers of secondary electrons. Radiation damage in both types of experiment may therefore be attributed to interactions between electrons produced by the "source" and atoms or molecules present within the "specimen".

In theory, it should be relatively straightforward to compare the quantitative results expressed in rads and in coulomb cm^{-2}. One important difference between the two units, however, is that rads are a measure of energy absorbed per gram of sample, whilst coulomb cm^{-2} refers to the total energy incident on the specimen. In radiation biological experiments, the sample thickness is such that some of the primary ionizing radiations and a proportion of the secondary electrons lose all of their energy by multiple collisions. Consequently, there are variations in linear energy transfer (LET) values between the beginning and end of the paths of the ionizing particles. In electron microscopy such a result is much less common because extremely thin specimens are employed. For precisely the same reason back scattering should also be reduced in EM work. The LET values used in radiation biology may not, therefore, be identical with those appropriate for electron microscopy.

There is another factor which may further complicate correlation of the two types of experiment. The rate of irradiation in terms of rad s^{-1} from a 1000 Curie cobalt-60 source is much lower than that which is normally encountered in electron microscopy (Toohey and Joy, 1972). Radiation repair processes are therefore more likely to be effective in compensating for damage sustained in some types of radiobiological experiments compared to that produced within an EM environmental chamber. Pulse radiolysis experiments, however, involve doses of over 10^5 rad in a few ns (McDonald *et al.*, 1971).

Normal viewing conditions in electron microscopy consist of a beam current of 10^{-2} amp cm^{-2} for a magnification of 10^4 (Reimer, 1965). The dose incident upon the specimen in one second will therefore be 10^{-2} coulomb cm^{-2}. Under these conditions, at a beam voltage of 100 kV, the dose absorbed by the specimen will be 4×10^9 rad s^{-1}.† A slightly lower value has been reported for a 60 kV beam (Reimer, 1965). The LET value for 60 kV electrons is approximately 1·06 eV nm^{-1}, since there is an inverse relationship between LET and accelerating voltage in thin films. Therefore, the dose corresponding to a beam current of 10^{-2} amp cm^{-2} at 60 kV for 1 s should be approximately 10^{10} rad. In HVEM work, on the other hand, the LET value at 1 MV is approximately 2×10^{-1} eV nm^{-1}. Since this LET value is maintained over the first μm of the path of a 1 MV electron, 200 eV are deposited in this thickness. This represents a dose of 2×10^9 rad s^{-1} if it is assumed that the specimen current density is the same.

If a lower current density were used, then the dose per unit time would be reduced. In the latter situation, however, the time of exposure would normally have to be lengthened proportionately in order to record the image, so no net advantage would be gained. When an image intensifier is employed, however, it should be possible to achieve some reduction in dosage (Imura *et al.*, 1971a).

A correlation between dosages known to produce structural damage in specimens examined in radiobiological and EM experiments at 100 kV is represented in Fig. 3. A similar scale, derived independently (Glaeser, 1971) is shown in Fig. 4.

The previous calculations refer to the dosage received by a specimen during its irradiation for 1 s. The relationships between dosage, time of irradiation and a number of other factors are included in Fig. 5. Although a period of several seconds is normally required for the photographic recording of an image, it is customary to reduce the beam

---

† Since one ampere is the current resulting from the passage of $6·25 \times 10^{18}$ electrons s^{-1} the specimen will be subjected to an electron flux of $6·25 \times 10^{16}$ electrons cm^{-2} s^{-1}. An accelerating voltage of 100 kV is frequently used. At this voltage, the LET of an electron in organic matter is 4×10^{-1} eV nm^{-1} (Stenn and Bahr, 1970). The specimen thickness chosen is, within limits, irrelevant since the final dose in rad is independent of the thickness. (The appropriate value of LET does depend on specimen thickness, however, $6·4 \times 10^{-1}$ eV nm^{-1} being a typical value for bulk samples (Glaeser, 1970)). If it is assumed that the specimen consists of a layer of organic material 2 nm thick, such a sample would absorb 0·8 eV from each electron. Since 1 eV is equal to $1·6 \times 10^{-12}$ ergs, the dosage may be expressed as 5×10^{16} eV cm^{-2} s^{-1} or 8×10^4 ergs cm^{-2} s^{-1}. Assuming a density of 1·0, the weight of a 1 cm^2 area of film of the thickness chosen would be 2×10^{-7} g. Since one rad is defined as the deposition of 100 ergs per gram of material, the dose absorbed by the specimen will be $(8 \times 10^4)/(100)(2 \times 10^{-7})$ rad s^{-1}.

current proportionately. The purpose of this procedure is to ensure an even exposure over the entire surface of the photographic emulsion.

It has been calculated that approximately 10^{-11} coulomb cm^{-2} are required at the plane of the emulsion in order to produce a photographic image (Valentine, 1966). A simple arithmetical calculation or reference to Fig. 5 will show that in order to attain a charge of this magnitude at the final image plane at a magnification of 10^4 the specimen must receive a dose of 10^{-3} coulomb cm^{-2} or 4×10^8 rad at 100 kV.

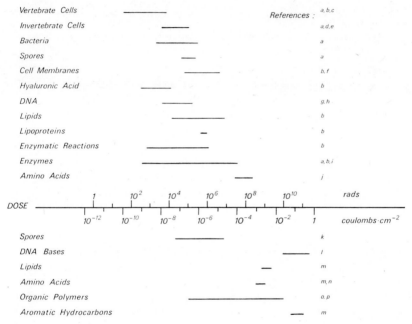

FIG. 3. Relationship between radiobiological effects expressed in rad and EM radiation effects expressed in coulomb cm^{-2}. The data on which this figure is based are taken from experimental results given by: (a) Alexander, 1965; (b) Kuzin, 1964; (c) Lippincott et al., 1970; (d) Ducoff et al., 1971; (e) Kimeldorf and Fortner, 1971; (f) Masurovsky et al., 1967; (g) Taylor et al., 1947; (h) Limperos and Mosher, 1950; (i) Booth, 1970; (j) Clark et al., 1970; (k) von Ardenne, 1939; (l) Crewe et al., 1970, 1971; (m) Reimer, 1965; (n) Glaeser et al., 1970; (o) Kobayashi and Sakaoku, 1965; (p) Bahr et al., 1965.

The effects of electron irradiation have also been studied on a qualitative basis, by comparing the intensities of individual diffraction spots or arcs. By means of selected area electron diffraction techniques, it has been possible to obtain information from irradiated regions of crystalline specimens; see Fig. 6.

It should always be borne in mind, however, that molecules in a crystalline state are possibly more resistant to radiation than the same molecules in an amorphous aggregation. Irradiation studies of copper phthalocyanine derivatives (Mayeda *et al.*, 1970b; Uyeda *et al.*, 1970) provide a specific molecular example. Halogenation of the 16 peripheral CH groups with chlorine increases the radiation resistance of the crystals by a factor of 30. It has been found, however, that halogenation of some non-crystalline organic materials usually makes them more susceptible to radiation damage (Bahr *et al.*, 1965). Destruction of crystalline and molecular organization is not always simultaneous

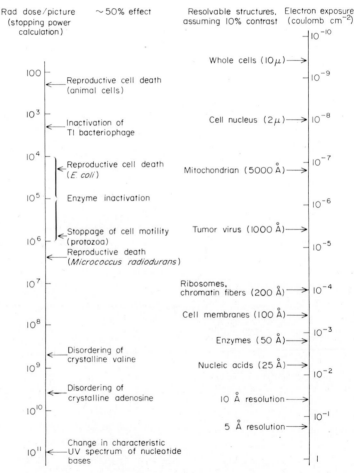

Fig. 4. Comparison of radiobiological and EM experimental results. (After Glaeser, 1971.)

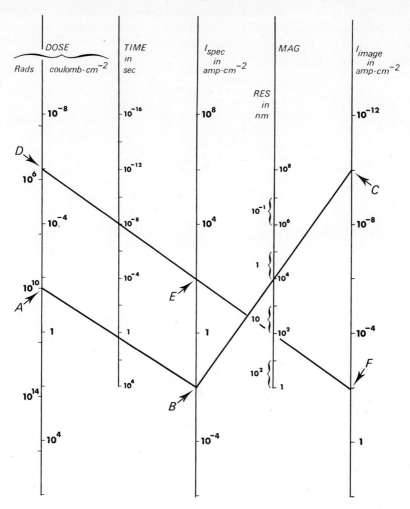

FIG. 5. Inter-relationships between the dosage received by a specimen and the conditions of operation of an electron microscope. "Time" refers to the period of irradiation within the electron microscope. "I_{spec}." refers to the beam current at the specimen. "Res." refers to resolution. "Mag." refers to the magnification of the final image which is recorded. "I_{image}" refers to the beam current at the plane of the image recording device. The lines joining the points labelled ABC correspond to conditions frequently employed in electron microscopy at 100 kV. Line DE represents a radiation dose at which 100% survival of unprotected *Micrococcus radiodurans* would occur, following a single exposure 10^{-8} s in duration at a specimen beam current of 100 amp cm^{-2} from a field emission source. In order to record an image, however, the magnification would have to be reduced to correspond with line EF. Image intensification of at least four orders of magnitude would be required to reduce the resolution to a useful value. Refer to section V(D) of the text.

(Stenn and Bahr, 1970). Phthalocyanine molecules may remain intact yet lose their crystallinity during irradiation, whilst tetracene molecules may be destroyed without visible alteration of the diffraction pattern of the sample (Reimer, 1965).

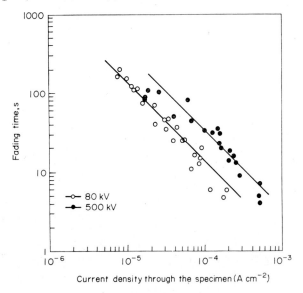

Fig. 6. Radiation damage curves for crystalline ℓ-valine. The time that a diffraction pattern persists at a given illumination intensity is plotted as a function of the current density at the object. (After Glaeser et al., 1970.)

Crystalline catalase is frequently used in electron diffraction experiments and it is generally assumed that its responses are representative of a typical protein molecule. The crystalline attributes of this specimen, however, should be considered. It has been demonstrated, for example, that the radiation sensitivities of dry preparations of amorphous and crystalline catalase differ (Setlow and Doyle, 1953). In addition, catalase is less susceptible to radiation damage than most proteins, perhaps because of the absence of sulphydryl groups within the enzyme (Barron, 1954).

Polyethylene, which is highly radiation sensitive, has been used as a test object for electron diffraction studies of irradiation damage (Stoyanova and Morozova, 1963). At those electron beam intensities which are normally employed in transmission microscopy, the electron diffraction pattern fades within a minute or less. Similar results occur when other crystalline organic specimens are irradiated with 100 kV electrons. The wide angle electron diffraction spacings from 0·1 to

0·4 nm vanish within a few seconds. Spacings of 1 to 2·5 nm remain somewhat longer, but also disappear gradually (Parsons, 1970). Image intensification techniques have, however, been able to prolong the period during which the diffraction pattern of polyethylene is maintained by a factor of up to 45 (Morrow and Horner, 1966, Mayeda et al., 1970b).

It has been suggested that the primary event occurring in molecular radiation damage consists of the ionization of carbon atoms. Secondary phenomena include the formation of carbon-carbon double bonds, cross-linking, chain scission, radical formation and the extrusion of hydrogen atoms (Kobayashi and Sakaoku, 1965). Whatever the relative sequence and importance of the various initial events may be, it seems fairly certain that the ultimate nature of radiation damage in polyethylene consists of the formation of cross-linkages between adjacent CH_2 groups, accompanied by the release of gaseous hydrogen (Reimer, 1965). Chemical analyses have been carried out on 1 to 5 μm thick films of commercial polyethylene subjected to irradiation by 75 kV electrons (Bahr et al., 1965). The samples had received 50% of the dose to which they would normally be exposed during focusing and image recording. It was found that 5% of the initial mass had been removed during irradiation and that the residue consisted of approximately 87·5% carbon and 12·5% hydrogen. Commercial polyethylene, however, is contaminated by additives such as anti-oxidants, low molecular weight compounds and catalyst residues (Phillips, 1970). The analytical data may not, therefore, be typical of pure polyethylene, which consists of 86% carbon and 14% hydrogen.

Damage to protein molecules undoubtedly contributes to the effects of radiation on living cells. Both general and specific radiation responses occur. Experiments have shown that irradiated protein molecules retain residues of elements other than carbon. For example, thin films of gelatin, whilst retaining 90% of their original carbon, also retain 60% of their oxygen, 75% of their hydrogen and approximately 90% of their nitrogen content (Bahr et al., 1965). In another protein, wheat gliadin, it has been concluded that random bond scission is responsible for most of the irradiation damage (Booth, 1970).

In certain proteins which contain sulphur it is thought that radiation damage ultimately becomes localized in the cystine residues (Gordy et al., 1955). Enzymes containing sulphydryl groups, such as the dehydrogenases, are extremely radiosensitive in dilute solution (Barron et al., 1949). The responses of enzymes in vitro, however, do not always correspond with those exhibited by the same molecules in intact cells (Roth and Eichel, 1955). Enzymes such as lysozyme and catalase, which do not contain sulphydryl groups, are considerably more resistant to irradiation (Forssberg, 1947; Proctor et al., 1952; Barron, 1954). In proteins which lack cystine, it has been suggested that radiation damage is concentrated within hydrogen bonds (Eidus, 1956). The inactivation of lysozyme, however, is now known to be related to specific reactions between hydroxyl radicals and tryptophan residues (Aldrich and Cundall, 1969).

When proteins are found in complexes with lipids, they are able to withstand doses as high as 10^6 r (Kuzin, 1964). The specific radiation damage which lipo-proteins sustain may involve the oxidation of double bonds in the lipid moiety (Chevallier and Burg, 1953).

The nucleic acid content of living organisms is well known to be susceptible to radiation damage. Structural alterations in untreated DNA molecules have been observed directly within the electron microscope (Williams and Fisher, 1970a). Viscosity and sedimentation measurements indicate that in irradiated solutions of DNA molecular scission takes place (Taylor et al., 1948; Hems, 1960).

Viruses, which contain both proteins and nucleic acids, are a particularly favourable type of biological specimen. They are small enough to be visualized in their entirety within the electron microscope and many of them are relatively simple in biochemical composition. Studies of some of the more specialized viruses have indicated that minute but discernible losses in fine structural details have occurred after electron irradiation. A degradation of bacteriophage T4 tail fibre structure, for example, results from a 30s exposure to the electron beam (Williams and Fisher, 1970b). Intensive studies of the effects of ionizing radiation on bacteriophage T7 viruses have been carried out recently (Dewey, 1970).

Bacterial spores have also been examined in the electron microscope on a number of occasions (Haskins, 1938; Siegel, 1970b). The physico-chemical properties of spores are such that their responses cannot be compared with those of fully hydrated and metabolically active cells. Spores of *Bacillus subtilis* ATCC 6633, for example, are insensitive to extremely low pressures and temperatures down to $-269°C$. Specimens of this nature ought to be useful test objects for the determination of radiation sensitivity in minimally hydrated proteins and other organic molecules (see Fig. 7). Electron irradiated spores of *Bacillus proteus vulgaris* have been cultured after being returned to standard temperature and pressure conditions (von Ardenne and Friedrich-Freksa, 1941). Other experiments indicate that spores of *Bacillus megaterium* exhibit 100% survival after receiving extremely low doses of $1·5 \times 10^{-6}$ and 4×10^{-6} coulomb cm^{-2} at 100 kV and 2 MV respectively. Higher doses resulted in decreased viabilities (Nagata and Fukai, 1971; Nagata and Ishikawa, 1971). Virtually no spores would have survived the level of dosage which would have been required to record a direct photographic image during irradiation.

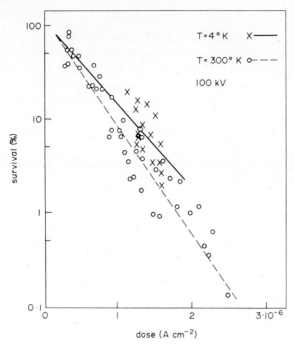

FIG. 7. The survival of electron irradiated spores of *B. subtilis* ATCC 6633 at different temperatures. (After Siegel, 1970b.)

Preliminary studies have been made of electron irradiation damage in fixed and embedded cells. Initial results have indicated that membranes in specimens treated with glutaraldehyde and osmium tetroxide show visible signs of damage. This occurs well within the minimum time normally required for focusing and image recording (Williams and Fisher, 1970b).

V. ORGANIC SPECIMENS IN ENVIRONMENTAL CHAMBERS

The responses to irradiation of hydrated molecules and structures are modified by a number of factors. These include the "oxygen effect", enhanced free radical production, the action of chemical protective agents and the influence of temperature variations. Attempts to preserve the viability of cells may be assisted by exploiting innate properties such as radiation resistance and repair mechanisms. However, the motility of cells and their contents makes the observation of living organisms exceptionally difficult.

A. *Environmental Chamber Construction and Techniques*

A number of attempts have been made to determine optimal conditions for the observation of aqueous specimens at voltages up to 100 kV. Chambers have been constructed in which the specimen is maintained in a hydrated condition at a pressure above that of the main part of the microscope column (Ito and Hiziya, 1958; Stoyanova and Mikhailovskii, 1959; Heide, 1960, 1962). Some of these chambers, however, have failed to fulfil all of the original expectations of the designers (Causey, 1968).

The extension of electron microscopy to higher voltages has stimulated fundamental developments in many fields of ultrastructural research. The technical capabilities of high voltage electron microscopy have been comprehensively described in recent reviews (Cosslett, 1967a,b, 1968; Dupouy, 1968). Since the penetration of electrons in organic material increases with beam voltage, it has become possible to observe specimens several μm thick in environmental chambers.

1. *Environmental chamber designs*

The majority of chambers which have been constructed may be divided into two categories. The chamber may either be exposed to the microscope column vacuum (Ruska, 1942; Ito and Hiziya, 1958; Parsons, 1969; Matricardi *et al.*, 1970; Swann and Tighe, 1971; Ward and Mitchell, 1972) or completely sealed off (Stoyanova and Mikhailovskii, 1959; Heide, 1962; Dupouy and Perrier, 1962; Escaig and Sella, 1966; Allinson, 1970a,b; Fukami *et al.*, 1970). In the former design, pressure is controlled dynamically by allowing a gaseous medium to flow over the specimen before being removed by accessory pumping systems. Details of three different dynamic chambers are shown in Figs. 8 and 9. Several typical static environmental chambers are illustrated in Figs. 10 to 13.

In theory static chambers might be expected to have certain advantages, since continuous control may be maintained over the pressure and composition of the environment throughout the specimen. In practice, however, these advantages seem to be outweighed by two other considerations. The presence of electron transparent windows strong enough to withstand significant pressure differentials and to remain impermeable to the environmental gases frequently leads to a serious reduction in resolution. Any tendency of the windows to rupture on exposure to water vapour or on irradiation would rapidly convert an initially static system into a dynamic one which would lack the ability to maintain an equilibrium pressure. Although both techniques continue to be improved, at present there seems to be a trend towards the development and use of dynamic rather than static systems.

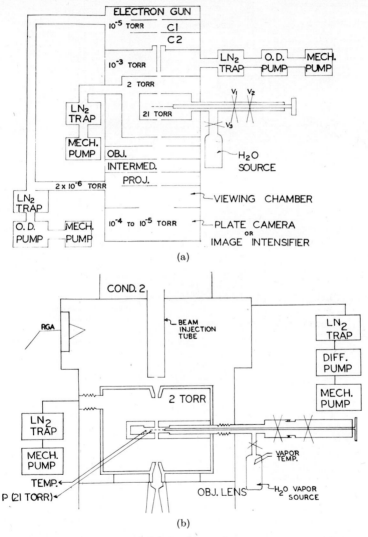

(a)

(b)

FIG. 8. Schematic diagrams and details of (a) a dynamic environmental chamber in relation to the rest of the microscope and (b) a two aperture dynamic environmental chamber. (After Moretz *et al.*, 1971.)

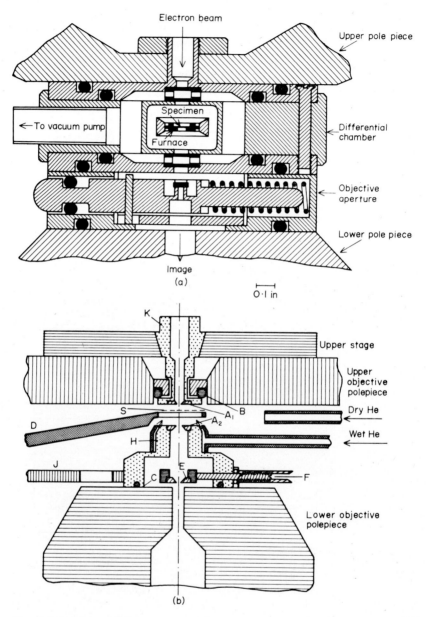

FIG. 9. Diagrams of different types of dynamic environmental chambers: (a) (after Swann and Tighe, 1971); (b) (after Ward and Mitchell, 1972).

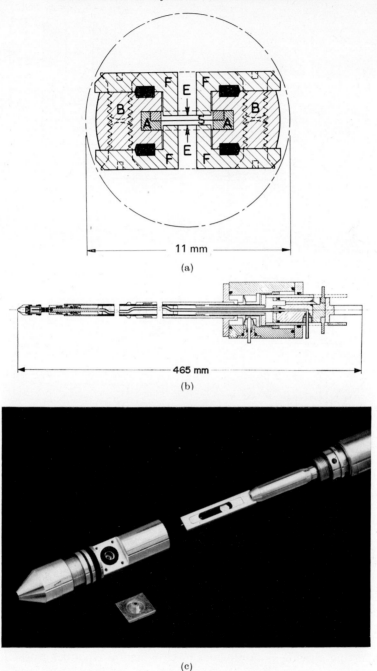

FIG. 10.(a) Cross-section of a static environmental chamber; (b) Diagram of the specimen holder rod and gas inlets; (c) Photograph of the specimen holder rod. (After Allinson, 1970b.) "Crown copyright reserved; National Physical Laboratory."

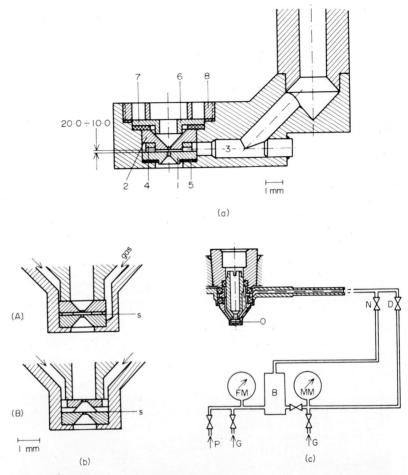

FIG. 11. Static environmental chambers: (a) after Stoyanova and Mikhailovskii, 1959; (b) after Heide, 1962; (c) after Heide, 1960.

2. *Environmental chamber windows and specimen supporting films*

In early types of environmental chambers one of the windows usually served a dual purpose by acting as the specimen supporting film. In at least one dynamic chamber design the two functions have been separated, allowing greater flexibility of specimen movement within the environmental chamber.

A wide variety of materials has been used for windows and for supporting specimens in aqueous environmental chamber work. Films have been prepared from both crystalline and amorphous materials.

Single crystals of mica, graphite, diamond or corundum have been tried in various chambers (Fernández-Morán, 1960a, 1966; Hale *et al.*, 1970). Amorphous collodion, reinforced with carbon and silicon oxide, has also been tried (Escaig and Sella, 1966). If it is proposed to use a collodion film to support the specimen without reinforcement, the film

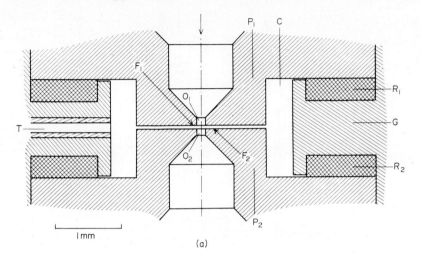

(a)

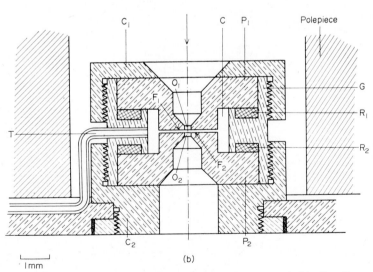

(b)

Fig. 12. Details of a static environmental chamber: (a) and (b) after Dupouy and Perrier, 1962.

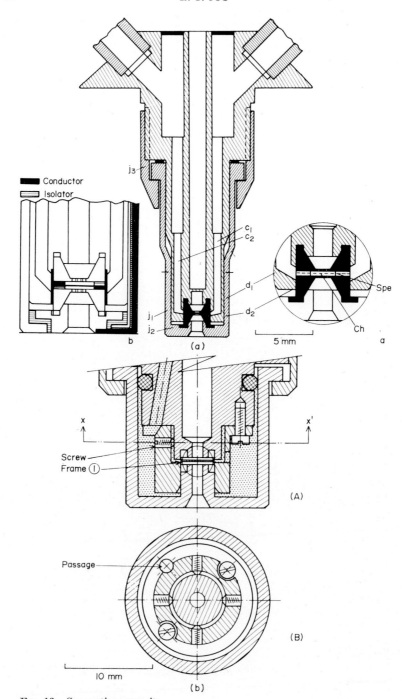

Conductor
Isolator

j3

c₁
c₂

d₁

j₁
j₂

d₂

b

(a)

5 mm

Spe

Ch

a

x   x′

Screw
Frame ①

(A)

Passage

10 mm

(B)

(b)

Fig. 13—*See caption opposite.*

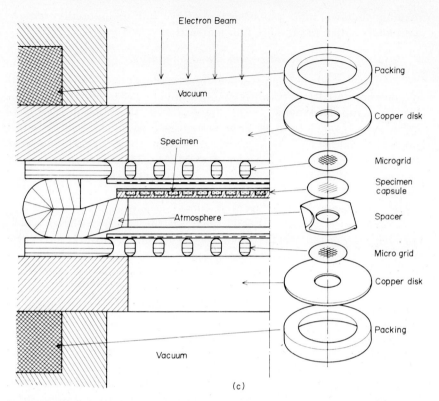

FIG. 13. Details of static environmental chambers: (a) after Escaig and Sella, 1966; (b) and (c) after Fukami *et al.*, 1970.

should be prepared on mercury rather than on water in order to render it impermeable to water vapour (Taylor, 1926; Abrams and McBain, 1944). The properties of certain embedding media are altered by contact with adjacent layers of other materials. The electron stability of Epon, for example, is diminished when it is included in a sandwich of carbon (Wachtel *et al.*, 1966).

Whether the specimen support film surface is hydrophilic or hydrophobic is of some importance. The natural properties of support films may be masked by introducing a layer of organic material which holds the specimen in place electrostatically (Dubochet *et al.*, 1971). Although this procedure has been used mainly with dried and stained specimens, it may be possible to adapt it for use with hydrated material.

It cannot be concluded that any particular specimen support film material has proved ideal for all applications. Specimens of widely varying chemical and physical properties will undoubtedly require completely different support film materials.

3. *Properties of the environmental chamber medium*

(a) *Oxygen content*. The presence of oxygen enhances damage caused by ionizing radiation (Crabtree and Cramer, 1933; Mottram, 1935; Anderson and Turkowitz, 1941). For example, the fraction of *E. coli* which survives a dose of 90 krad is increased significantly if a buffer solution equilibrated with nitrogen rather than oxygen is used (Burnett *et al.*, 1951; Hollaender *et al.*, 1951). The radiosensitivity of various cells is altered by a factor of approximately three when anoxic conditions are employed (de Serres, 1961).

The mechanism of the "oxygen effect" is a complex one and has been reviewed elsewhere (Wood, 1958). Of the two hypotheses which have been suggested, the first involves the ionization of water molecules and the production of free radicals. These are subsequently thought to create peroxides which are responsible for the secondary damage. The second hypothesis postulates that oxygen reacts directly with organic molecules at a primary position in the sequence of events leading to radiation damage.

Regardless of the type of cell, there is a specific oxygen content, below which radiosensitivity is markedly reduced (Gray, 1959). The critical concentration lies in the vicinity of 1 to 10 mg litre^{-1} (Hollaender and Stapleton, 1953) or at a partial pressure of less than 1% oxygen (Howard-Flanders and Alper, 1957). In environmental chamber experiments, inert gases such as argon (Stoyanova and Morozova, 1963), helium or nitrogen (Heide, 1962; Swann and Tighe, 1971) are often employed in order to prevent oxygen from coming into contact with the specimen during irradiation.

Cells may also be protected from the oxygen effect by the addition of hydrogen donors such as $Na_2S_2O_4$ and simple sulphydryl compounds. Various theories attempting to explain the protective properties of substances such as cysteamine have been considered in detail elsewhere (Revesz and Bergstrand, 1963; Sinclair, 1969). It is known that $Na_2S_2O_4$ is able to remove dissolved oxygen from a solution (Burnett *et al.*, 1952). Other protective chemicals which are reducing compounds may be able to accomplish the same result.

In environmental chamber work, therefore, it is desirable to use a low concentration of oxygen and to add protective chemicals when appropriate. Both techniques will interfere with some of the physiological reactions of the cell. This disadvantage is preferable, however, to the complete destruction of cells by ionizing radiation.

(b) *Water content.* In conventional electron microscopical techniques, water is completely removed from the specimen. In many environmental chamber experiments, however, it is a requisite that some water shall be present. Whether hydration of a specimen is advantageous or not depends upon the response of the organic molecules concerned. Excessive dehydration must be avoided when nucleic acids are examined since the secondary structure of the molecules depends upon hydrogen bond interactions with adjacent water molecules. Dehydration alone, uncomplicated by thermal or radiation damage, is sufficient to interfere with the molecular and crystalline structural order of DNA. A similar interpretation may be placed on the results of X-ray and electron diffraction studies of catalase (Longley, 1967; Parsons and Matricardi, 1972). In contrast, polyribonucleotide and polyamino acid preparations maintain their ability to yield an electron diffraction pattern even when exposed to the microscope column vacuum (Parsons, 1966).

In dynamic environmental chamber experiments, water vapour may be included in the gaseous medium circulated to a specimen (refer to Fig. 14). Although resolution is obviously impaired by the presence of water vapour, images of dislocation fringes were still visible in some regions of the original micrographs under the conditions specified for Fig. 14(c).

The accumulation of liquid water droplets upon the specimen produces areas from which an exceptionally high proportion of electrons are scattered. Liquid water seems to be significantly more electron opaque than objects of higher absolute density (see Fig. 15). It has even been suggested that water could be used as an electron dense or negative stain for organic materials (Moretz *et al.*, 1970). The deposition of electron dense regions of liquid water has also been observed in static designs of environmental chambers (Allinson, 1971). In every instance in which water droplets have been observed on supporting films (Heide, 1962; Parsons and Moretz, 1970; Ward and Mitchell, 1972) they have exhibited a characteristically high electron density.

One structural peculiarity which is sometimes seen in droplets of water is a halo effect, in which a central dense portion of the droplet is surrounded by a less dense region. Frequently the increase in density is gradual (see Fig. 16). At other times, however, the halo seems to be relatively constant in density, with a sudden increase in density at the edge of the central region, as in Fig. 15. There are a number of possible explanations. Water vapour could have been deposited on both sides of the specimen at "cold" points. Alternatively, the properties of the solid/liquid interface or contamination by residual hydrocarbons may affect the surface tension forces present. It is also conceivable that two different varieties of water are present (Moretz *et al.*, 1970).

FIG. 14. Stainless steel specimen observed in 1·5 mm thick dynamic environmental chamber in: (a) Helium at 10^{-5} torr; (b) He at 760 torr; (c) He saturated with water at 760 torr. (After Swann, 1972).

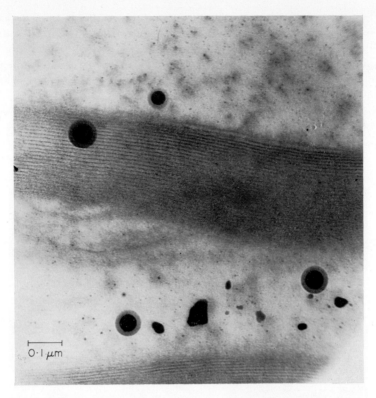

FIG. 15. Water droplets on a thin araldite section of OsO_4 fixed nerve myelin maintained in a low temperature stage cooled by liquid nitrogen and observed at 100 kV. The specimen was exposed to vacuum on both sides.

It is possible that the excessively dense appearance of microorganisms observed in HVEM environmental chamber experiments (Dupouy *et al.*, 1960; Stoyanova, 1961, 1966a) may be due more to the high scattering of electrons by water molecules than to "carbonization" of the specimen. If this is so, then in any specimens in which intracellular detail is observed, the extent of hydration must remain a matter for speculation until it becomes possible to make quantitative measurements. The recommended mode of operation in one type of static environmental chamber included the removal of excess water, ostensibly in order to decrease the production of free radicals (Stoyanova and Morozova, 1963). It may be found that the application of dynamic chamber methods will result in the partial dehydration of intact cells and living organisms. It is to be hoped that this problem is not a serious one.

The presence of water in an environmental chamber may be expected to enhance the production of indirect ionization. The free radicals produced by the irradiation of water act as electron acceptors and remove electrons from atoms in macromolecules in their immediate vicinity. Although the mechanism and effects of the production of free radicals are reasonably well understood, the quantitative relationship between water content and free radical production is a complex one. It has been demonstrated that radiation damage is proportional to the water content of a specimen (Stapleton and Hollaender, 1952). However, it is necessary to specify water content or hydration precisely.

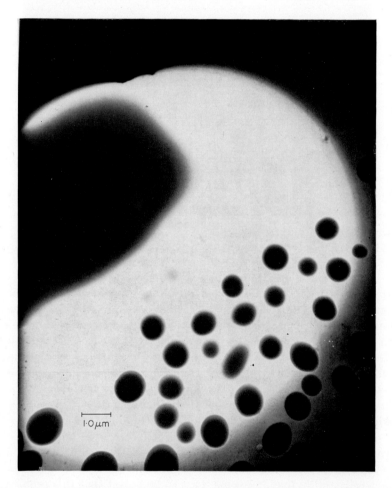

Fig. 16. Water droplets observed in a dynamic environmental chamber. (After Parsons, 1971.)

For example, "desiccated" spores of *Aspergillus terreus* contain 25% water by weight whilst "dry" spores contain approximately 42%. When spores are suspended in excess water they contain no more than 80% by weight. Within these limits of hydration, the radiation damage does not vary by more than a factor of two. If bound water could be almost entirely removed it might be possible to effect a considerable improvement in radiation resistance.

Water content and oxygen content seem to be additive in their effects (de Serres, 1961). A combination of dehydration and anoxia leads to a radioprotective increase by a factor of five in *Saccharomyces cerevisiae*. In this experiment dehydration was accomplished by immersion in 6·9 M glycerol. Since this compound is itself a radioprotective agent, however, the results cannot be interpreted solely in terms of dehydration and anoxia.

(c) *Environmental temperature.* In designing environmental chambers in which the temperature of the medium and specimen is to be controlled, a decision must be made as to whether or not freezing is to be allowed. In providing a heat sink with sufficient capacity to counteract the instantaneous influence of the electron beam, however, the specimen may inadvertently be frozen. A sophisticated system of temperature sensing and control is required if the medium is to be prevented from freezing.

The probability of freezing may be reduced by the introduction of one of a number of compounds which can lower the freezing point of the aqueous solution. Since dimethyl sulphoxide (DMSO) is employed both for this purpose and for protection against the effects of ionizing radiation, DMSO may be an ideal solute for certain types of cells. Other types of cryo-protective solutes, such as glycerol, ethanol, methanol, ethylene-glycol and dimethyl formamide are also available for use (Meryman, 1971).

It should be possible to avoid thermal damage by cooling the specimen directly. However, the deleterious effects of freezing may outweigh those of heating. With some materials physical damage accompanies the phase change from liquid to solid and is difficult to avoid, no matter how quickly or by what method the temperature is lowered.

In hydrated specimens, the rate of freezing before irradiation can be a critical factor. In certain types of cells, slow rates of freezing may lead to a disruption of the cell membranes. A generalization that rapid freezing is not deleterious to the ultrastructural features of cells has led to the development of the preparative technique of freeze etching. There are some types of cell, however, in which slow rates of freezing are advantageous. In cells which are expected to retain their physiological properties after freezing and thawing, the nature of the rewarming regime may prove to be a critical factor.

Under certain irradiation conditions it is advantageous for the specimen to be cooled. This is usually effective, however, only if the specimen is maintained continuously at a low temperature during irradiation, observation and image recording. The cooling of biological objects to temperatures well below the freezing point of water is a technique of long standing (Marton, 1934). Liquid nitrogen cold stages have been developed for a number of different types of electron microscope (Dvoryankin, 1960; Watanabe et al., 1960; Fernández-Morán, 1960a,b,c, 1962; Hedley and McGeagh, 1963; Wayte and Thornton, 1967; Herrell and Ferrier, 1969; Heide and Urban, 1970). Experimental stages have also been developed for operation at liquid helium temperatures (Venables, 1963; Piercy et al., 1963; Valdrè and Goringe, 1965; Watanabe and Ishikawa, 1967; Venables et al., 1968; Fernández-Morán, 1970). Cold stages have frequently been employed either to prevent heating damage or to study the phase changes of metallurgical and inorganic specimens. At least one cold stage, however, has been constructed specifically for research into the effects of radiation at temperatures between -269 and $+27\,^{\circ}\mathrm{C}$ (Heide and Urban, 1970). The details and size of this stage may be compared with those of an earlier model designed for operation at 100 kV, using liquid nitrogen as a coolant (Heide, 1965b). It is readily apparent that HVEM techniques have involved substantial increases in the complexity of the equipment and also in its flexibility.

The most obvious method of cooling an environmental chamber involves the direct attachment of a heat sink. This method may be limited, however, by the thermal conductivity of the supporting film and is probably inefficient with dry or isolated aqueous specimens. An alternative method consists of cooling the gaseous medium outside the microscope before it is circulated past the specimen (Krause, 1937).

Ultrathin frozen sections of unfixed material have been transferred directly from the freeze sectioning apparatus to a conventional electron microscope and kept frozen on a cold stage during examination (Fernández-Morán, 1962). In such experiments there is an inherent danger that sublimation of water vapour from the ice will occur. The factors governing sublimation during electron irradiation include the temperature at which the specimen is maintained and the pressure to which the specimen is exposed. Under conditions in which sublimation may be prevented, the ability of ice to scatter electrons must be considered.

Published micrographs indicate that ice crystals deposited from residual water vapour are no less electron opaque than the thin droplets of water depicted in Fig. 16. The material was identified as ice by means of its characteristic crystalline shape and by correlated electron diffraction patterns (Fernández-Morán, 1960d,e). Since ice is as opaque as liquid water, the advantages of using frozen specimens in electron microscopy would consist of a reduction in specimen movement and the restriction of radiation damage, in some materials, to the status of a latent phenomenon.

HVEM techniques have enabled much thicker frozen specimens to be examined. The increasing availability of freezing attachments for ultramicrotomes (Persson, 1970, 1972; Christensen and Paavola, 1972) should facilitate the observation of unfixed preparations in a frozen condition. Such equipment has been designed specifically for the preparation of sections which are normally treated with electron dense stains either before or after freezing. However, the freezing attachments could be used to produce sections for examination in the electron microscope whilst still frozen and unstained. It has been found advantageous to add gelatin to the specimen before freeze-sectioning (Bernhard and Viron, 1971; Bernhard, 1972).

B. *Specimen Viability during and after Irradiation*

1. *Bacteria*

Cultures of *Bacillus mycoides* and *B. mesentericus* have been examined in a "moist" condition in environmental chamber experiments at 60 to 65 kV (Stoyanova *et al.*, 1960a). When cells of *B. mycoides* were returned to a growth medium after an initial irradiation, it was claimed that structural evidence for continued growth could be seen in subsequent electron micrographs (Stoyanova and Nekrasova, 1960). It was reported that no appreciable morphological changes occurred in cells exposed to 5×10^6 r. Cell wall deterioration was noticed at 10^7 to 10^8 r and a total fixation or polymerization of the cells occurred at 10^9 r or greater. Subsequent publications have indicated that the actual conditions of irradiation involved beam currents of 3×10^{-5} amps cm^{-2} for periods of up to fifty seconds (Stoyanova, 1966b). Reference to Fig. 5 reveals that all of the doses reported should probably be increased by two orders of magnitude.

It has also been claimed that certain micro-organisms have remained viable after HVEM examination in an environmental chamber. After samples of *Corynebacterium diphtheriae*, *Bacillus anthracomorphe*, *B. subtilis* and *Staphylococci* were irradiated and cultured, it was reported that they were able to produce new colonies (Dupouy and Perrier, 1962; Dupouy, 1968). However, the precise dosage received by the specimens was not recorded, so that it is difficult to estimate the probability of survival of the species concerned from a radiological point of view. It would be useful if quantitative methods of assessing the dosage (Weiss, 1952; Kartha, 1970) could be standardized and followed as a matter of routine in all laboratories concerned with experiments of this nature. This is necessary because the radiation tolerance of different strains of the same species is variable. Although the LD_{50} dose for *E. coli*, for example, has been quoted as 10^4 r (Linton, 1971), there are several strains of this species which are known to be more resistant to ionizing radiation (Engel and Adler, 1961).

Micrococcus radiodurans, which has an LD_{50} of approximately 7×10^5 r, is one of the most resistant organisms known to radiation biologists (Dewey and Michael, 1970a). A review of the variation of radio-sensitivity in this organism during its growth cycle has been published (Serianni and Bruce, 1968). Numerous theories have been proposed to explain the unusually high resistance of the species. These have included energy transfer mechanisms, post-irradiation DNA repair processes, the presence of radical trapping sulphydryl compounds and physiological or biochemical structural changes. An explanation of the high resistance might be of significance in attempts to protect other types of cell. Until such an explanation is forthcoming, however, *M. radiodurans* is an obvious choice for environmental chamber experiments.

2. *Other types of cells*

Unicellular organisms with LD_{50} values intermediate between those of *E. coli* and *M. radiodurans* include yeast (3×10^4 r), *Amoeba* (10^5 r) and *Paramecium* (3×10^5 r) (Linton, 1971). There are also a number of multicellular organisms which are more resistant than *E. coli*; the NC-4 strain of the slime mould *Dictyostelium discoideum*, for example, has a D_{10} of 3×10^5 r (Cleveland and Deering, 1971).

Preliminary low resolution observations have been made of hydrated erythrocytes and unicellular pond water micro-organisms, by means of a scanning electron microscope used in a transmission mode of operation (Swift and Brown, 1970). Although movement of individual cells was observed, only static photographs have been published and no viability studies were carried out on the irradiated specimens.

Pond water protozoans have also been observed by conventional transmission microscopy (Ishikawa and Nagata, 1971). Some initial observations of *Scenedesmus* have been attempted in a static environmental chamber at 750 kV (Nagata and Ishikawa, 1972). Electron scattering by the water in the preparation, however, led to a reduction in contrast between specimen and background.

In many types of insects, the somatic cells in adult forms do not divide mitotically during the remainder of the life of the individual and seem to be relatively highly resistant to radiation. Doses of 5×10^4 r have little effect on cells from many of the tissues of *Diptera* and *Hymenoptera* (Ducoff *et al.*, 1971). Cells from these sources would also seem to be favourable subjects for further investigation.

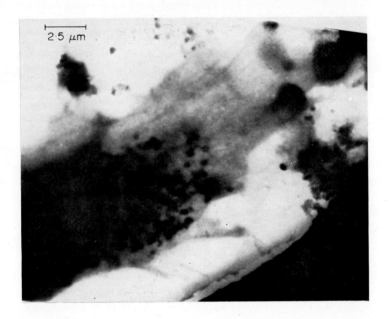

Fig. 17. Human melanoma cells, hydrated and observed in a dynamic environmental chamber at 800 kV. (After Matricardi *et al.*, 1972.)

In general, the radiation resistance of cells of higher organisms is not as great as that of micro-organisms. Certain types of melanomas, however, appear to be relatively resistant to radiation (Dewey and Michael, 1970b). Advantage could be taken of this characteristic until technical advances enable more susceptible varieties of cells to be examined. Some environmental chamber observations of neoplastic cells have already been accomplished (Subjeck *et al.*, 1972) (see Fig. 17).

A major advantage which living cells possess is their ability to repair some types of molecular radiation damage by biochemical reactions.

In vegetative bacteria, for example, a "dark-repair" mechanism has been described in which damaged single stranded regions of DNA are removed and replaced by resynthesized segments (Linton, 1971). Metabolic repair of DNA also occurs in vertebrate cells subjected to ionizing radiation (Elkind and Kamper, 1970).

Post irradiation repair may be enhanced by altering slightly the temperature of the medium in which the specimen is maintained. Optimal temperatures have been determined for different strains of *E. coli*; although these vary, they generally lie below the usual growth temperature (Stapleton *et al.*, 1953). Strains of other species of bacteria, yeast and mammalian cells have exhibited similar temperature responses (Gunter and Kohn, 1958; Beer *et al.*, 1963).

A rational approach towards the reduction of radiation damage could include several of the following techniques: (1) the use of specimens which are innately radiation-resistant; (2) utilization of low beam intensities and image intensification; (3) alterations of the physical environment; and (4) the protection of specimens by chemical compounds. Although the protective techniques referred to in section V(A) may not seem to be significant individually, a combination of such techniques could prove to be additive in their effects. In this event living cells might be irradiated for a sufficiently long period to enable an image to be recorded at a magnification high enough to yield information not obtainable by light microscopy.

C. *Specimen Thickness and Heterogeneity*

The complex ultrastructure of organic specimens necessitates the use of as high a resolution as can be obtained without the production of damage through radiation phenomena. Radiation damage has been demonstrated in thin sections of cellular material fixed in glutaraldehyde and osmium tetroxide and embedded in Epon (Williams and Fisher, 1970b).

The limiting thickness of sections of fixed material which can be examined at high resolution and without radiation damage is 2 μm at 500 kV and 3 μm at 1 MV (Hama and Porter, 1969; Nagata *et al.*, 1969; Ris, 1969). In sections as thick as these, however, the overlapping of structural elements presents serious difficulties which can best be solved by stereoscopic techniques.

Sections of retinal rods and other preparations, from 0·5 to 1 μm in thickness, have been examined successfully by stereo HVEM techniques (Ris, 1969; Hama and Nagata, 1970; Hudson and Makin, 1970; Nakanishi *et al.*, 1971; Cosslett, 1971). One practical difficulty occurs, however, in the examination of this type of specimen. Only structures two of whose dimensions are relatively small, such as particles or fibrils, may be visualized in their entirety. Extensive regions of complex planar structures, such as complete organelle or cell surface membranes, have not yet been adequately resolved in thick sections of fixed material. Presumably the same difficulty will be encountered in the examination of whole cells in environmental chambers.

Calculations of the number of multiple overlapping stereo pairs required to reconstruct an entire membrane have been carried out (Cooper and Joy, 1971). The number needed is related to the average radius of curvature of the structure. Relatively small objects require fewer stereo pairs. A complete stereo reconstruction of a membrane with radius of curvature of 15 nm could be obtained from eight stereo pairs, whilst fifty-two would be required for a cell membrane whose radius of curvature is 0·37 μm. Work of this nature could best be carried out in those dynamic environmental chambers in which the specimen can be rotated independently.

D. *Specimen Motility*

The movement of a biological specimen in a liquid environment will limit the resolution obtainable in environmental chamber work. The motion of entire cells may result either from active innate processes or passive physical external phenomena. Previously published electron micrographs of hydrated specimens may have depicted cells maintained in an extremely thin film of water. Consequently, surface tension forces could have immobilized the specimens during the time required for photographic recording. This situation exists whether the specimens are maintained in static or dynamic environmental chambers. If the specimens were grown on a supporting film by means of tissue culture techniques, however, cellular stability might be attained even in the presence of moderately thick layers of water. The difficulty concerning contrast between water and organic material still remains to be solved, however.

An even more serious problem arises from the intracellular movement of cytoplasmic regions. Even in those cells which do not exhibit active cytoplasmic streaming or cyclosis, the molecules in solution, colloidal particles and unattached cell organelles are subjected to the forces resulting in Brownian motion. Using equations for average translation, it has been calculated that a colloidal particle of gold 100 nm in diameter will be displaced by a distance equal to its own radius in $2·5 \times 10^{-3}$ s (Abrams and McBain, 1944). Since the motion is random,

the distance travelled from the starting point is not directly proportional to time. After 1 s, the same particle will have arrived at a
position approximately 2 µm away from its initial position. Since it
does this by a devious route, however, the prospects for recording a
recognizable photographic image over this period of time seem to be
very poor. A particle ten times as large would be translated through a
distance of 0·6 µm in 1 s. It has also been calculated that an organic
molecule whose diameter, including bound water, is about 1 nm will
travel 27·6 µm during an interval of 1 s (Einstein, 1926). Therefore
high resolution images of structures within an aqueous specimen may
best be recorded by using exposure times much shorter than those
employed at present.

Since it is impossible to avoid Brownian motion at room temperature,
one effective way of increasing resolution would be to use a greatly
increased beam current for an extremely short period of time. Flash
electron microscopy with exposure times of 10^{-6} to 10^{-13} s have been
alluded to (Fernández-Morán, 1960e; Hoppe, 1970), but no practical
demonstration of the technique has yet been made. Field emission
gun illuminating systems could be used to provide beam currents of
100 amp cm^{-2} (Siegel, 1970a). Reference to Fig. 5 indicates that the
dosage would be significantly reduced under these conditions of beam
current and irradiation time. A recordable image could be obtained,
however, only by sacrificing resolution and magnification to such an
extent that the technique would cease to have any value. The advantage
of short scanning times in image intensification systems (Imura et al.,
1971a) is not applicable in this particular situation, since the illumination time is many orders of magnitude smaller in comparison. If
methods of producing even higher beam currents were to become
available in the future, ultra-short exposure times could then be
utilized effectively. Such techniques would also have the advantage
that they would enable micrographs of a specimen to be obtained
before oxygen effects and secondary molecular damage had occurred
(Dewey and Boag, 1959; Epp et al., 1968; Dewey, 1969; Kessaris et al.,
1971; Weiss, 1972).

Specimen motility becomes even more critical if the thickness of the
specimen is such that stereo photographs are required. The normal
procedure for producing a pair of stereo images involves taking an
initial photograph and then tilting the specimen before taking a
second photograph. This method can only be used if the specimen
remains stationary on the specimen supporting film. Because of the
inherent motility of living cells, stereo examination would be possible
only if ultra-short exposure times were practicable and a method of

taking stereo micrographs from two different directions simultaneously were developed.

VI. The Application of Environmental Chamber Methods to Biological Problems

Dynamic environmental chamber observations of the electron diffraction patterns of membrane preparations have already been made (Moretz *et al.*, 1972) and further work is in progress towards the direct visualization of hydrated membranes and macromolecules. If such environmental chamber experiments are successful they will be extremely helpful in resolving some of the more controversial problems of cell membrane studies.

The "unit membrane" concept attempted to include many different varieties of cellular membranes within a single structural category (Robertson, 1960). It was suggested that the structure which was visible in the electron microscope was related to a bimolecular lipid leaflet covered by protein layers at both surfaces. Gradually, however, evidence has accumulated which supports a "structural subunit" membrane model characterized by micellar arrangements of lipids and protein molecules extending partially across the thickness of the membrane (Benson, 1968, Sjöstrand, 1970). Although various physical methods of investigating protein conformation and interactions in membranes have been used, their results have neither supported unequivocally the structural subunit model nor disproved the applicability of the unit membrane theory (Korn, 1969). A compromise model has been suggested in which the lipids are arranged both in micelles and in bimolecular leaflets and the protein is arranged both in layers and subunits (Glauert, 1968).

Difficulties in assessing the relative merits of the membrane structural theories arise because membranes prepared by dissimilar techniques differ in their physical appearance. Although artifacts produced by EM preparative techniques are relatively unimportant when interpreting the general ultrastructural features of the cell, they are critical in very high resolution interpretations of the macromolecular structures which are present.

Environmental chamber equipment could be used to observe the ultrastructural changes which take place during the intermediate stages of conventional EM preparative techniques. Observation of the complete sequence would enable better assessments to be made of variations in ultrastructure produced by a particular technique.

Environmental chamber experiments are especially suitable for

12

studying the effects of ionizing radiation on organic material. It is probable that the destruction of lipoprotein membranes is one of the factors contributing to cellular radiation damage. There is experimental evidence from conventional EM studies that interphasic death in muscle cells (Portela *et al.*, 1971) and erythrocytes (Prince and Little, 1971) is directly related to radiation damage in cell membranes. This results in massive increases in permeability to water and specific ions. Enzyme release could also occur as a result of cell membrane permeability changes. Post-irradiation storage for several hours at slightly lower than normal temperatures, however, minimizes catabolic reactions and assists the cell in repairing radiation damage (Alexander, 1965). These phenomena should now be studied in environmental chambers in order to discover methods by which radiation damage may be alleviated.

Processes such as membrane solubilization (Engelman, 1968; Zahler, 1968) and reconstitution (Racker and Horstman, 1967) could also be studied in environmental chambers. Further developments in contrast stop and other types of dark-field microscopy should simplify some of the problems connected with the study of unstained materials.

If the resolution attainable in environmental chamber work can ultimately be improved to permit the observation of individual macromolecules, much useful information could be obtained. The precipitation products of certain inorganic reactions have already been observed and identified within the electron microscope (Wiesenberger, 1965). If analogous organic reactions could be carried out completely within environmental chambers, biochemical and histochemical molecular interactions could be studied more effectively. It might be possible, for example, to exploit those staining reagents which interact with specific amino-acids in poly-peptides or bases in nucleic acids (Beer, 1965).

VII. Summary

This review is not restricted to past achievements and contemporary developments but is also concerned with speculations about the future of environmental chamber work. The subjects considered in the preceding sections are so diverse in nature that some attempt to relate the various topics is appropriate at this point. It is hoped that the information gathered will be of assistance in the design of new types of environmental chamber systems.

Dark-field methods of illumination used in conjunction with environmental chamber techniques are capable of producing 2 nm resolution in relatively thin unfixed material. It does not seem possible, however, to exceed this resolution in specimens up to 1 μm in thickness, even at high voltages. Sections as thick as 2·5 μm are unlikely to yield resolutions lower than 10 nm.

Of the interactions which take place between specimen and incident beam, temperature increases are probably less deleterious than "radiation effects". Ionization and bond disruption caused by inelastic scattering cannot be disregarded under most operating conditions, but are less serious at very high accelerating voltages. Conversely, the effects of elastic scattering and atomic displacement are increased in HVEM work. The extent to which these radiation phenomena lead to alterations in ultrastructure depends partly upon the radiation sensitivity of the types of molecules which are present. The radiation dosage received by organic specimens in those environmental chambers which are now in use is fairly high, by radiobiological standards. Although a few micro-organisms are naturally resistant to radiation, it would appear that the majority of biological specimens which are irradiated in an unprotected condition are liable to sustain serious molecular damage.

There are various methods by which radiation damage may be reduced or circumvented. It may be necessary to employ one or more of these artifices in order to enable some specimens to survive the amount of electron irradiation required for the recording of an image. Further developments in image intensification techniques seem to present the most likely solution to the problem of reducing radiation to an acceptable level. In addition, full use has not yet been made of chemicals which are able to protect specimens against radiation damage. Nor have the techniques necessary for flash electron microscopy yet been developed to a state in which they are practicable.

Some bacteria and other unicellular organisms have apparently survived EM examination. The resolution and contrast in the relevant micrographs is unsatisfactory, however. Further development of stereoscopic techniques might improve this situation. Contrast is affected adversely by high water content in a specimen. It does not seem possible at present to examine organic specimens in a continuous layer of water. Brownian movement of macromolecules and cell contents also limits the degree of hydration of specimens observed within environmental chambers.

The examination of frozen sections may avoid the difficulties arising from Brownian motion, but the problem of specimen contrast still remains. Although there are many problems yet unsolved, it is reasonable to expect that ultimately techniques will be developed which will enable cellular reactions to be observed within the electron microscope.

ACKNOWLEDGEMENTS

The experimental work, the results of which are shown in Fig. 15, was carried out at the Cavendish Laboratory during the tenure of a NSF fellowship and with the assistance of N.I.H. grant No. BPD-10,252(C2).

I am grateful to Dr. V. E. Cosslett for his valuable suggestions concerning the preparation of this paper. My thanks are also due to all those who have provided information or illustrations of their environmental chamber work.

REFERENCES

Abrams, I. M. and McBain, J. W. (1944). *J. appl. Phys.* **15**, 607–609.

Agar, A. W., Revell, R. S. M. and Scott, R. D. (1949). *In* "Proceedings of the Conference on Electron Microscopy, Delft", pp. 52–54. Nijhoff, The Hague.

Aldrich, J. E. and Cundall, R. B. (1969). *Int. J. Radiat. Biol.* **16**, 343–358.

Alexander, P. (1965). *In* "Atomic Radiation and Life". Penguin Books, Harmondsworth, Middlesex.

Allinson, D. L. (1970a). *In* "Handbook of Conference on the Applications of High Voltage Electron Microscopy, A.E.R.E., Harwell, April 2–3", p. 25.

Allinson, D. L. (1970b). *In* "Microscopie Électronique 1970", proceedings of the Seventh International Congress for Electron Microscopy, Grenoble (P. Favard, ed.), Vol. I, pp. 169–170. Société Française de Microscopie Électronique, Paris.

Allinson, D. L. (1971). (Personal communication.)

Anderson, K. (1968). *J. Phys., E.* **1**, 601–603.

Anderson, R. S. and Turkowitz, H. (1941). *Am. J. Roentg.* **46**, 537–541.

Bahr, G. F. and Zeitler, E. (1965). *Lab. Invest.* **14**, 955–977.

Bahr, G. F., Johnson, F. B. and Zeitler, E. (1965). *Lab. Invest.* **14**, 1115–1133.

Barron, E. S. G. (1954). *Radiat. Res.* **1**, 109–124.

Barron, E. S. G., Dickman, S., Muntz, J. A. and Singer, T. P. (1949). *J. gen. Physiol.* **32**, 537–552.

Beer, J. Z., Lett, J. T. and Alexander, P. (1963). *Nature, Lond.* **199**, 193–194.

Beer, M. (1965). *Lab. Invest.* **14**, 1020–1025.

Benson, A. A. (1968). *In* "Membrane Models and the Formation of Biological Membranes" (L. Bolis and B. A. Pethica, eds.), pp. 190–202. North-Holland, Amsterdam.

Bernhard, W. (1972). *J. Microsc. (Fr.)* **13**, 143–144.

Bernhard, W. and Viron, A. (1971). *J. Cell Biol.* **49**, 731–746.

Booth, M. R. (1970). *J. Sci. Fd. Agric.* **21**, 145–147.

Burnett, W. T., Morse, M. L., Burke, A. W. and Hollaender, A. (1952). *J. Bact.* **63**, 591–596.

Burnett, W. T., Stapleton, G. E., Morse, M. L. and Hollaender, A. (1951). *Proc. Soc. exp. Biol. Med.* **77**, 636–638.

Causey, G. (1968). *J. Anat.* **103**, 587.

Chevallier, A. and Burg, C. (1953). *Annls. Nutr. Aliment.* **7**, 81–95.

Christensen, A. K. and Paavola, L. G. (1972). *J. Microsc. (Fr.)* **13**, 147–148.

Clark, J., Kushelvsky, A. P. and Slifkin, M. A. (1970). *Radiation Effects*, **2**, 303–304.

Cleveland, R. F. and Deering, R. A. (1971). *Radiat. Res.* **47**, 292.

Considine, K. T. (1969). Ph.D. thesis, University of Cambridge.

Cooper, R. E. and Joy, R. T. (1971). (Unpublished).

Cosslett, A. (1960). *Jl R. microsc. Soc.* **79**, 263–271.

Cosslett, A. (1961). *In* "Proceedings of the European Regional Conference on Electron Microscopy, Delft, 1960" (A. L. Houwink and B. J. Spit, eds.), Vol. II, pp. 678–681. De Nederlandse Vereniging voor Electronenmicroscopie, Delft.

Cosslett, V. E. (1967a). *Sci. Prog., Oxf.* **55**, 15–34.

Cosslett, V. E. (1967b). *Jl R. microsc. Soc.* **87**, 53–76.

Cosslett, V. E. (1968). *Sci. J.* **4**, (12), 38–44.

Cosslett, V. E. (1970). *Ber. (Dtsch.) Bunsenges. Phys. Chem.* **74**, 1171–1175.

Cosslett, V. E. (1971). *Phil. Trans. R. Soc.* **B261**, 35–44.

Cowley, J. M. and Grinton, G. R. (1970). *In* "Microscopie Électronique 1970", proceedings of the Seventh International Congress for Electron Microscopy, Grenoble (P. Favard, ed.), Vol. I, pp. 59–60. Société Française de Microscopie Électronique, Paris.

Crabtree, H. G. and Cramer, W. (1933). *Proc. R. Soc.* **B113**, 238–250.

Crewe, A. V., Isaacson, M. and Johnson, D. (1970). *In* "Proceedings of the 28th Annual Meeting of the Electron Microscope Society of America, Houston" (C. J. Arceneaux, ed.), pp. 262–263. Claitor's Publishing Division, Baton Rouge, La.

Crewe, A. V., Isaacson, M. and Johnson, D. (1971). *Nature, Lond.* **231**, 262.

Dewey, D. L. (1969). *Radiat. Res.* **38**, 467–474.

Dewey, D. L. (1970). *Radiat. Res.* **44**, 345–358.

Dewey, D. L. and Boag, J. W. (1959). *Nature, Lond.* **183**, 1450–1451.

Dewey, D. L. and Michael, B. D. (1970a). *In* "1970 Annual Report of the Research Unit in Radiobiology, Mount Vernon Hospital, Northwood, Middlesex", pp. 46–47.

Dewey, D. L. and Michael, B. D. (1970b). *Ibid.*, p. 48.

Dubochet, J., Ducommun, M., Zollinger, M. and Kellenberger, E. (1971). *J. Ultrastruct. Res.* **35**, 147–167.

Ducoff, H. S., Crossland, J. L. and Vaughan, A. P. (1971). *Radiat. Res.* **47**, 299–300.

Dupouy, G. (1968). *In* "Advances in Optical and Electron Microscopy" (R. Barer and V. E. Cosslett, eds.), Vol. 2, pp. 167–250. Academic Press, London and New York.

Dupouy, G. (1971). (Personal communication).

Dupouy, G. and Perrier, F. (1962). *J. Microsc. (Fr.)* **1**, 167–192.

Dupouy, G. and Perrier, F. (1969). *Z. angew. Phys.* **27**, 224–227.

Dupouy, G., Perrier, F. and Durrieu, L. (1960). *C. r. hebd. Séanc. Acad. Sci., Paris*, **251**, 2836–2841.

Dupouy, G., Perrier, F. and Durrieu, L. (1962). *C. r. hebd. Séanc. Acad. Sci., Paris* **254**, 3786–3791.

Dupouy, G., Perrier, F. and Verdier, P. (1966). *J. Microsc. (Fr.)* **5**, 655–668.

Dupouy, G., Perrier, F., Enjalbert, L., Lapchine, L. and Verdier, P. (1969). *C. r. hebd. Séanc. Acad. Sci., Paris*, **B268**, 1341–1345.

Dvoryankin, V. F. (1960). *Soviet Physics, Crystallography*, **4**, 415–434.

Eidus, L. K. (1956). *Biofizika* **1**, 544–554.

Eidus, L. K. and Ganassi, E. E. (1960). *Biophysics*, **5**, 594–604.

Einstein, A. (1926). *In* "Investigations on the Theory of the Brownian Movement" (R. Fürth, ed.), Methuen, London.

Elkind, M. M. and Kamper, C. (1970). *Biophys. J.* **10**, 237–245.

Engel, M. S. and Adler, H. I. (1961). *Radiat. Res.* **15**, 269–275.

Engelman, D. M. (1968). *In* "Membrane Models and the Formation of Biological Membranes" (L. Bolis and B. A. Pethica, eds.), pp. 203–228. North-Holland, Amsterdam.

Ennos, A. E. (1953). *Br. J. appl. Phys.* **4**, 101–106.

Ennos, A. E. (1954). *Br. J. appl. Phys.* **5**, 27–31.

Epp, E. R., Weiss, H. and Santomasso, A. (1968). *Radiat. Res.* **34**, 320–325.

Erickson, H. P. and Klug, A. (1970). *Ber. (Dtsch.) Bunsenges. Phys. Chem.* **74**, 1129–1137.

Escaig, J. and Sella, C. (1966). *In* "Proceedings of the Sixth International Congress for Electron Microscopy, Kyoto", Vol. I, pp. 177–178. Maruzen, Tokyo.

Fernández-Morán, H. (1960a). *J. appl. Phys.* **31**, 1840.

Fernández-Morán, H. (1960b). *In* "Fast Fundamental Transfer Processes in Aqueous Biomolecular Systems", pp. 33–37. Dept. of Biology, M.I.T., Cambridge, Mass.

Fernández-Morán, H. (1960c). *J. appl. Phys.* **31**, 1840–1841.

Fernández-Morán, H. (1960d). *Ann. N.Y. Acad. Sci.* **85**, 689–713.

Fernández-Morán, H. (1960e). *op cit* 1960b, pp. 26–32.

Fernández-Morán, H. (1962). *Circulation*, **XXVI**, 1039–1065.

Fernández-Morán, H. (1966). *In* "Proceedings of the Sixth International Congress for Electron Microscopy, Kyoto", Vol. I, pp. 13–14. Maruzen, Tokyo.

Fernández-Morán, H. (1970). *In* "Proceedings of the Seventh International Congress for Electron Microscopy, Grenoble", Vol. II, pp. 91–92. Société Française de Microscopie Électronique, Paris.

Forssberg, A. (1947). *Nature, Lond.* **159**, 308–309.

Fukami, A., Etoh, T., Ishihara, N., Katoh, M. and Fujiwara, K. (1970). *In* "Proceedings of the Seventh International Congress for Electron Microscopy, Grenoble", Vol. I, pp. 171–172. Société Française de Microscopie Électronique, Paris.

Glaeser, R. M. (1970). *In* "Proceedings of the 28th Annual Meeting of E.M.S.A., Houston", pp. 260–261. Claitor's Publishing Division, Baton Rouge, La.

Glaeser, R. M. (1971). *J. Ultrastruct. Res.* **36**, 466–482.

Glaeser, R. M., Budinger, T. F., Aebersold, P. M. and Thomas, G. (1970). *In* "Proceedings of the Seventh International Congress for Electron Microscopy, Grenoble", Vol. I, pp. 463–464. Société Française de Microscopie Électronique, Paris.

Glauert, A. M. (1968). *Jl R. microsc. Soc.* **88**, 49–70.

Gordy, W., Ard, W. B. and Shields, H. (1955). *Proc. natn. Acad. Sci. U.S.A.* **41**, 983–1004.

Gray, L. H. (1959). *Radiat. Res. Suppl.* **1**, 73–101.

Gunter, S. E. and Kohn, H. I. (1958). *Bact. Proc.* 1958, 34.

Haine, M. E. (1957). *J. scient. Instrum.* **34**, 9–15.

Haine, M. E. and Einstein, P. A. (1962). *Proc. Instn elect. Engrs* **B109**, 185–195.

Hale, K. F., Henderson Brown, M. and Allinson, D. L. (1970). *In* "Proceedings of the Seventh International Congress for Electron Microscopy, Grenoble", Vol. I, pp. 297–298. Société Française de Microscopie Électronique, Paris.

Hall, C. E. (1966). "Introduction to Electron Microscopy," McGraw-Hill, New York.

Hama, K. and Nagata, F. (1970). *J. Cell. Biol.* **45**, 654–659.

Hama, K. and Porter, K. R. (1969). *J. Microsc. (Fr.)* **8**, 149–158.

Hashimoto, H., Kumao, A., Suzuki, S. and Yotsumoto, H. (1970). *In* "Proceedings of the Seventh International Congress for Electron Microscopy, Grenoble", Vol. I, pp. 351–352. Société Française de Microscopie Électronique, Paris.

Haskins, C. P. (1938). *J. appl. Phys.* **9**, 553–561.

Hedley, J. A. and McGeagh, J. (1963). *J. scient. Instrum.* **40**, 484–486.

Heide, H. G. (1960). *Naturwissenschaften*, **47**, 313–317.

Heide, H. G. (1962). *J. Cell Biol.* **13**, 147–152.

Heide, H. G. (1965a). *Lab. Invest.* **14**, 1134–1139.

Heide, H. G. (1965b). *Lab. Invest.* **14**, 1140–1146.

Heide, H. G. and Urban, K. (1970). *In* "Proceedings of the Seventh International Congress for Electron Microscopy, Grenoble", Vol. II, pp. 107–108. Société Française de Microscopie Électronique, Paris.

Hems, G. (1960). *Nature, Lond.* **186**, 710–712.

Herrell, D. J. and Ferrier, R. P. (1969). *J. Phys. E (J. scient. Instrum.)* **2**, 548–549.

Hillier, J. (1948). *J. appl. Phys.* **19**, 226–230.

Hollaender, A. and Stapleton, G. E. (1953). *Physiol. Rev.* **33**, 77–84.

Hollaender, A., Stapleton, G. E. and Martin, F. L. (1951). *Nature, Lond.* **167**, 103–106.

Hoppe, W. (1970). *Ber. (Dtsch.) Bunsenges. Phys. Chem.* **74**, 1090–1100.

Howard-Flanders, P. and Alper, T. (1957). *Radiat. Res.* **7**, 518–540.

Hudson, B. and Makin, M. J. (1970). *J. Phys. E (J. scient. Instrum.)* **3**, 311.

Imura, T., Saka, H., Doi, M. and Okamoto, N. (1971a). *Jap. J. appl. Phys.* **10**, 654.

Imura, T., Saka, H., Todokoro, H. and Ashikawa, M. (1971b). *J. phys. Soc. Japan*, **31**, 1849.

Ishikawa, I. and Nagata, F. (1971). *J. Electron Microsc., Chiba Cy*, **20**, 219.

Ito, T. and Hiziya, K. (1958). *J. Electron Microsc., Chiba Cy*, **6**, 4–8.

Kartha, M. (1970). *Radiat. Res.* **42**, 220–231.

Kessaris, N. D., Weiss, H. and Epp, E. R. (1971). *Radiat. Res.* **47**, 295–296.

Kimeldorf, D. J. and Fortner, R. W. (1971). *Radiat. Res.* **46**, 52–63.

Kleinschmidt, A. K. (1970a). *Biophys. J.* **10**, 88a.

Kleinschmidt, A. K. (1970b). *Ber. (Dtsch.) Bunsenges. Phys. Chem.* **74**, 1190–1196.

Kobayashi, K. and Ohara, M. (1966). *In* "Proceedings of the Sixth International Congress for Electron Microscopy, Kyoto", Vol. I, pp. 579–580. Maruzen, Tokyo.

Kobayashi, K. and Sakaoku, K. (1965). *Lab. Invest.* **14**, 1097–1114.

König, H. (1948). *Naturwissenschaften*, **35**, 261–265.

Korn, E. D. (1969). *In* "Theoretical and Experimental Biophysics, A Series of Advances" (A. Cole, ed.), Vol. 2, pp. 1–67. Marcel Dekker, New York.

Krause, F. (1937). *Naturwissenschaften*, **25**, 817–825.

Kuzin, A. M. (1964). "Radiation Biochemistry" translated by Y. Halperin. Israel Program for Scientific Translations, Jerusalem.

Lapchine, L. and Enjalbert, L. (1971). *C. r. hebd. Séanc. Acad. Sci., Paris*, **D272**, 3092–3093.

Leduc, E. H. and Bernhard, W. (1962). *In* "Symposia of the International Society for Cell Biology" (R. J. C. Harris, ed.), Vol. I, pp. 21–44. Academic Press, New York and London.

Lenz, F. (1954). *Z. Naturf.* **9a,** 185.

Lenz, F. (1970). *Ber. (Dtsch.) Bunsenges. Phys. Chem.* **74,** 1187–1190.

Limperos, G. and Mosher, W. A. (1950). *Am. J. Roentg.* **63,** 681–690.

Linton, A. H. (1971). *In* "Micro-organisms" (L. E. Hawker and A. H. Linton, eds.), pp. 193–218. Arnold, London.

Lippert, W. (1961). *In* "Proceedings of the European Regional Conference on Electron Microscopy, Delft", Vol. II, pp. 682–685. De Nederlandse Vereniging voor Electronenmicroscopie, Delft.

Lippert, W. (1962). *Optik,* **19,** 145–155.

Lippincott, S. W., Bender, R., Foelsche, T., Azzam, N., Montour, J. and Rogers, C. (1970). *Archs Path.* **89,** 416–420.

Longley, W. (1967). *J. molec. Biol.* **30,** 323–327.

McDonald, J., Pinkerton, A., Weiss, H. and Epp, E. R. (1971). *Radiat. Res.* **47,** 353–354.

Makin, M. J. (1968). *Phil. Mag.* **18,** 637–653.

Makin, M. J. (1970). *In* "Proceedings of the Seventh International Congress for Electron Microscopy, Grenoble", Vol. II, pp. 213–214. Société Française de Microscopie Électronique, Paris.

Marton, L. (1934). *Nature, Lond.* **133,** 911.

Marton, L. (1935). *Bull. Acad. r. Belg. Cl. Sci.* **21,** 553–564.

Masurovsky, E. B., Bunge, M. B. and Bunge, R. P. (1967). *J. Cell Biol.* **32,** 497–518.

Matricardi, V. R., Hausner, G. G. and Parsons, D. F. (1970). *In* "Proceedings of the 28th Annual Meeting of E.M.S.A., Houston", pp. 542–543. Claitor's Publishing Division, Baton Rouge, La.

Matricardi, V. R., Moretz, R. C. and Parsons, D. F. (1972a). *Science, N.Y.* (in press).

Matricardi, V. R., Moretz, R. C. and Parsons, D. F. (1972b). *Biochim. Biophys. Acta* (submitted for publication).

Matricardi, V. R., Subjeck, J. and Parsons, D. F. (1972). *In* "Proceedings of the 30th Annual Meeting of E.M.S.A., Los Angeles", pp. 180–181. Claitor's Publishing Division, Baton Rouge, La.

Mayeda, M., Yamamoto, T., Watanabe, M. and Kitamura, N. (1970a). *Jap. J. appl. Phys.* **9,** 1183.

Mayeda, M., Yamamoto, T., Watanabe, M. and Kitamura, N. (1970b). *In* "Proceedings of the 28th Annual Meeting of E.M.S.A., Houston", pp. 548–549. Claitor's Publishing Division, Baton Rouge, La.

Meryman, H. T. (1971). *Cryobiology* **8,** 173–183.

Millonig, G. and Marinozzi, V. (1968). *In* "Advances in Optical and Electron Microscopy" (R. Barer and V. E. Cosslett, eds.), Vol. 2, pp. 251–341. Academic Press, London and New York.

Molière, G. (1947). *Z. Naturf.* **2a,** 133–145.

Möllenstedt, G. (1949). *Optik, Stuttg.* **5,** 499–517.

Moretz, R. C., Hausner, G. G. and Parsons, D. F. (1970). *Biophys. J. Abstr.* **10,** 132a.

Moretz, R. C., Hausner, G. G. and Parsons, D. F. (1971). *In* "Proceedings of the 29th Annual Meeting of E.M.S.A., Boston", pp. 44–45. Claitor's Publishing Division, Baton Rouge, La.

Moretz, R. C., Hausner, G. G. and Parsons, D. F. (1972). *Biophys. J. Abstr.* **12,** 254a.

Morrow, D. R. and Horner, J. A. (1966). *R.C.A. Sci. Instrum. News*, **11**, No. 1, pp. 1–10.

Mottram, J. C. (1935). *Br. J. Radiol.* **8**, 32–39.

Nagata, F. and Fukai, K. (1971). Reported at "U.S.—Japan Seminar on High Voltage Electron Microscopy", Honolulu, Sept. 20–24, 1971.

Nagata, F. and Ishikawa, I. (1971). *J. Electron Microsc., Chiba Cy.* **20**, 219–220.

Nagata, F. and Ishikawa, I. (1972). *Jap. J. appl. Phys.* **11**, 1239–1244.

Nagata, F., Hama, K. and Porter, K. R. (1969). *J. Electron Microsc., Chiba Cy.* **18**, 106–109.

Nakanishi, Y. H., Utsumi, S., Liu, I. and Yoshii, G. (1971). *J. Electron Microsc., Chiba Cy.* **20**, 252.

Nathan, R. (1970). *In* "Proceedings of the 28th Annual Meeting of E.M.S.A., Houston", p. 28. Claitor's Publishing Division, Baton Rouge, La.

Ohr, S. M. and Noggle, T. S. (1970). *In* "Proceedings of the 28th Annual Meeting of E.M.S.A., Houston", pp. 52–53. Claitor's Publishing Division, Baton Rouge, La.

Ottensmeyer, F. P. (1969). *Biophys. J.* **9**, 1144–1149.

Parsons, D. F. (1966). *In* "Proceedings of the Sixth International Congress for Electron Microscopy, Kyoto", Vol. II, pp. 121–122. Maruzen, Tokyo.

Parsons, D. F. (1969). *In* "Current Developments in HVEM—a Conference at the U.S. Steel Corporation Research Center, Monroeville, Pa., June 17–19, 1969", pp. 8–9.

Parsons, D. F. (1970). *In* "Some Biological Techniques in Electron Microscopy" (D. F. Parsons, ed.), pp. 1–68. Academic Press, New York and London.

Parsons, D. F. (1971). *In* "Cell Membranes; Biological and Pathological Aspects", pp. 30–37. The American Association of Pathologists and Bacteriologists.

Parsons, D. F. and Matricardi, V. R. (1972). *Biophys. J. Abstr.* **12**, 51a.

Parsons, D. F. and Moretz, R. C. (1970). *In* "Proceedings of the Seventh International Congress for Electron Microscopy, Grenoble", Vol. I, pp. 497–498. Société Française de Microscopie Électronique, Paris.

Persson, A. (1970). *In* "Proceedings of the Seventh International Congress for Electron Microscopy, Grenoble", Vol. I, pp. 421–422. Société Française de Microscopie Électronique, Paris.

Persson, A. (1972). *J. Microsc. (Fr.)* **13**, 162.

Phillips, W. A. (1970). *Proc. R. Soc.* **A319**, 565–581.

Piercy, G. R., Gilbert, R. W. and Howe, L. M. (1963). *J. scient. Instrum.* **40**, 487–489.

Portela, A., Garfunkel, M., Vaccari, J., Dolbue, A. M., Stewart, P. A. and Perez, J. C. (1971). *Radiat. Res.* **47**, 704–715.

Powers, E. L., Webb, R. B. and Ehret, C. F. (1959). *Expl. Cell Res.* **17**, 550–554.

Prince, E. W. and Little, J. B. (1971). *Radiat. Res.* **47**, 321–322.

Proctor, B., Coleman, M. and Goldblith, S. (1952). *J. Bact.* **63**, 337–339.

Racker, E. and Horstman, L. L. (1967). *J. biol. Chem.* **242**, 2547–2551.

Rauth, A. M. and Simpson, J. A. (1964). *Radiat. Res.* **22**, 643–661.

Reimer, L. (1959). *Z. Naturf.* **14b**, 566–575.

Reimer, L. (1965). *Lab. Invest.* **14**, 1082–1096.

Reimer, L. and Christenhusz, R. (1962). *Z. angew. Phys.* **14**, 601–607.

Revesz, L. and Bergstrand, H. (1963). *Nature, Lond.* **200**, 594–595.

Reynolds, G. T. (1968). *In* "Advances in Optical and Electron Microscopy"

(R. Barer and V. E. Cosslett, eds.), Vol. 2, pp. 1–40. Academic Press, London and New York.

Riemersma, J. C. (1970). *In* "Some Biological Techniques in Electron Microscopy" (D. F. Parsons, ed.), pp. 69–99. Academic Press, New York and London.

Ris, H. (1969). *J. Microsc. (Fr.)* **8**, 761–766.

Robertson, J. D. (1960). *Prog. Biophys. biophys. Chem.* **10**, 343–418.

Roth, J. S. and Eichel, H. J. (1955). *Biol. Bull. mar. biol. Lab.*, *Woods Hole*, **108**, 308–317.

Ruska, E. (1942). *Kolloidzeitschrift*, **100**, 212–219.

Ruthemann, H. (1942). *Naturwissenschaften*, **30**, 145.

Sabatini, D. D., Bensch, K. and Barrnett, R. J. (1963). *J. Cell Biol.* **17**, 19–58.

Sabatini, D. D., Miller, F. and Barrnett, R. J. (1964). *J. Histochem. Cytochem.* **12**, 57–71.

Sakitani, Y., Ozasa, S., Fujita, H. and Ohji, K. (1971). *J. Electron Microsc.*, *Chiba Cy.* **20**, 218–219.

Scherzer, O. (1970). *Ber. (Dtsch.) Bunsenges. Phys. Chem.* **74**, 1154–1167.

Schidlovsky, G. (1965). *Lab. Invest.* **14**, 1213–1233.

Serianni, R. W. and Bruce, A. K. (1968). *Radiat. Res.* **36**, 193–207.

de Serres, F. J. (1961). *In* "Microbial Reaction to Environment; 11th Symposium of the Society for General Microbiology; held at the Royal Institution, London, April, 1961", pp. 196–216. Cambridge University Press, London.

Setlow, R. and Doyle, B. (1953). *Archs Biochem. Biophys.* **46**, 31–38.

Siegel, B. M. (1970a). *Ber. (Dtsch.) Bunsenges. Phys. Chem.* **74**, 1175–1181.

Siegel, G. (1970b). *In* "Proceedings of the Seventh International Congress for Electron Microscopy, Grenoble", Vol. II, pp. 221–222. Société Française de Microscopie Électronique, Paris.

Sinclair, W. K. (1969). *Radiat. Res.* **39**, 135–154.

Sjöstrand, F. S. (1970). *In* "Proceedings of the Seventh International Congress for Electron Microscopy, Grenoble", Vol. 3, p. 11. Société Française de Microscopie Électronique, Paris.

Stapleton, G. E. and Edington, C. W. (1956). *Radiat. Res.* **5**, 39–45.

Stapleton, G. E. and Hollaender, A. (1952). *J. cell. comp. Physiol.* **39**, suppl. 1, 101–113.

Stapleton, G. E. Billen, D. and Hollaender, A. (1953). *J. cell. comp. Physiol.* **41**, 345–357.

Stenn, K. and Bahr, G. F. (1970). *J. Ultrastruct. Res.* **31**, 526–550.

Sternheimer, R. M. (1961). *In* "Methods of Experimental Physics, Vol. 5—Nuclear Physics, Part A" (L. C. L. Yuan and C. S. Wu, eds.), pp. 1–89. Academic Press, New York and London.

Stoyanova, I. G. (1961). *Bull. Acad. Sci. USSR phys. Ser.* **25**, 715–721.

Stoyanova, I. G. (1966a). *In* "Proceedings of the Sixth International Congress for Electron Microscopy, Kyoto", Vol. II, pp. 265–266. Maruzen, Tokyo.

Stoyanova, I. G. (1966b). *In* "Proceedings of the Sixth International Congress for Electron Microscopy, Kyoto", Vol. I, pp. 581–582. Maruzen, Tokyo.

Stoyanova, I. G. and Mikhailovskii, G. A. (1959). *Biophysics*, **4**, No. 4, 116–126.

Stoyanova, I. G. and Morozova, T. P. (1963). *Soviet Phys. Dokl.* **8**, 161–163.

Stoyanova, I. G. and Nekrasova, T. A. (1960). *Soviet Phys. Dokl.* **5**, 1117–1121.

Stoyanova, I. G., Nekrasova, T. A. and Biryuzova, V. I. (1960a). *Soviet Phys. Dokl.* **5**, 433–436.

Stoyanova, I. G., Nekrasova, T. A. and Zaides, A. L. (1960b). *Soviet Phys. Dokl.* **5**, 209–211.

Subjeck, J., Matricardi, V. and Parsons, D. F. (1972). *Biophys. J. Abstr.* **12**, 54a.

Sugata, E., Nishitani, Y., Kaneda, S., Tateishi, M. and Yokoya, H. (1956). *In* "Proceedings of the International Conference on Electron Microscopy, London, 1954" (R. Ross, General Editor; V. E. Cosslett, Chairman of the Editorial Committee), pp. 452–459. Royal Microscopical Society, London.

Swann, P. R. (1972). (Personal communication).

Swann, P. R. and Tighe, N. J. (1971). *Jernkont. Annlr.* **155**, 497–501.

Swann, P. R., Swann, G. R. and Wray, G. P. (1970). *In* "Hand bookof the Conference on the Applications of High Voltage Electron Microscopy, A.E.R.E., Harwell, April 2–3", p. 22.

Swift, J. A. and Brown, A. C. (1970). *J. Phys., E.* **3**, 924–926.

Taylor, B., Greenstein, J. P. and Hollaender, A. (1947). *Cold Spring Harb. Symp. quant. Biol.* **12**, 237–246.

Taylor, B., Greenstein, J. P. and Hollaender, A. (1948). *Archs. Biochem.* **16**, 19–31.

Taylor, J. (1926). *J. scient. Instrum.* **3**, 400–404.

Thach, R. E. and Thach, S. S. (1970). *In* "Proceedings of the Seventh International Congress for Electron Microscopy, Grenoble", Vol. I, pp. 465–466. Société Française de Microscopie Électronique, Paris.

Thach, R. E. and Thach, S. S. (1971). *Biophys. J.* **11**, 204–210.

Toohey, M. and Joy, R. T. (1972). (Unpublished).

Uyeda, N., Kobayashi, T., Suito, E., Harada, Y. and Watanabe, M. (1970). *In* "Proceedings of the 28th Annual Meeting of E.M.S.A., Houston", pp. 524–525. Claitor's Publishing Division, Baton Rouge, La.

Valdrè, U. and Goringe, M. J. (1965). *J. scient. Instrum.* **42**, 268–269.

Valentine, R. C. (1965). *Lab. Invest.* **14**, 1334–1340.

Valentine, R. C. (1966). *In* "Advances in Optical and Electron Microscopy" (R. Barer and V. E. Cosslett, eds.), Vol. 1, pp. 180–203. Academic Press, London and New York.

von Ardenne, M. (1939). *Z. tech. Phys.* **20**, 239–242.

von Ardenne, M. and Friedrich-Freksa, H. (1941). *Naturwissenschaften*, **29**, 521–528.

von Borries, B. and Glaser, W. (1944). *Kolloidzeitschrift*, **106**, 123–128.

Venables, J. A. (1963). *Rev. scient. Instrum.* **34**, 582–583.

Venables, J. A. and Bassett, D. C. (1967). *Nature, Lond.* **214**, 1107–1108.

Venables, J. A., Ball, D. J. and Thomas, G. J. (1968). *J. Phys., E.* **1**, 121–126.

Wachtel, A. W., Gettner, M. E. and Ornstein, L. (1966). *In* "Physical Techniques in Biological Research" (A. W. Pollister, ed.), Vol. IIIA, pp. 173–250.

Ward, P. R. and Mitchell, R. F. (1972). *J. Phys., E.* **5**, 160–162.

Watanabe, H. (1956). *J. Phys. Soc. Japan*, **11**, 112–119.

Watanabe, H. and Ishikawa, I. (1967). *Jap. J. appl. Phys.* **6**, 83-88.

Watanabe, M., Okazaki, I., Honjo, G. and Mihama, K. (1960). *In* "Fourth International Conference on Electron Microscopy, Berlin", Vol. I, pp. 90–93. Springer-Verlag, Berlin.

Watson, J. H. L. (1947). *J. appl. Phys.* **18**, 153–161.

Wayte, R. C. and Thornton, P. R. (1967). *J. scient. Instrum.* **44**, 806–808.

Weiss, H. (1972). *Radiat. Res.* **50**, 441–452.

Weiss, J. (1952). *Nucleonics*, **10**, July, pp. 28–31.

Wiesenberger, E. (1965). *Lab. Invest.* **14**, 1026–1040.

Williams, R. C. and Fisher, H. W. (1970a). *Biophys. J.* **10**, 53a.

Williams, R. C. and Fisher, H. W. (1970b). *In* "Proceedings of the 28th Annual Meeting of E.M.S.A., Houston", pp. 304–305. Claitor's Publishing Division, Baton Rouge, La.

Wood, T. H. (1958). *A. Rev. nucl. Sci.* **8**, 343–386.

Yamaguchi, S. (1956). *Z. angew. Phys.* **8**, 221–222.

Zahler, P. (1968). *In* "Membrane Models and the Formation of Biological Membranes" (L. Bolis and B. A. Pethica, eds.), pp. 181–189. North-Holland, Amsterdam.

Author Index

(Numbers in italics refer to pages in the References at the end of each chapter)

A

Abrams, I. M., 297, 327, 339, *344*
Abrikosov, A. A., 205, *236*
Adler, H. I., 336, *346*
Aebersold, P. M., 309, 313, 316, *346*
Agar, A. W., 307, *344*
Aharanov, Y., 250, 253, *295*
Ajeian, R., 289, 290, *295*, *296*
Aldrich, J. E., 318, *344*
Alexander, P., 313, 338, 342, *344*
Allinson, D. L., 320, 323, 325, 329, *344*, *346*
Alper, T., 328, *347*
Amboss, K., 217, *236*
Anderson, K., 309, *344*
Anderson, R. S., 328, *344*.
Anderson, T. W., 69, *79*
Ard, W. B., 317, *346*
Ashikawa, M., 310, *347*
Azzam, N., 313, *348*

B

Bacon, G. E., 179, *199*
Bahr, G. F., 45, *79*, 113, *114*, 193, *198*, 304, 305, 312, 313, 314, 316, 317, *344*, *350*
Bainbridge, J. E., 40, *42*
Ball, D. J., 334, *351*
Balladore, J.-L., 225, *237*
Balossier, G., 235, *236*
Barrnett, R. J., 306, *350*
Barron, E. S. G., 316, 317, 318, *344*
Bartels, P. H., 45, *79*
Bassett, D. C., 310, *351*
Bayh, W., 253, *295*
Beadle, C., 44, *79*
Beer, J. Z., 338, *344*
Beer, M., 342, *344*
Bender, R., 313, *348*
Bensch, K., 306, *350*
Benson, A. A., 341, *344*
Beorchia, A., 223, *236*
Bergstrand, H., 328, *349*

Berjot, C., 220, *236*
Berjot, G., 223, *236*
Bernhard, W., 304, 335, *344*, *347*
Billen, D., 338, *350*
Biryuzova, V. I., 298, 335, *350*
Boag, J. W., 340, *345*
Boersch, H., 222, 223, *236*, 240, 254, *295*
Bohm, D., 250, 253, *295*
Bonhomme, P., 220, 223, 224, 235, *236*
Bonjour, P., 225, 226, 227, *236*
Booth, M. R., 313, 317, *344*
Born, M., 164, 182, *198*, 242, 260, *295*
Bostanjoglo, O., 222, 223, *236*, 293, *295*
Broglie, L. de, 246, 270, *295*
Brown, A. C., 336, *351*
Bruce, A. K., 336, *350*
Budinger, T. F., 309, 313, 316, *346*
Bunge, M. B., 313, *348*
Bunge, R. P., 313, *348*
Burg, C., 318, *344*
Burge, R. E., 168, 177, 179, *198*
Burke, A. W., 328, *344*
Burnett, W. T., 328, *344*
Bussler, P., 197, *198*

C

Campbell, D., 5, *42*
Carvalko, J. R., 57, *79*
Causer, R., 39, *42*
Causey, G., 320, *344*
Chambers, R. G., 253, *295*
Chester, P. F., 207, *236*
Chevallier, A., 318, *344*
Christenhusz, R., 305, *349*
Christensen, A. K., 335, *344*
Clark, J., 313, *344*
Cleveland, R. F., 336, *345*
Cohen, M. S., 240, 241, *295*
Coleman, M., 318, *349*
Coles, W., 87, *88*
Considine, K. T., 299, *345*
Cooper, R. E., 339, *345*

Y

Yamaguchi, S., 306, *352*
Yamamoto, T., 310, 314, 317, *348*
Yokoya, H., 298, *351*
Yoshii, G., 338, *349*
Yotsumoto, H., 310, *347*

Z

Zahler, P., 342, *352*
Zaides, A. L., 298, *351*
Zeitler, E., 193, *198*, 304, 313, 314, 317, *344*
Zerbst, H., 228, 231, *236*
Zollinger, M., 300, 303, 327, *345*

Subject Index

A

Abbe theory, 243, 244, 245, 286
Aberration, 163, 165, 167, 187, 211, 214, 216, 217, 244, 245, 287, 288, 298
    chromatic, 165, 181, 193, 298
    in solenoid electron lens, 216
    spherical, 165, 167, 173, 175, 193, 196, 197, 198, 244, 298
    in superconducting electron lens, 211, 214, 216, 234
Achromobacter, 301, 302
Adenosine crystals, 314
Aharanov and Bohm effect, 252, 253
ALGOL, 45
Amoeba, 336
Aperture, 101, 176, 182, 183, 187
Aspergillus terrens, 333
Automatic microscope
    finding and framing, 53–55
    image analysis, 60–72
    image display, 55–60
    oscillating scanner, 50–53
    stage positioning, 53
    in white blood cell differential count, 50

B

Bacillus anthracomorphe, 335
Bacillus megaterium, 310, 318
Bacillus mesentericus, 335
Bacillus mycoides, 335
Bacillus proteus vulgaris, 318
Bacillus subtilis, 318, 319, 335
Bacteria, 305
    radiation damage, 335, 336, 343
Bacteria, vegetative
    radiation damage repair, 338
Bacterial flagella, 300, 301, 302
Bacterial spores
    radiation damage, 318, 319
Bacteriophage, 314
    radiation damage, 318

Bausch and Lomb "blister" microscope
    construction, 35
    operation, 35
Bausch and Lomb in-cell microscope, 35
Biological specimen damage
    in amorphous state, 314
    by atomic displacement, 308, 309
    avoidance, 303, 304, 306, 309, 310, 342, 343
    by contamination, 303, 304
    in crystalline state, 314
    dosage required, 312, 313, 314, 315, 343
    by electrostatic charge, 304, 305
    by ionization, 307, 308
    by ionizing radiation, 306–309, 313, 335–338, 342
    nature, 317, 318
    by sublimation, 304
    by temperature, 305, 306, 343
Biological specimens
    cytoplasmic streaming, 339
    homogeneity, 339
    irradiation effects, 303–309, 311–319, 335–338, 343
    motility, 339, 340
    staining, 46, 47, 49, 54, 76, 102
    thickness, 338, 339
    viability, 335–338
Blood cells
    classification, 45, 46
Brachet "Telemicroscope"
    construction, 36, 37
    operation, 36
Bronze, 156
Brownian motion
    in liquid biological specimens, 339, 340, 343

C

Cancer research, 99
Carbon, amorphous, 308

Cumulative Index of Authors

Cumulative Index of Titles